Underground Space Design

Part 1: Overview of Subsurface Space Utilization

by Raymond L. Sterling, Ph.D., P.E.
Associate Professor and Director
Underground Space Center
University of Minnesota

Part 2: Design for People in Underground Facilities

by John Carmody
Associate Director
Underground Space Center
University of Minnesota

Designed and Illustrated by John Carmody

Underground Space Center
Department of Civil and Mineral Engineering
University of Minnesota

This book was prepared as part of a joint research project between the Underground Space Center at the University of Minnesota, USA, and the Institute of Technology of the Shimizu Corporation, Japan.

VAN NOSTRAND REINHOLD
New York

Library of Congress Catalog Card Number 92-33460
ISBN 0-442-01383-3

Printed in the United States of America

Van Nostrand Reinhold
115 Fifth Avenue
New York, New York 10003

Chapman & Hall
2-6 Boundary Row
London SE1 8HN, England

Thomas Nelson Australia
102 Dodds Street
South Melbourne 3205
Victoria, Australia

Nelson Canada
1120 Birchmount Road
Scarborough, Ontario
M1K 5G4, Canada

16 15 14 13 12 11 10 9 8 7 6 5 4 3 2 1

Library of Congress Cataloging-in-Publication Data

Carmody, John.
Underground space design : a guide to subsurface utilization and design for people in underground spaces / John Carmody and Ray Sterling.
p. cm.
Includes bibliographical references.
ISBN 0-442-01383-3
1. Underground construction. 2. Underground architecture. I. Sterling, Raymond. II. University of Minnesota. Underground Space Center. III. Title
TA712.C254 1993
721'.04673--dc20 92-33460
CIP

Contents

Foreword

A life of comfort and safety is the perpetual desire of humanity. To achieve this desire, suitable space is required for dwellings and workplaces as well as for various necessary functions such as energy production and storage, mobility, and many others. However, fulfilling this need for suitable space is becoming more and more difficult in many areas of the world due to a growing shortage of urban land. Also, concern has been rising over the social costs of above-grade construction. For example, railways and highways cannot be constructed above grade without deterioration of the landscape.

Spurred by these factors, interest in underground space utilization is increasing throughout the world. Recent technological advancements have enabled builders to overcome prior restrictions that had largely precluded underground construction. Through the delicate integration of both above- and below-ground development, construction will now be able to progress extensively. A wide range of facilities—such as energy plants, which are indispensable to development—may thus be located underground to allow for more effective use of the surface land.

Many underground projects have already been proposed and successfully carried out worldwide, and extensive research and development plans have been implemented. In Japan, interest in underground space utilization has increased significantly since the late 1980s. Among many proposals for underground development are parking lots, power transformation plants, gymnasia, multipurpose halls with music and conference functions, exhibition halls, pedestrian networks, water channels for flood control, as well as conventional underground highways and subways. Many Japanese research and development projects have been established jointly by the government, universities, and corporations. Committees and study groups are now producing multifarious results that not only address construction technology but also extend to planning, safety, disaster prevention, and other areas.

Research and development results from Japan and many other countries have been shared at gatherings with international audiences, evidence of the broad worldwide interest in underground space utilization. The first international Earth Sheltered Building Conference was held in 1983 in Sydney, Australia. The second and third conferences were held in 1986 in

Minneapolis, USA, and in 1988 in Shanghai, China, respectively. The fourth conference, titled "Urban Underground Utilization '91 – International Conference on Underground Space and Earth Sheltered Buildings," was held in Tokyo in 1991.

These conferences covered the full spectrum of underground technology – from hard technology such as structures to soft technology such as environmental issues, disaster prevention, and so on. It is important to note that technology related to the environment is not limited to the physical environment, but includes the consideration of physiology and psychology of the occupants as well.

Shimizu Corporation, one of Japan's largest construction firms, organized a project team designed to strengthen the company's expertise in meeting the needs of society. In 1988, the team proposed a future underground city plan titled "Urban Geo-Grid Plan." This underground city plan is the first of its kind, as it provides society with a realistic chance to eliminate the dark images associated with the underground.

In an effort to enhance academic activity, Shimizu entered a planned research cooperation with the University of Minnesota, one of the most prominent universities emphasizing underground technology. Shimizu donated a professorship to Professor R.L. Sterling of the University of Minnesota in 1987 to promote the study of underground space.

Along with the professorship, Shimizu has also concluded a five-year agreement with the University of Minnesota to implement joint research on the planning of underground space with Professor R.L. Sterling and J.C. Carmody. The results are published in this guidebook. It introduces underground planning, with a focus on environmental considerations. It is rewarding not only to the University of Minnesota and Shimizu Corporation, but also to society as a whole, as we strive to provide information for underground space utilization to improve our lives for the future.

I hope this guidebook will be helpful to those who take part in underground design and utilization emphasizing environmental influences.

Yorihiko Ohsaki
Executive Vice President
Shimizu Corporation

Preface

Over the past century we have witnessed a rapid growth in the use of underground facilities for an expanding variety of purposes. Why is this? What are the implications for the future of society? Should people be required to work in underground facilities, or should underground space be used solely for mechanical or transit services and low occupancy functions such as storage? It is important to try to answer these questions if underground space is to be put to its highest use in the service of humankind.

This book results from the joint research interests of Shimizu Corporation's Institute of Technology in Japan and the Underground Space Center at the University of Minnesota. Out of these mutual interests, a five-year joint research program was initiated with emphasis in understanding the effect of underground spaces on people and developing design strategies for making underground facilities as acceptable as possible. The results of these investigations are presented in this book.

Because this effort has evolved into two complementary but essentially separate components, the book naturally separates into two parts. Part 1 is an overview of underground space use. It introduces some broad trends contributing to increased underground space usage and reviews the need for careful planning of the underground (Chapter 1); discusses more comprehensively the issues that may present advantages or disadvantages for underground facilities (Chapter 2); describes and classifies types of underground space and their uses (Chapter 3); and describes historical development and current uses of underground space (Chapter 4). Since the entire field of underground uses (including mining, oil wells, utilities, transportation tunnels, etc.) is too broad to be covered in a single volume, a decision was made in this book to try to be as all-inclusive as possible in areas such as classification of uses, but to concentrate description and discussion on urban and especially people-oriented uses of underground space. Part 1 provides the context in which the design issues for people in underground space can be understood.

Part 2 deals with the design of underground facilities for use by people. The idea of being underground frequently elicits negative associations and images. Moreover, the actual experience of people in underground facilities suggests a number of psychological and physiological concerns. Chapter 5 defines these problems by exploring the commonly accepted images of underground space and by reviewing research on actual experience in underground and windowless spaces. Chapter 6 discusses the methodology for developing design guidelines to alleviate these concerns, summarizes the design guidelines for underground facilities that appear in Chapters 7 through 11, and discusses the larger context of underground space design in urban environments. Chapters 7 through 11 address five major aspects of building design that are important in improving the environment for people underground. These are: exterior and entrance design (Chapter 7), layout and spatial configuration (Chapter 8), interior design elements and systems (Chapter 9), lighting (Chapter 10), and life safety (Chapter 11). Within each of these chapters is a discussion of specific design issues and problems, a statement of design objectives, and a presentation of several possible design responses (referred to as patterns). The problems and solutions presented have applicability to most enclosed environments even if not located underground.

The authors would like to emphasize a few key points as you read this book. First, while the focus of the book is on people in underground space, this should not be taken as implying that having people work or stay underground is ideal. Similarly, the use of underground space is also not a goal in its own right. Both are manifestations of a struggle to maintain an effective, attractive, and ecologically sound environment for our expanding population. This struggle to improve services and better our surface environment has to use as its base the inherited development patterns of our societies. While we espouse a preference for "people above—things below," the reality is that even service functions need people to staff and maintain them and that sometimes the overall good of a community is served by locating people-oriented uses below ground. Many examples of such cases are given in Part 1. What we can strive to do is ensure that we create the most acceptable environments for people both below and above ground.

Raymond Sterling
John Carmody

Acknowledgments

The preparation of this book has taken more than four years and has been made possible by the generous support of Shimizu Corporation of Japan as part of a joint research project between their Institute of Technology and the Underground Space Center at the University of Minnesota. The authors would like to extend a special thanks to Dr. Ohsaki and Dr. Ota, who made this project possible. Also we appreciate the efforts of the people in Shimizu with whom we worked the most closely. These are Dr. Kobayashi, Dr. Miyake, and Dr. Hane of the Institute of Technology; Mr. Inoue, Mr. Shindo, and Mr. Denda of the Technology Division; and Mr. Yagi of S-Technology in Boston.

In a broad-ranging book of this kind, we have drawn extensively on the work of other researchers and authors to present a comprehensive picture of the topics involved. It is our intention to give specific references to information, ideas, and data at an appropriate level that will lead the reader to further in-depth information or background reading. If we have missed some appropriate references, please let us know and we will add a correction in future editions.

Gathering information for *Part 2: Design for People in Underground Facilities* was a particularly challenging task because the subject matter is scattered throughout many disciplines. This task was aided greatly by Dr. James Wise, who provided numerous references and helpful direction at the beginning of the project. Dan Montello reviewed the manuscript and provided useful suggestions and additional references related to wayfinding and spatial orientation.

We are very grateful to Olivier Huet, who provided us with a description of the life safety systems at Les Halles in Paris. Huet was a visiting scholar at our Center and has often assisted us.

Within the Underground Space Center, we would like to acknowledge the work undertaken by Pamela Snopl in editing the book and helping with the desktop publishing aspects of the project development. We would also like to acknowledge Sara Hanft and Andrea Spartz for typing the manuscript, Lester Shen for assistance with some of the diagrams, Donna Ahrens for editorial assistance, and Janine Hanson Ess and Bridget Schloesser for contributing several drawings.

Raymond Sterling
John Carmody

Part 1: Overview of Subsurface Space Utilization

by Raymond Sterling

CHAPTER 1

by Raymond Sterling

Introduction to Underground Space Utilization

The rapid growth of world civilization will have a significant impact on the way humans live in the future. As the global population increases and more countries demand a higher standard of living, the world must provide more food and greater energy and mineral resources to sustain this growth. The difficulty of doing this is compounded by three broad trends: the conversion of agricultural land to development uses; the increasing urbanization of the world's population; and growing concern for the maintenance and improvement of the environment, especially regarding global warming and the impact of population growth. Underground space utilization, as this chapter describes, offers opportunities for helping address these trends.

Figure 1-1: Underground space is increasingly being viewed as an underutilized resource to alleviate problems found in congested urban environments.

By moving certain facilities and functions underground, surface land in urban areas can be used more effectively, thus freeing space for agricultural and recreational purposes. Similarly, the use of terraced earth sheltered housing on steeply sloping hillsides can help preserve precious arable flat land in mountainous regions. Using underground space also enables humans to live more comfortably in densely populated areas while improving the quality of life.

On an urban or local level, the use of underground facilities is rising to accommodate the complex demands of today's society while improving the environment. For example, both urban and rural areas are requiring improved transportation, utility, and recreational services. The state of traffic congestion in many urban areas of the world is at a critical level for the support of basic human living, and it is difficult if not impossible to add new infrastructure at ground level without causing an unacceptable deterioration of the surface environment or an unacceptable relocation of existing land uses and neighborhoods.

On a national level in countries around the world, global trends are causing the creation and extension of mining developments and oil or gas recovery at greater depths and in more inaccessible or sensitive locations. These trends have also led to the development of improved designs for energy generation and storage systems as well as national facilities for dealing with hazardous waste (including chemical, biological, and radioactive waste), and improved high-speed national transportation systems. All these developments involve use of the underground.

This chapter focuses on a primary issue spurring underground space utilization—growing land use pressures—as well as the need for careful planning of the underground and potential environmental benefits. Future directions for underground development are also discussed. A more comprehensive discussion of benefits and drawbacks to underground space use occurs in Chapter 2.

Land Use Pressures

Placing facilities underground is a promising method for helping ease land use pressures caused by the growth and urbanization of the world's population. Although the average population density in the world is not large, the distribution of population is very uneven. A map of population density shown in Figure 1-2 indicates that large areas of the world are essentially uninhabited. These areas are for the most part deserts, mountainous regions, or regions of severe cold that do not easily support human habitation.

If one examines China, for example, the average population density is approximately 100 persons per square kilometer, but the vast majority of the one billion-plus population lives on less than 20 percent of the land area. This is the fertile land that can support food production. However, due to population growth, urbanization, and economic growth, this same land must now support extensive transportation systems, industrial and

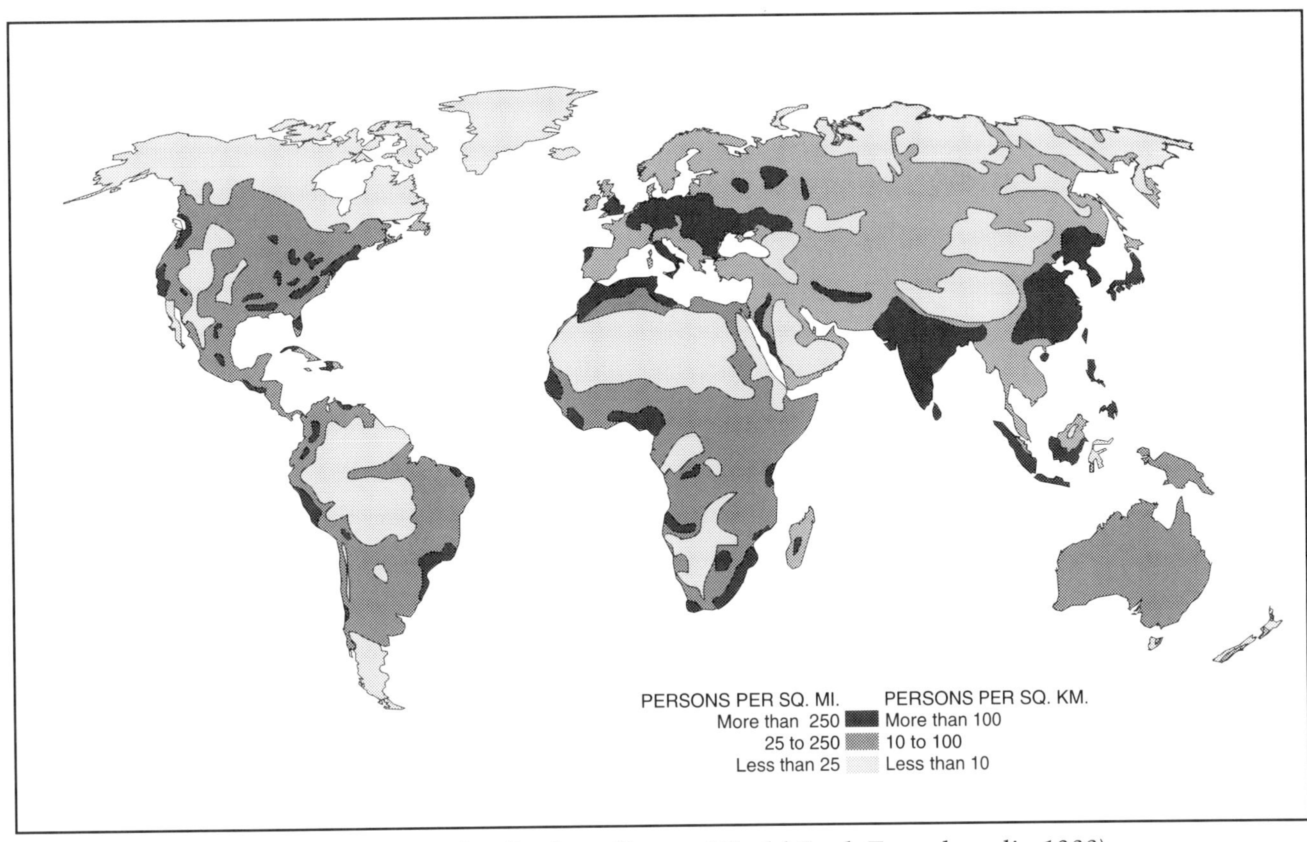

Figure 1-2: World population density distribution. (Source: World Book Encyclopedia *1988)*

commercial developments, and increasing demands for housing. As the population and economy grow, the land available for agriculture shrinks, and the problems of transporting food and raw materials to an urban population increase. By the year 2000 it is estimated that 70 percent of the world's population will inhabit urban areas.

The same trends are evident in Japan, where approximately 80 percent of the land area is mountainous, 90 percent of the population lives on the coastal plains, and economic development is concentrated in relatively few economic centers. The flat-lying land is generally the most fertile and is historically the region of settlement. Other factors adding to population density include the traditional building style, which is low-rise, and Japanese laws that contain strong provisions for maintenance of access to sunlight. Also, to retain domestic food production capability, the Japanese government has protected agricultural land from development. The combination of these historical and political factors together with a strong migration of businesses and individuals to the economic centers has created enormous land use pressures. The result is an astronomically high cost of land in city centers (as high as US$500,000 per square meter) and difficulty in providing housing, transportation, and utility services for the population. Typical business employees cannot afford to live near the city center where they work and may have to commute one to two hours each way from an affordable area. To service the expanding metropolitan area, public agencies must upgrade roads and build new transit lines and utilities. Land costs for such work are so high that in central Tokyo, the cost of land may represent over 95 percent of the total cost of a project.

In addition to population density, other factors in growing urban areas may stimulate underground space development. Table 1-1 shows the residential population density of the world's largest cities. It is interesting to note that the average population densities in the major Japanese connurbations (Tokyo-Yokohama and Osaka-Kobe-Kyoto) are not among the highest of major urban areas in the world. Hong Kong is by far the most densely populated city, with a density in 1985 of 104,480 persons per square kilometer (270,750 persons per square mile) by this calculation. At the other end of the scale of the world's major cities is Dallas, with a total population half as large as Hong Kong's but a 1985 population density of only 2,290 persons per square kilometer (5,933 persons per square mile).

Much discussion concerning use of the underground often revolves around the density of cities in Europe and Japan, but as the table shows, most European, North American, and Japanese cities are near the bottom of the list of the world's largest cities in terms of population density. This illustrates that other factors—such as historical and cultural development patterns, demands for business and personal mobility, and the greater expectations for a spacious and pleasant environment that accompany economic growth—are at least as important in stimulating underground development as mere density. Thus, the relative population densities in Table 1-1 indicate that continued economic development in the most densely populated cities of the world will create a need for underground development that could more than rival that experienced in European and Japanese cities today.

The problems of land use pressures and the related economic effects of high land prices are of great interest in the study of the potential uses of underground space. When surface space is fully utilized, underground space becomes one of the few development zones available. It offers the possibility of adding needed facilities without further degrading the surface environment. Without high land prices, however, the generally higher cost of constructing facilities underground is a significant deterrent to their use. When underground facilities are not economically competitive, they must be justified on aesthetic, environmental, or social grounds—luxuries which many developing nations cannot afford at present and which developed nations are reluctant to undertake except in areas of special significance.

As land prices rise, however, placing facilities underground becomes more attractive economically because it is usually not necessary to pay for the full cost of the surface land under which the facility is built. Appendix A provides an analysis of the combined unit building area costs (i.e., \$ per m^2) for land acquisition plus construction of a surface facility and an underground facility. Figures 1-3 and 1-4 compare these combined costs for variations in the permitted floor area ratio for the building aboveground, the cost of land per unit area, and the easement cost for the underground space. The permitted floor area ratio controls the total floor area of buildings relative to the site area available. For example, if a building occupies an entire site, a floor area ratio

Table 1-1: Population density of major world cities.

City, Country	Population in 1985	Area 1985 (sq mi)	Density 1985 (pop/sq mi)
Hong Kong	5,415,000	20	270,750
Ho Chi Minh City, Vietnam	3,250,000	31	104,839
Shenyang, China	4,086,000	39	104,769
Dhaka, Bangladesh	3,283,000	32	102,594
Ahmadabad, India	3,037,000	32	94,906
Tianjin, China	4,622,000	49	94,327
Chengdu, China	2,260,000	25	90,400
Shanghai, China	6,698,000	78	85,871
Harbin, China	2,518,000	30	83,933
Cairo, Egypt	8,595,000	104	82,644
Alexandria, Egypt	2,660,000	35	76,000
Pusan, South Korea	3,996,000	54	74,000
Bangalore, India	3,685,000	50	73,700
Casablanca, Morocco	2,495,000	35	71,286
Surabaya, Indonesia	2,962,000	43	68,884
Teheran, Iran	7,354,000	112	65,660
Lahore, Pakistan	3,603,000	57	63,211
Madrid, Spain	4,137,000	66	62,682
Bogota, Colombia	4,711,000	79	59,633
Caracas, Venezuela	2,993,000	54	55,426
Rangoon, Burma	2,558,000	47	54,426
Delhi, India	6,993,000	138	50,673
Calcutta, India	10,462,000	209	50,057
Kinshasha, Zaire	2,794,000	57	49,018
Bangkok, Thailand	4,998,000	102	49,000
Wuhan, China	3,048,000	65	46,892
Naples, Italy	2,862,000	62	46,161
Lima, Peru	5,447,000	120	45,362
Manila, Phillippines	8,485,000	188	45,132
Barcelona, Spain	3,842,000	87	44,161
Madras, India	4,983,000	115	43,330
Rome, Italy	2,944,000	69	42,667
Ankara, Turkey	2,338,000	55	42,509
Guangzhou, China	3,248,000	79	41,114
Bucharest, Romania	2,095,000	52	40,288
Taipei, Taiwan	5,550,000	138	40,217
Kiev, Ukraine	2,489,000	62	40,175
Seoul, South Korea	13,655,000	342	39,958
Rio de Janeiro, Brazil	10,116,000	260	38,907
Belo Horizonte, Brazil	3,059,000	79	38,782
Beijing, China	5,608,000	151	37,139
Santiago, Chile	4,700,000	128	36,719
Guadalajara, Mexico	2,746,000	78	32,205
Baghdad, Iraq	3,371,000	97	34,753
Hyderabad, India	3,022,000	88	34,341
Karachi, Pakistan	6,351,000	190	33,426
Sao Paulo, Brazil	14,911,000	451	33,062
St. Petersburg, Russia	4,569,000	139	32,871
Singapore, Singapore	2,556,000	78	32,769
Istanbul, Turkey	5,389,000	165	32,661
Mexico City, Mexico	16,901,000	522	32,377
Monterrey, Mexico	2,351,000	77	30,532
Athens, Greece	3,352,000	116	28,034
Osaka-Kobe-Kyoto, Japan	13,562,000	495	27,397
Moscow, Russia	9,873,000	379	26,050
Tokyo-Yokohama, Japan	25,434,000	1089	23,356
Buenos Aires, Argen.	10,750,000	535	20,093
Paris, France	8,633,000	432	19,983
Toronto, Canada	2,972,000	154	19,299
Montreal, Canada	2,827,000	164	17,238
Budapest, Hungary	2,297,000	138	16,645
Nagoya, Japan	4,452,000	307	14,502
Milan, Italy	4,635,000	344	13,474
Manchester, UK	4,151,000	357	11,627
New York, USA	14,598,000	1274	11,458
Berlin, Germany	3,033,000	274	11,069
Porto Allegre, Brazil	2,536,000	231	10,978
Lagos, Nigeria	6,054,000	58	10,810
London, UK	9,442,000	874	10,803
Essen, Germany	7,604,000	704	10,801
Jakarta, Indonesia	8,122,000	76	10,686
Bombay, India	10,137,000	95	10,670
Sydney, Australia	3,396,000	338	10,047
Birmingham, UK	2,211,000	223	9,915
San Francisco, USA	3,790,000	428	8,855
Melbourne, Australia	2,852,000	327	8,722
Los Angeles, USA	9,638,000	1110	8,682
Philadelphia, USA	4,025,000	471	8,546
Chicago, USA	6,511,000	762	8,544
Boston, USA	2,470,000	303	8,152
Miami, USA	3,123,000	448	6,971
Washington, USA	2,456,000	357	6,880
Houston, USA	2,104,000	310	6,787
Detroit, USA	3,133,000	468	6,694
Dallas, USA	2,486,000	419	5,933

Note: Cities are defined as continuous built-up areas with a population density of at least 5000 persons per square mile. Large nonresidential areas are excluded in density calculations. (Source: *World Almanac* 1989) of 5 would permit up to a five-story building. The combined costs are compared by plotting the breakeven ratio of underground to surface construction costs (excluding land). This indicates how much more expensive the underground construction can be to remain an economic alternative. Figure 1-3 assumes that the underground building has two stories, that the surface construction costs US$1500 per square meter, and that the easement cost for the underground building is 20 percent of the cost of the overlying surface land area. Figure 1-4 assumes the same surface construction cost but that the easement cost of the underground space is zero. These parameters and the analysis are explained further in Appendix A.

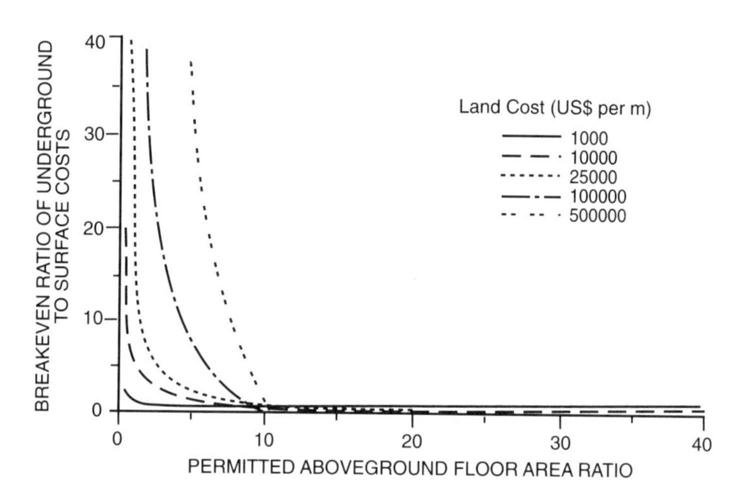

Figure 1-3: Breakeven cost ratio: underground easement cost 20%.

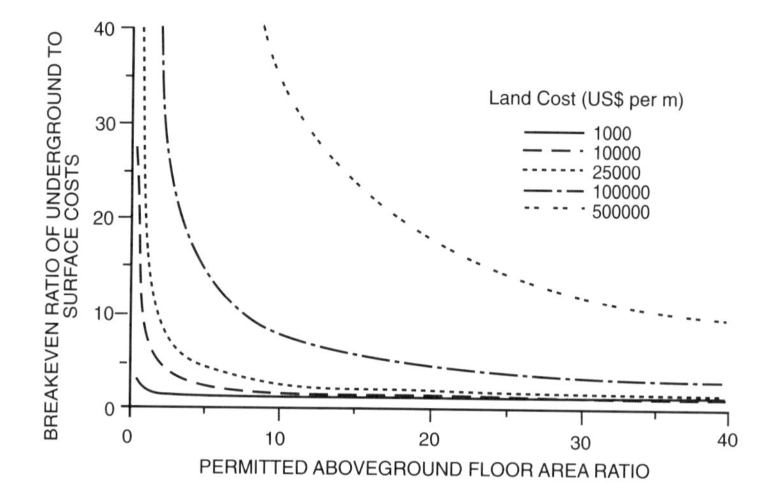

Figure 1-4: Breakeven cost ratio: no underground easement cost.

Curves for five values of land cost are illustrated. The highest value of US$500,000 per square meter is representative of the highest land values in Tokyo in 1989 (Kuwabara 1988). The value of $25,000 per square meter is representative of the highest 1989 land values in Manhattan, New York (Downes 1989). For comparison, the highest 1989 land values in Hong Kong were around US$14,000 per square meter (Vail 1989).

The curves show that at relatively low urban land values of $1000 per square meter, underground construction must cost essentially the same as surface construction to be economically competitive. At high land values, however, the competitive construction costs depend greatly on the cost of the underground easement and on the permitted land area ratio aboveground. Figure 1-3 shows a crossover in relative costs at a land area ratio of 10. This crossover point is dependent on the easement cost and the number of stories constructed below ground. Tokyo provides an extreme case with very large breakeven cost ratios against buildings with land area ratios of less than 10, but even at New York land prices, underground construction costs can be 2.1 times those of surface construction in buildings with land area ratios of 6.

When there are no easement costs associated with using the subsurface, there is no crossover point and, for example, the breakeven underground construction cost ratios against a building with land area ratio of 10 are 1.07, 1.7, 2.7, 7.7, and 34 times the surface construction cost for the respective land values of 1000, 10,000, 25,000, 100,000, and 500,000 US$ per square meter.

It is clear from the above analysis that as land use pressures increase and/or land prices rise there will be an economically driven trend towards the construction of high-rise buildings and increased use of underground facilities. In fact, since either trend will tend to increase the local urban density and create a demand for additional service facilities, there will be a reinforcing impact on the land use pressures and an increased demand for transportation and utility services for which no surface land is available. The intense interest in Japan in providing new urban services underground is an example of this trend. In this regard, it is important to plan the types of new underground facilities wisely. Planning must be effectively controlled and should be used to maintain the desired surface environment, or else the secondary development implications of subsurface projects on the surface environment should be anticipated.

The issue of the cost of underground easements also raises an important planning dilemma. It is desirable to build underground facilities as cheaply as possible so that they can be used economically to solve urban problems. If no value is assigned to space underground, however, there are none of the normal economic pressures to help rationalize the appropriate use of the underground and minimize the volume of this resource usurped by individual uses (Riera 1990). This is an important issue for underground planning and may be dealt with by assigning an internal value to various underground zones for use in design trade-off studies. This is currently done for economic evaluations of highway projects in terms of the value of travel time saved and the economic cost of anticipated accidents versus road standards.

Planning of Underground Space

Effective planning for underground utilization should be an essential precursor to the development of major underground facilities. This planning must consider long-term needs while providing a framework for reforming urban areas into desirable and effective environments in which to live and work. If underground development is to provide the most valuable long-term benefits possible, then effective planning of this resource must be conducted. Unfortunately, it is already too late for the near-surface zones beneath public rights-of-way in older cities around the world. The tangled web of utilities (see Figure 1-5) commonly found is due to a lack of coordination and the historical evolution in utility provision and transit system development.

The underground has several characteristics that make good planning especially problematical:

- Once underground excavations are made, the ground is permanently altered. Underground structures are not as easily dismantled as surface buildings.
- An underground excavation may effectively reserve a larger zone of ground required for the stability of the excavation.
- The underground geologic structure greatly affects the types, sizes, and costs of facilities that can be constructed, but the knowledge of a region's subsurface can only be inferred from a limited number of site investigation borings and previous records.
- Large underground projects may require massive investments with relatively high risks of construction problems, delays, and cost overruns.
- Traditional planning techniques have focused on two-dimensional representations of regions and urban areas. This is generally adequate for surface and aboveground construction but it is not adequate for the complex three-dimensional geology and built structures often found underground. Representation of this three-dimensional information in a form that can readily be interpreted for planning and evaluation is very difficult.

In Tokyo, for example, the first subway line (Ginza Line) was installed as a shallow line (10 meters deep) immediately beneath the existing layer of surface utilities. As more subway lines have been added, uncluttered zones can only be found at the deeper underground levels. The new Keiyo JR line in Tokyo is 40 meters deep. A new underground super highway from Marunouchi to Shinjuku has been proposed at a 50-meter depth. For comparison, the deepest installations in London are at approximately a 70-meter depth although the main complex of works and sewers is at less than 25 meters (Hillman 1983). Compounding these issues of increasing demand is the fact that newer transportation services (such as the Japanese Shinkansen bullet trains or the French TGV) often require larger cross-section tunnels, straighter alignments,

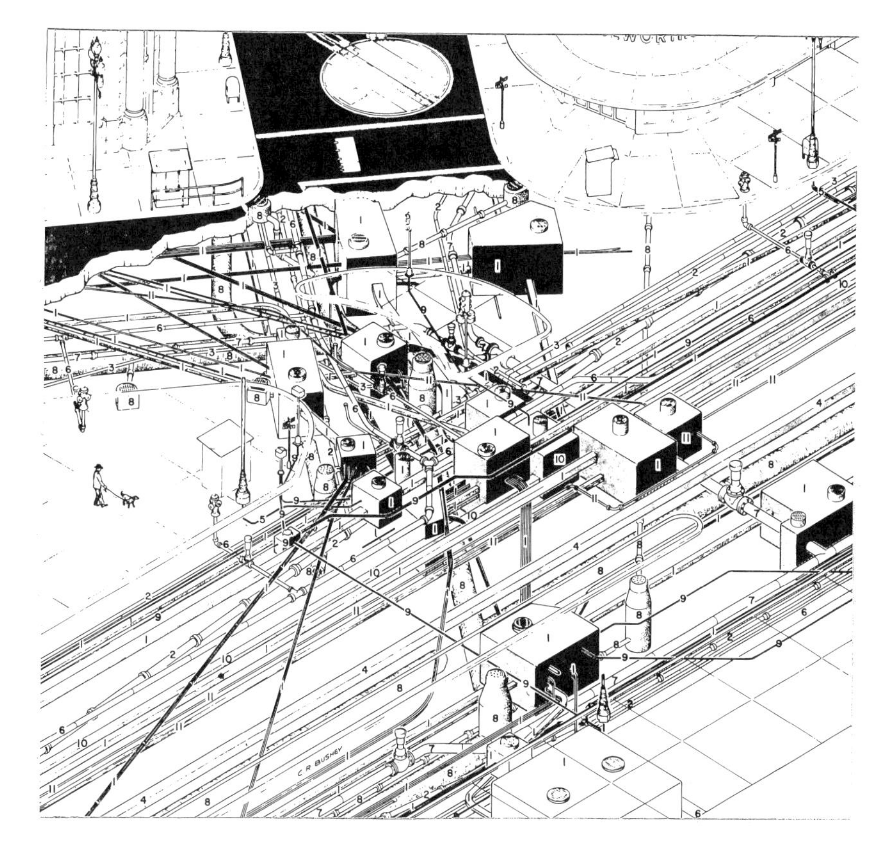

Figure 1-5: Subsurface utilities at street intersection in San Francisco. (Source: AWPA 1971)

and flatter grades. If space is not reserved for this type of use, very inefficient layouts of the underground beneath urban areas can occur. Use of the underground in the past has been based mostly on a first-come, first-served basis with principal attention focused on minimizing the cost of that increment of underground development. Space allocation for shallow utilities beneath roadways is practiced (APWA 1971), but examples of more comprehensive utility planning are more difficult to find. Even when considerable attention is focused on underground planning (Jansson and Winqvist 1977; Sterling and Nelson 1982; Saari 1988), it is not easy to impact actual practices.

A common problem in the development of a rational underground development structure is that a higher initial investment is required to reap future planning and cost benefits. Very often these future benefits or costs are not monetarized—as in the case of the value of the ground beneath public rights-of-way (mentioned in the evaluation of land cost implications) or the social cost of continually tearing up streets to repair and upgrade shallow utilities. This financial problem, which has been a major impetus in attempts to encourage common utility tunnels, has been overcome only rarely except when a single authority has overall responsibility for all utility provision.

The importance of "ground level" is an issue that bears examination in the planning of underground space to separate service uses such as transportation and utilities from pedestrian- and recreation-oriented uses such as walkways, plazas, gardens, and parks. When an underground structure is created and the surface restored to support traffic or plantings, a new artificial ground surface has in effect been created—cut off from the natural ground environment below. For widespread use of the underground, it will usually be cheaper to create a false ground level above the original ground level to provide separation of public and service facilities, thus saving the excavation and lateral ground support costs. Taken to its extreme this could provide a new surface environment at the roof levels of essentially conventional buildings (see Figure 1-6). For buildings on sloping sites, a single ground level is an arbitrary concept anyway. What is ground level on one side of a building may be one floor above or below ground on the other side of the building.

Although the concept has limited applicability to existing urban areas or to cities that grow slowly from small villages, it can have applicability in "new town" developments and in the redevelopment of sections of existing built-up areas. The redevelopment of the La Defense area in Paris is an example of the creation of a pedestrian platform above the original grade to serve as the "ground level" of the buildings in the development (Figure 1-7). This use of a platform level, which simplifies traffic circulation, service access, and the provision of utilities below, has been credited as an important feature in the success of this large development (LeComte 1990).

Figure 1-6: Multistory structures with landscaped roofs create a new ground level. (Source: Shimizu Bulletin *1988)*

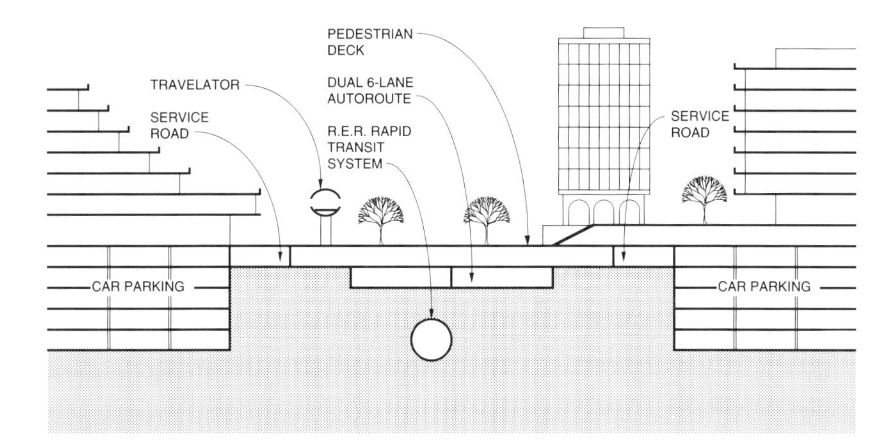

Figure 1-7: Schematic section of La Defense development in Paris, France. A new ground level is created by placing a pedestrian deck two levels above existing grade. In effect, the normal grade level becomes underground space. (Source: O'Reilly 1978)

PLANNING AT DIFFERENT GOVERNMENTAL LEVELS

Planning for future underground space use is an important activity at all levels of government but will encompass different emphases, planning techniques, and levels of detail at the national, regional, and local levels.

At the national and regional level, the broad geologic environments and resources represented by different regions must be examined in the context of existing human uses, significant national facility needs, and development trends. The examination and reservation of sites for nuclear waste repositories is an example of a national planning need. National and regional planning can identify important mineral resources, especially favorable geologic environments for certain functions, and also special geologic conditions which should be preserved. Although these large-scale planning efforts require three-dimensional geologic information, the site reservation and planning efforts for the most part can be handled effectively using two-dimensional maps.

At the urban and local level it becomes necessary to prioritize among potentially competing underground uses. The geologic conditions, existing underground structures, and space utilization plans must be understood in a fully three-dimensional setting. When underground facilities are constructed they should be used to solve urban problems without creating new ones, and spaces should be designed so that they can be adapted to future uses as readily as possible. Large spans and adequate floor-ceiling heights can promote such flexibility. For example, car parking structures with minimum ceiling heights may not be appropriate for later conversion to a higher use such as a shopping center. More future flexibility is provided if higher ceilings are used initially or if parts of the structure can be removed later without affecting ground support.

Planning for urban underground utilization involves a physical inventory of the geologic setting relative to surface topography, existing surface uses, anticipated development, and urban planning

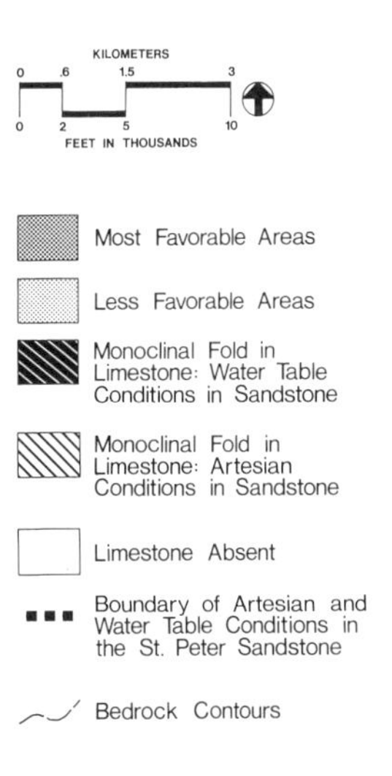

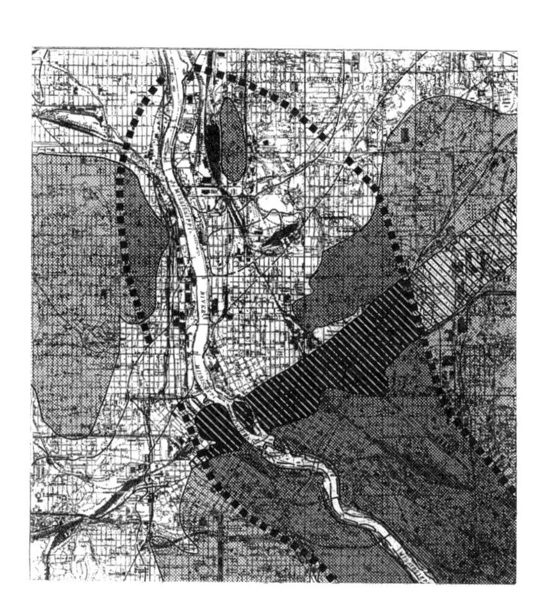

Figure 1-8: Potential areas for mined space development in Minneapolis, Minnesota. (Source: Sterling and Nelson 1982)

goals. The information must then be correlated with the varying degree of viability or ease of construction for various types of underground facilities. Construction costs, maximum clear spans, the potential for environmental damage, and ease of access to the underground levels all will be important in planning decisions and will potentially change with depth and location within the urban area. Geologic potential thus can be matched with needs and urban planning goals to identify the best sites for different types of underground functions. Figure 1-8 illustrates the results of a planning process to identify the best site for underground commercial/industrial development in Minneapolis, Minnesota. From this study, access from the river bluffs to the potential underground site was preserved and a master plan for development of the site has been prepared (Sterling and Nelson 1982).

OWNERSHIP AND ADMINISTRATIVE PROCEDURES

Another example of far-reaching changes that can occur as a result of consideration of the future value of the underground is that underground ownership and historical administrative procedures may be questioned.

In Japan, consideration is currently being given in the Japanese Diet to public ownership of the underground at depths further than 50 meters below the ground surface. This is a radical change from the current status of ownership to the center of the earth. The Japanese reconsideration of their land ownership provisions has been spurred not only by high surface land and underground easement costs, but also by the administrative delays the individual easement process can cause.

A recent survey by the International Tunnelling Association revealed a surprising variety of underground ownership structures and administrative procedures worldwide. A synopsis of conditions in the 19 countries responding to the survey is included in Appendix C.

Even if land ownership structures are not radically changed, forethought can substantially ease later problems. Today, when downtown redevelopment sites in Minneapolis are packaged and released to a developer, the ownership of the underground below the main surface bedrock layer is retained by the city. Over a period of a few decades this can result in substantial capture of the central urban underground for a city.

Another change may be in the type of building foundation used. Deep pile foundations are used in many cities founded on poor estuary soils. Timber piles are very sensitive to rotting under future water table fluctuations, and deep piles in general usurp a large volume of the urban underground as unproductive space. Deep basements usually provide an alternate foundation scheme for large buildings and provide usable underground space. They may also restrict future underground uses less than piling systems do (Hou and Shu 1988).

FUTURE DIRECTIONS FOR SUBSURFACE PLANNING

In response to the many concerns related to effective planning of the underground, the International Tunnelling Association has established a policy statement on subsurface planning. The statement provides clear directions for this newly emerging aspect of planning.

> *The subsurface is a resource for future development similar to surface land or recoverable minerals. Once an underground opening is created, the subsurface can never be restored to its original condition and the presence of this opening can affect all future uses of the surface and the subsurface in its vicinity. These factors require responsible planning for all uses of the underground to ensure that the resource is not damaged or usurped by uncoordinated first uses.*
>
> *The awareness of the underground option among planners, developers and financiers should be increased so that subsurface planning issues are properly addressed. Subsurface planning should be an integral part of the normal land use planning process.*
>
> *National, regional and local policies should be prepared to provide guidelines, criteria and classifications for assessing appropriate uses of underground space, identifying geologic conditions, defining priority uses and resolving potential utilization conflicts. Site reservation policies should be established for important future uses and for especially favorable geologic conditions.*
>
> *It is recommended that every region or city establish a permanent record-keeping system for the maintenance of detailed records of the use of the subsurface. This record-keeping should be coordinated by a single agency to ensure compatible and complete records and should include "as built" records rather than project plans. Records should include activities, such as groundwater extraction and deep pile foundations, which affect the potential use of the subsurface but which may not be classed as specific subsurface facilities.*

INITIATION OF UNDERGROUND DEVELOPMENTS

Identification and planning of advantageous uses of the underground for a region does not necessarily result in these ideas being actualized. Since underground space utilization is not the choice of first resort for most planners and builders, there is a natural barrier to its use even when circumstances are favorable. Investigation of underground developments around the world indicates that both a favorable environment for underground space use (in terms of site or physical advantage) and a trigger for the adoption of the method of construction must be present for significant development to occur.

These issues are often operative in the adoption of underground solutions to national and urban problems. Most potential underground projects are limited less by a lack of technical knowledge to create and safely occupy the facility than by the political and social reluctance to pursue the alternative. Barriers to adoption may include uncertain legal and administrative rules which can cause long delays in decision-making and costly lawsuits, as well as unnecessarily restrictive safety regulations and prohibitions against underground or windowless working environments. A common problem is that underground solutions often cost more than surface solutions but their environmental benefits do not receive economic evaluations. Another problem occurs in the division of responsibilities among agencies or departments charged with environmental protection. Use of the underground almost inevitably represents at some level a potential risk of degradation of the subsurface environment. Thus, an agency charged with groundwater protection may resist use of the underground even though the overall environmental benefits of a project far outweigh its drawbacks.

For urban areas, underground utility development naturally grows as a community grows but certain factors may cause rapid changes in the level of use. Community decisions to locate electric, telephone, and cable service below ground can make sudden changes in demand for underground services. Major government initiatives to reduce urban congestion, speed intercity travel, or improve the environment can likewise cause sudden increases in the demand for underground construction.

An example of this trend is the current underground placement of the downtown section of the Boston expressway in the United States. Originally constructed as an elevated freeway, the growth of traffic and the environmental blight of the elevated structure prompted a project in which the downtown section of the freeway will be routed underground. This will remove a major visual barrier that now separates rapidly developing areas of the city and will provide new development land. A further illustration of this trend was the proposal by private interests to place a downtown section of the Gardiner expressway in Toronto, Canada, underground, at no cost to the city but in return for development rights on the land surface reclaimed (*Toronto Star* 1989).

For industrial and commercial projects the stimuli or triggers are less clear. They vary according to the type of industry and their physical and locational needs. Manufacturing, distribution, or service industries that have strong preferences for central urban

Figure 1-9: Underground rail transit systems are often the catalyst for more extensive underground commercial developments. This underground shopping center is one of many created adjacent to underground metro stations in Montreal, Canada.

locations and industries with particular physical requirements (such as freezer storage or low-vibration manufacturing) are the prime candidates. Unless the economic advantage is large, however, companies are unlikely to use underground facilities for proactive reasons. They are more likely to use the underground only when viable surface options are unavailable due to land pressures or planning restrictions.

One of the few positive triggers for underground development other than physical necessity is the creation of new underground transit systems (Figure 1-9). Following the initial transit stimulus, large underground commercial developments have grown through private investment.

Although the lack of technology may not be the major stumbling block to more widespread underground development in most areas of the world, it will still be very important in the cost-effectiveness of underground construction and in improving the ability to construct larger span openings in poor geologic conditions. The high cost of underground construction together with the increasing need for underground solutions provides a major incentive and opportunity for technological innovation. Technological advances will increase the scope of uses that can be placed underground, and cost reductions will increase the utilization of more conventional underground projects. The advances made in the microtunneling field allowing remote guidance of tunnelled small diameter utilities serve as an example of the kind of technological stimulation that can trigger a widespread increase in the use of the underground.

Research needs and opportunities around the world vary with the economic situation, geologic constraints, and the nature of the construction industry. Improvements in underground construction systems, which typically involve many interrelated aspects for success, are more easily developed by large companies or institutions with strong markets for systemized construction and the incentive to improve and refine. Long-term national programs with steady and competitive markets for underground construction appear to be effective in stimulating the technological innovation that substantially improves the technological capability and cost-effectiveness of underground construction.

Environmental Benefits of Underground Space Usage

Another major trigger for underground space usage is the growing international concern over the environment, which has led to attempts to rethink the future of urban and industrial development. The major concerns in balancing economic development versus environmental degradation and world natural resource limitations revolve around several key issues. These are:

- The increasing consumption of energy compared to the limited reserves of fossil fuels available to meet future demand.
- The effect on the global climate of burning fossil fuels.
- The pollution of the environment from the by-products of industrial development.
- The safe disposal of hazardous wastes generated by industrial and military activities.

Preserving the environment and extending the life of the world's resources while promoting economic growth and maintaining individual life styles will be complex if not impossible. However, a high standard of living and high gross domestic product (GDP) do not have to be proportionately dependent on resource consumption and environmental degradation. Figure 1-10 charts the Total Fuel Energy Requirement (TFER) per capita versus

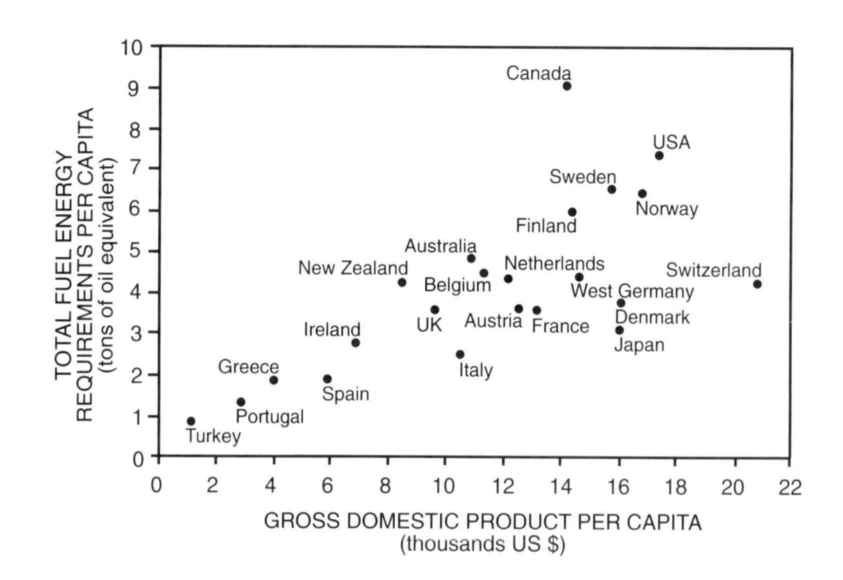

Figure 1-10: Total fuel energy requirement per capita versus gross domestic product per capita for OECD countries in 1986.

T.F.E.R. data source: Energy Balance of OECD Countries 1985/86 (IEA 1988).
G.D.P. data source: National Account Statistics 1986 (United Nations 1989).
Note: Only countries with populations greater than one million are included.

the Gross Domestic Product (GDP) per capita for nations belonging to the Organization for Economic Cooperation and Development (OECD). Only nations with populations larger than 1 million are shown. There are significant differences among these more developed nations. The more energy-efficient developed nations such as those in western Europe and Japan use only half the energy per capita as the United States and Canada for a similar level of per capita GDP. The historical availability and price of fuel have had major impacts on these discrepancies as has the overall size of the country, but the figures demonstrate that continued economic development, while being more resource conscious, is possible.

Underground space utilization can help solve the environmental/resource dilemma in several ways. Underground facilities are typically energy conserving in their own right. More importantly, by using underground space, higher urban densities can be supported with less impact on the local environment. In addition to the obvious benefit of preserving green space and agricultural land, there is strong evidence that higher urban density can lower fuel resource consumption.

Figure 1-11 is a graph of gasoline use per capita versus population density for selected world cities (based on 1980 figures—Newman and Kenworthy 1989). The strong relationship between urban density and gasoline consumption is clear, but it is also interesting to note the wide range in gasoline consumption once the population density drops below 10 persons per acre.

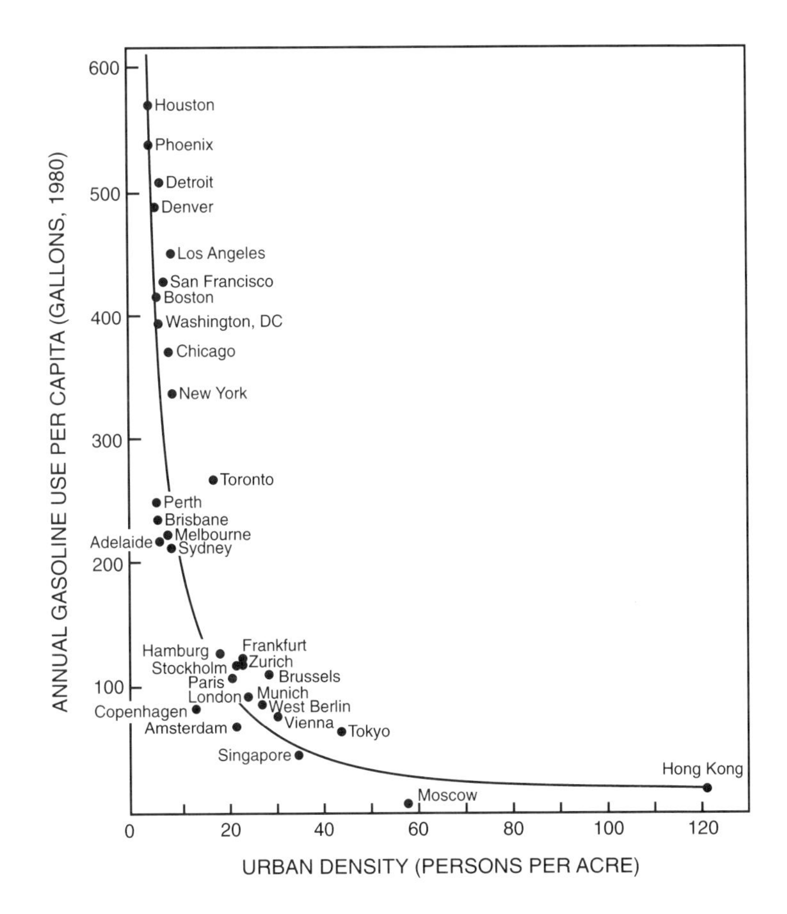

Figure 1-11: Annual gasoline use per capita versus urban density – 1980. (Source: Newman and Kenworthy 1989)

Table 1-2: Gasoline use and land use variables in global cities – 1980.

City	Gasoline gallons per capita	Total population density	Total job density	Inner population density	Inner job density	Outer population density	Outer job density	Jobs in city center	Proportion of jobs in city center (%)	Proportion of population in inner city (%)	Average work trip length (miles)
U.S. cities	446	5.7	2.8	18.2	12.1	4.5	2.0	364,180	12	27	8.1
Australian cities	227	5.7	2.4	9.7	10.9	5.3	1.6	107,736	16	17	7.5
Toronto	265	16.2	8.1	23.1	15.4	13.8	5.8	142,645	13	36	8.1
European cities	101	21.9	12.6	36.8	32.0	17.4	8.1	265,505	19	41	5.0
Asian cities	42	64.8	28.8	18.8	119.8	46.6	17.8	785,225	19	32	2.5
Moscow	3	56.2	---	---	---	---	---	---	---	---	---
Correlation with gasoline*		-.5778	-.6571	-.3917	-.4846	-.5751	-.5912	-.1026	-.5027	-.4577	+.7620
Significance		0.000	0.000	0.0150	0.003	0.000	0.000	0.291	0.002	0.005	0.000

* Correlations are on all 32 separate cities in the sample.
Source: Newman and Kenworthy 1989.

Table 1-3: Gasoline use and land use variables in global cities – 1980.

City	Total transit passenger miles	Rail transit passenger miles	Total passenger miles on transit (%)	Journey to work			Road supply (ft/capita)	Parking spaces per 1000 CBD workers	Average speed of traffic (mph)	Average speed of transit (mph)		
				Car	Public transit	Walk/ bike				Bus	Train	LRT
U.S. cities	324	162	4.4	83	12	5	21.6	380	27	12	26	11
Australian cities	532	306	7.5	76	19	5	28.5	327	27	13	24	14
Toronto	1,227	673	16.7	63	31	6	8.9	198	---	12	21	10
European cities	1,112	801	24.8	44	35	21	6.9	211	19	12	27	11
Asian cities	1,900	1,112	64.1	15	60	25	3.3	67	15	9	22	8
Moscow	>2,647	>1,886	>9.5	2	74	24	1.3	---	28	13	>26	11
Correlation with gasoline*	-.7191	-.5484	-.7530	+.8733	-.8201	-.7301	+.6918	+.5754	+.7034	+.2734	-.0481	+.2602
Significance	0.000	0.001	0.000	0.000	0.000	0.000	0.000	0.000	0.000	0.072	0.410	0.184

* Correlations with gasoline use per capita are for all 32 separate cities in the sample.
Source: Newman and Kenworthy 1989.

Tables 1-2 and 1-3, also from Newman and Kenworthy, provide additional insight into the relationships between population density, job density, transportation use, and energy consumption.

An assessment of the implications of these data concerning national and urban efficiency is that in a future of rising resource costs and increasing resource scarcity, the least efficient nations and cities will be put at a competitive disadvantage. Adaptation to such changing circumstances may eventually cause a substantial restructuring of past urban and national development trends. Low-density urban sprawl totally dependent on the automobile, as has occurred in many areas of the United States, is not likely to be as economically viable in the future.

Underground development will be an important tool in reshaping our urban areas to meet the challenges of the future without destroying their heritage or worsening their surface environment.

The Future of Underground Space Development

Although existing underground facilities throughout the world provide some models for future development, they are all limited in scale, in use, or in their lack of a comprehensive vision for the total city environment. As a complement to more detailed planning and research studies, it is useful to examine the visions of extensive underground complexes, even entire cities, that have been proposed by futuristic planners and designers. A few examples of these visions are presented here and at various locations throughout the book. Most of the illustrations require little explanation since they are essentially visual concepts.

Visionary underground networks of space have been proposed as a comprehensive solution to congestion and environmental problems in many urban areas. In Paris, a multilevel underground city containing many functions and systems beneath the Seine River was envisioned in the 1960s (Figure 1-12). This concept was used to promote the eventual Les Halles development.

The unique geology in the Minneapolis-St. Paul area has led to several proposals since 1970 envisioning a complete layer of underground space beneath the existing city. Under the congested University of Minnesota, underground space at a depth of 30 meters could contain parking, transit, library archives, laboratories, service delivery, district heating, and utilities (Figure 1-13). In the central city of Minneapolis, underground space is envisioned for expansion of laboratories, manufacturing, and storage directly beneath offices and existing facilities on the surface. This type of

Figure 1-12: Concept for development beneath the Seine River in Paris.

space can be created with little surface disruption and can be expanded in small increments as required.

In the 1970s an American architect, Gunnar Birkerts, suggested the creation of major subterranean corridors containing transportation systems, utilities, manufacturing, and storage facilities. These corridors could be used to revitalize existing urban areas and direct future growth and development. The most undesirable but necessary urban functions are underground, leaving open space on the surface above. The highest density residential development would occur along the corridors.

Recently, the high level of interest in underground space in Japan has resulted in similar visionary concepts. The Shimizu "Geo-Grid" concept (Figure 1-14) was one of the first of these proposals. It involves concentrated nodes of underground service and community functions connected by high-speed underground transport and communication links (*Shimizu Bulletin* 1988). Many national ministries, city governments, and other large companies have also developed underground concepts. The large-diameter underground service sphere developed by the Ministry of Trade and Industry is the most concrete of these proposals. The MITI concept is being backed by a US$150 million, seven-year investment in the technological developments necessary to construct such large-span spheres deep in the saturated soft ground beneath Tokyo. Another concept, the Alice City Network, envisions deep cylindrical buildings extending into the ground with central atria providing natural light to the underground community centers.

Geotech '90, a conference and exhibition held in Tokyo in April 1990, was a major forum for the underground industry in Japan. More than a dozen underground concepts were displayed, ranging from the typical transit and utility uses to underground corridors that are envisioned as places for a communication network protected during disasters. Such corridors could also effectively transport both waste and energy between substations in the city and central generation and disposal sites outside the city. This approach not only relieves congestion but also can provide more efficient energy generation and recycling of waste materials. These concepts are all intended to permit a major upgrade of the city infrastructure that will eventually enable the surface to be rebuilt with more open space and a more efficient, attractive overall environment.

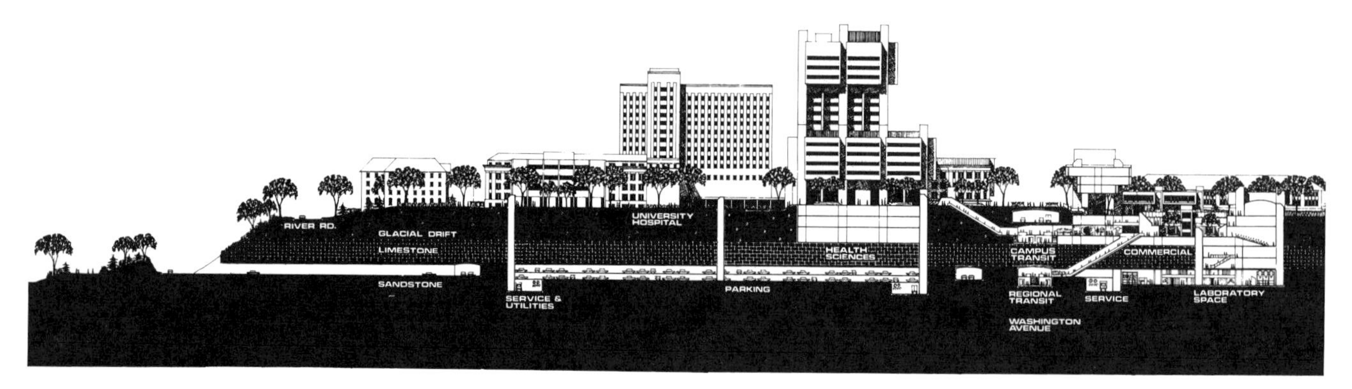

Figure 1-13: Concept for underground development at the University of Minnesota. (Drawing: John Carmody)

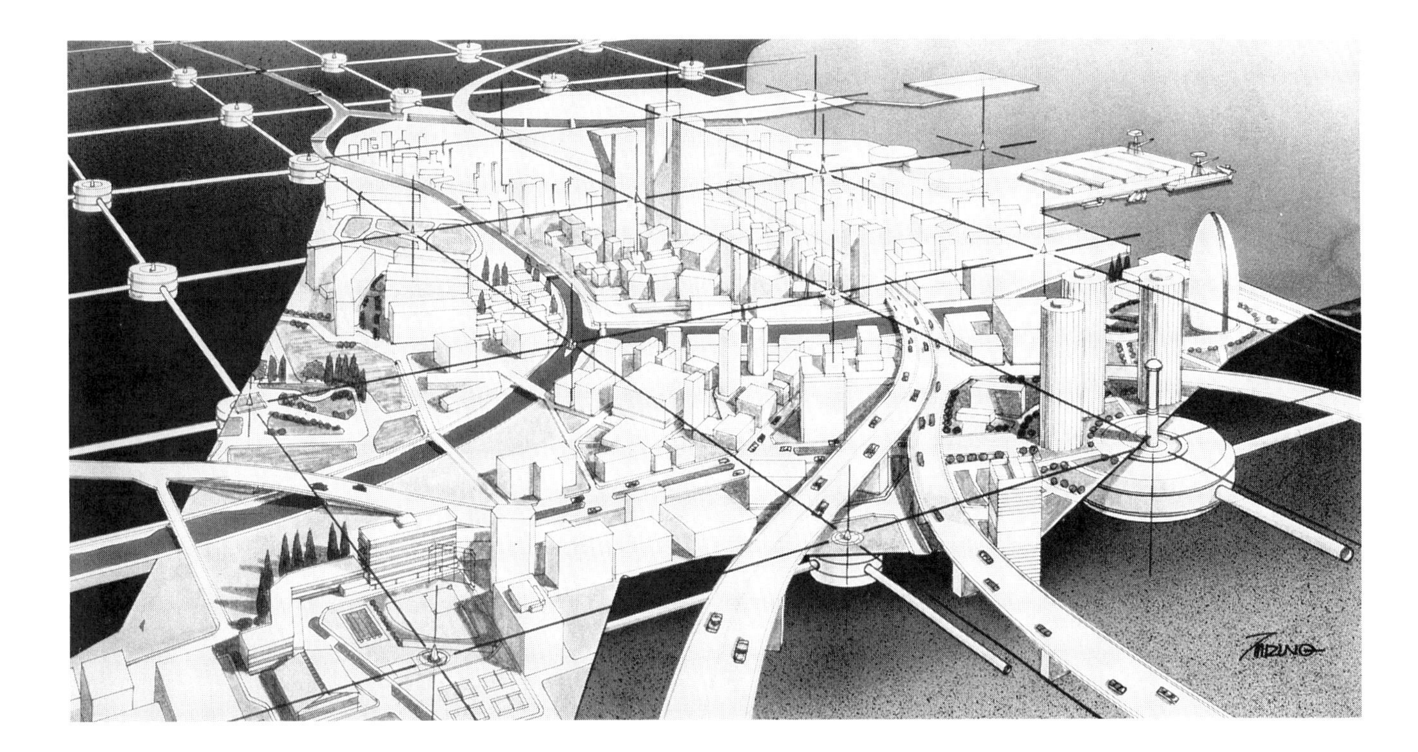

Figure 1-14: Geo-Grid concept for Tokyo developed by Shimizu Corporation. This illustrates an extensive network of underground space beneath Tokyo that can provide improved infrastructure and more open space on the surface in a congested urban environment.

When completely new cities are envisioned for the future, the underground often is a major component, as illustrated by the work of the architect Paolo Soleri over the last 30 years. In science fiction, future cities often are depicted as self-contained, climate-controlled units frequently located underground for protection from the elements and possibly from a hazardous or polluted environment. In this case, underground cities on earth differ little from bases created on the moon or other isolated environments.

Visions of future underground development—some positive, some negative—are frequent subjects of science fiction writers. E.M. Forster's short story, *The Machine Stops*, envisions a world in which people have adapted to living in small pods underground connected to anyone in the world by advanced communications and supplied with life necessities and cultural opportunities by the central machine. Cut off from the need to provide for their existence and dependent on artificial systems, they are tragically vulnerable when the machine stops. A slightly different theme can be found in H.G. Wells' *The Time Machine*, in which surface dwelling elite, the "Eloi," have become vulnerable to a literal underclass, the "Morlocks," who were gradually evolved by the Eloi to provide all their needs out-of-sight below ground.

There are many positive literary and scientific visions of underground uses in the future. Soviet physicist Andre Sakharov and science fiction writer Isaac Asimov, in addition to the architects and planners mentioned above, have all stressed the importance of underground space use in the future of our built environment. To avoid the cautionary visions of what the underground could become while developing the positive attributes it can provide in an environmentally insecure future, it is critical that human and social goals be an important part of the vision for future underground development.

CHAPTER 2

by Raymond Sterling

Benefits and Drawbacks of Underground Facilities

Chapter 1 introduced several global trends that are providing increased impetus for underground space utilization. This chapter presents in more detail the many advantages of locating facilities underground, and also systematically discusses the drawbacks of underground facilities.

Choosing to Build Underground

Given the wide range of types and sizes of underground facilities, the discussion below should be considered only as a discussion of potential factors for choosing to build a facility underground. Individual projects may only involve a few issues providing significant advantages or disadvantages. It is also important to note that one of the prime considerations in developing underground space is location. Thus, the issue is often not merely choosing between an underground facility and a surface facility on the same site, but determining whether alternate locations, types of construction, and perhaps alternate means of achieving the desired end result without construction are appropriate.

Figure 2-1 illustrates a simplified, generic decision process for evaluation of a major public or business project. First, there is usually a problem to be solved—for example, a needed facility expansion or provision of a new service. This can be met by construction of a new facility or service in a particular vicinity but also potentially by reducing demand for the new facility (using conservation techniques for energy or water facilities, for example). If a new facility is to be considered seriously, then several alternative sitings and construction types may be examined with differing attributes in functionality, cost, ease of permitting, and uncertainty. For example, a high-cost option of siting a new surface structure in downtown Tokyo may be compared with an underground structure also in downtown Tokyo or a surface structure in a suburban area. One of the principal issues to be weighed will be the relative importance of a location in the downtown area — a decision unrelated to any specific features of the construction.

Table 2-1 provides in chart form the principal advantages and disadvantages generally associated with underground space use. Direct benefits of a particular project are separated from indirect societal benefits with little relevance to an individual user (unless the environmental benefits are linked to permit costs, tax incentives, etc.). Physical benefits are likewise separated from those benefits that can be expressed in actual cost benefits to a

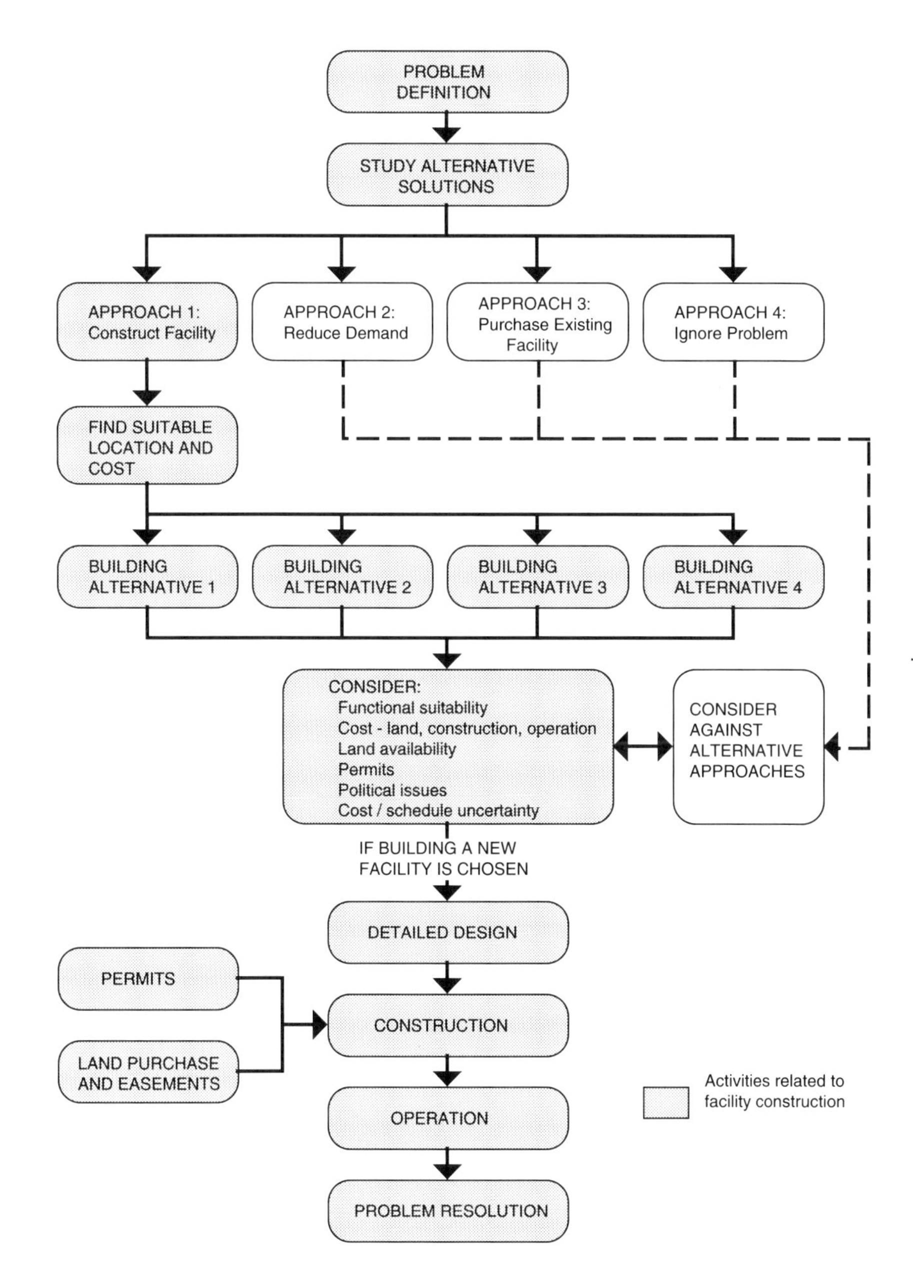

Figure 2-1: Decision-making process for evaluation of building alternatives.

Table 2-1: Benefits and drawbacks of underground facilities.

MAJOR ISSUES	SUBCATEGORY	POTENTIAL BENEFITS	POTENTIAL DRAWBACKS
PHYSICAL AND INSTITUTIONAL ISSUES	LOCATION	Proximity Lack of surface space Service provision Status	Unfavorable geology Uncertain geology
	ISOLATION	Climatic thermal, severe weather, fire, earthquake Protection noise, vibration, explosion, fallout, industrial accident Security limited access, protected surfaces Containment hazardous materials, hazardous processes	Climatic thermal, flooding Communication Human issues psychological acceptability, physiological concerns, fire safety, personal safety
	PRESERVATION	Aesthetics visual impact, interior design Environmental natural landscape, ecology, run-off Materials	Aesthetics visual impact, building services, skillful design Environmental site degradation, drainage, pollution
	LAYOUT	Topographic freedom 3-dimensional planning	Ground support Span limitations Access limitations Adaptability Sewage removal
	INSTITUTIONAL		Easement acquisition Permits Building code Investment uncertainty
LIFE CYCLE COST	INITIAL COST	Land cost savings Construction savings no structural support, weather independent, scale Sale of excavated materials or minerals Savings in specialized design features	Confined work conditions Ground support Limited access Ground excavation, transportation, and disposal Cost uncertainty geological, contractual, institutional delays
	OPERATING COST	Maintenance Insurance Energy use	Equipment/materials access Personnel access Ventilation and lighting Maintenance and repair
SOCIETAL ISSUES		Land use efficiency Transportation and circulation efficiency Energy conservation Environment/aesthetics Disaster readiness National security Less construction disruption	Environmental degradation Permanent changes Embodied energy

project. Although some physical benefits can be measured in terms of cost, others such as aesthetic issues must be balanced within a decision-making framework.

Following the basic structure of the chart, the nature of each listed issue is amplified in the rest of this chapter. Where appropriate, several references are provided to papers or reports relevant to the issue being discussed.

Potential Physical Benefits

LOCATION

Locational advantages for underground structures include the ability to build in close proximity to existing facilities or on otherwise unbuildable sites. For some projects, such as essential utilities, the location may be predetermined, which in turn may mandate underground construction due to the utility type or surface restrictions. Building decisions also may be affected by the status of certain locations within a city or urban area, which may translate into a premium being paid for a downtown location. For example, a higher cost for underground construction may be acceptable if it permits a downtown location for a facility that otherwise would have to be located further from the city center.

ISOLATION

Isolational advantages relate to the physical characteristics of typical underground spaces and their surrounding ground environment. The ability to isolate structures within a mass of earth provides the following specific advantages.

Climate

Thermal. In most regions of the world the temperature within the soil or rock at depths of less than 500 meters represents a moderate thermal environment compared with the extremes of surface temperatures (see Figure 2-2 for an example). These moderate temperatures and the slow response of the large thermal mass of the earth provide a wide range of energy conservation and energy storage advantages:

- Conduction losses from the building envelope in cold climates are reduced.
- Heat gain through the exterior envelope from both radiation and conduction is avoided in hot climates.
- Earth-contact cooling is possible in hot climates.
- Energy requirements are reduced for tempering air infiltration.
- Peak heating and cooling loads are reduced due to large thermal inertia.

Carmody and Sterling (1983, 1985) provide more complete discussions of the energy issues involved in underground buildings. Energy advantages for other types of underground facilities are discussed in Chapter 4 under the various uses of underground space.

Severe weather. Underground structures are naturally protected from hurricanes, tornadoes, thunderstorms, hail, and most other natural phenomena (Moreland 1981). The most vulnerable portions of underground structures are the surface access points for entry, light, or view. Underground structures can also resist structural damage due to floodwaters, although special isolation provisions are necessary to prevent inundation of the structure itself.

Fire. Underground structures provide a natural protection against external fires. The ground is incombustible and provides excellent thermal isolation to the structure beneath. Access points are again the most vulnerable. Brush fires are a relatively common hazard in some regions of the world such as Australia and California. Urban fires are a major concern during other calamities such as a major earthquake or during wartime.

Earthquake. Underground structures have several intrinsic advantages in resisting earthquake motions:

- The ground motions at the ground surface are amplified by the presence of surface waves.
- Structures below ground are usually designed to support significant ground loads and hence earthquake loadings may not provide massive increases in loadings.
- Structures below ground are constrained to move with the ground motion, so there is not the same opportunity for amplification of ground motions by structural oscillation effects as there is aboveground.

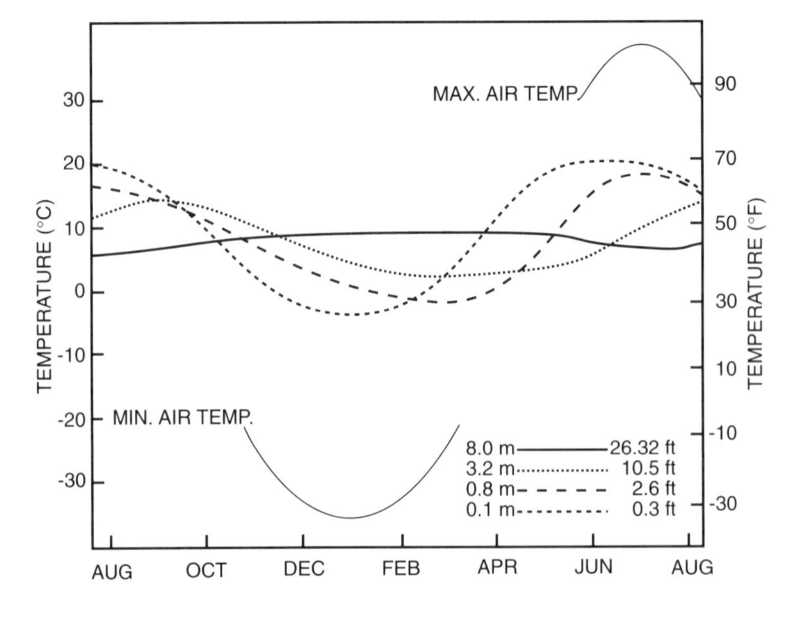

Figure 2-2: Annual temperature fluctuations in Minneapolis, Minnesota.

Figure 2-3: An Australian house damaged by a brush fire.

Earthquakes will damage underground structures at fault movement locations, and special care must be taken in lightly supported blocky rock structures which could be loosened during ground movements. In general, however, experience with underground structures during earthquakes has been excellent.

Protection

Noise. Small amounts of earth cover are very effective at preventing the transmission of airborne noise. This attribute can be very important for structures located in exceptionally noisy locations such as those adjacent to freeways and major airports. Surface openings provide the major transmission path for noise to the interior.

Vibration. Major vibration sources in urban areas include road and highway traffic, trains, subways, industrial machinery, and building HVAC systems. High technology manufacturing systems require environments with increasingly stringent limits on vibration amplitudes, velocities, and accelerations. If the vibration sources are at or near the ground surface, levels of vibration will diminish rapidly with depth below ground and distance from the source. High frequency vibrations are eliminated more quickly with depth than low frequency vibrations.

Explosion. As with noise and vibration, the earth will absorb the shock and vibrational energy of an explosion. Arching of the soil across even shallow-buried structures greatly increases the peak air pressures that a structure can withstand. Once structural protection has been achieved, the access points must be designed to prevent the passage of high air overpressures.

Fallout. Radioactive fallout consists of radioactive dust particles that settle on the ground or on other surfaces following a release of radiation into the air. The majority of the types of radiation present in fallout from an atomic bomb can be absorbed by several inches of concrete, steel, or earth. A major benefit of

Figure 2-4: Seward town houses in Minneapolis use earth berms to protect against freeway noise.

underground structures in this regard, in addition to their heavy structures and earth cover, is the limited number of openings to the surface. All building openings and the ventilation system must be properly protected to provide adequate fallout protection (Moreland 1981; Chester et al. 1983; Chester and Zimmerman 1987; Winqvist and Mellgren 1988; Saari 1988).

Industrial accident. Explosion, fallout, and similar catastrophic protection is not solely related to military uses—many industrial facilities have a significant potential for explosions and toxic chemical release. Also, terrorists often strike non-military targets. Underground structures, especially if provided with the ability to exclude or filter contaminated outside air, can be valuable emergency shelter facilities.

Security

Limited access. The principal security advantage for underground facilities is that access points are generally limited and easily secured. This limitation of entry and exit points also seems to inhibit would-be intruders or thieves.

Inaccessibility. The structure of the facility away from surface openings is generally not directly accessible. Excavation or tunneling for unauthorized access is time consuming and can be monitored with relative ease.

Containment

Containment is the inverse function of protection. With containment, the goal is to prevent a damaging release from the facility to the surface ecosystem.

Hazardous materials. Hazardous material storage underground can take advantage of the protection, isolation, and security of the facility. Proper design and geological siting can provide very low probabilities of hazardous material leakage and of any such leakage being transported to the surface environment. Hazardous materials include both high- and low-level nuclear wastes and hazardous chemicals that are not disposed of by chemical alteration or incineration.

Hazardous processes. Containment of a hazardous (e.g., potentially explosive) process below ground can limit the effect of an explosion on the surrounding community. Several major industrial accidents over the past two decades have highlighted this concern, and protective earth berms to deflect blast waves upward are now required for some surface facilities.

PRESERVATION

Aesthetics

Visual impact. A fully or partially underground structure has less visual impact than an equivalent surface structure. This may be important in siting facilities in sensitive locations or when industrial facilities must be sited adjacent to residential areas. The increasing requirement for all utility services to be placed below ground is primarily a visual impact decision.

Interior character. An underground structure can provide an interior character quite different from that of a surface structure. Combinations of tunnels, chambers, and natural rock structures in a quiet, isolated space have inspired many religious expressions. At the other end of the spectrum the hustle, noises, and smells of a busy subway system also can provide a memorable aesthetic experience.

Environmental Advantages

Natural landscape. This is similar to the limited visual impact mentioned earlier but specifically relates to the preservation of a natural landscape in keeping with the local environment.

Figure 2-5: Church in the Rock in Helsinki exploits the unique design opportunities with underground construction.

Figure 2-6: Solaria house in New Jersey, USA, illustrates environmental advantages of earth sheltered buildings including preservation of the natural vegetation and reduced rainfall run-off. (Architect: Malcolm Wells)

Ecological preservation. When natural vegetation is preserved through the use of underground structures, less damage is inflicted on the local and global ecological cycle. Plant life, animal habitat, and plant transpiration and respiration are maintained to a greater extent than with surface construction.

Rainfall retention. Results of the preserved ground surface are that percolation of rainfall to replenish groundwater supplies is encouraged and storm water run-off is reduced. This reduction in run-off permits smaller storm sewers, detention basins, and treatment facilities and also reduces the potential for flooding.

Materials

Underground structures may offer advantages in terms of preservation of the structure itself or preservation of objects stored within the structure. For example, embalmment followed by entombment has been very successful in preserving corpses from ancient civilizations. Likewise, food preservation is often enhanced by the moderate and constant temperature conditions and the ability to maintain a sealed environment that restricts the growth of insect populations and fungi (see Chapter 4).

LAYOUT

Advantages in the layout of underground facilities derive primarily from the freedom (within geological, cost, and land ownership limitations) to plan a facility or an urban system in three dimensions rather than being tied to surface facilities controlled by topographic and existing land use constraints (Fairhurst 1976). Transportation and utility tunnels in areas of rugged topography are independent from the topographic constraints. Deep subway systems need not be physically constrained by existing surface land uses (although legal obstacles often limit this freedom). Likewise, a pumped-storage scheme may use a deep underground reservoir connected by shaft to a surface reservoir when the region does not have favorable topography for a conventional dual surface reservoir scheme.

Life Cycle Cost Benefits

Direct financial benefits are calculated by estimating the life cycle cost impacts of the benefits provided by an underground facility. These benefits may be in terms of initial cost or operating cost.

Initial Cost/Land Cost Savings

The most likely initial cost saving is in a reduced cost for the land purchase necessary to carry out the project. Land or easement costs for an underground project may range from a full purchase of the site for projects that essentially usurp the surface use to a very low percentage of the land value if no impact on the existing surface use will occur and the surface owner would have little opportunity in developing a use at the depth proposed (see Table 2-2 for examples of easement cost ratios to surface land cost). As illustrated in Chapter 1, in areas with extremely high land costs, the cost of land purchase can dominate all the initial cost decisions.

Table 2-2: Examples of easement cost versus depth.

	Depth(m)	Value(%)*
Belgium	>6	10
	3.25 - 6	20
	1 - 3.25	30
Germany	50 - 90	0.25
	35 - 50	0.5
	25 - 35	1
	20 - 25	2
	15 - 20	3
	10 - 15	4
	<10	5

*Expressed as a percentage of the surface value.
Source: *Legal and Administrative Issues in Underground Space Use* (ITA 1990).

Construction Savings

Although underground structures typically cost more to construct than equivalent surface structures, some combinations of geological environment, scale of facility, and type of facility may provide direct savings in construction cost. An example of this is the Scandinavian experience with large oil storage caverns. Figure 2-7 illustrates the change in the cost of underground oil storage facilities with the size of the facility. Underground structures may

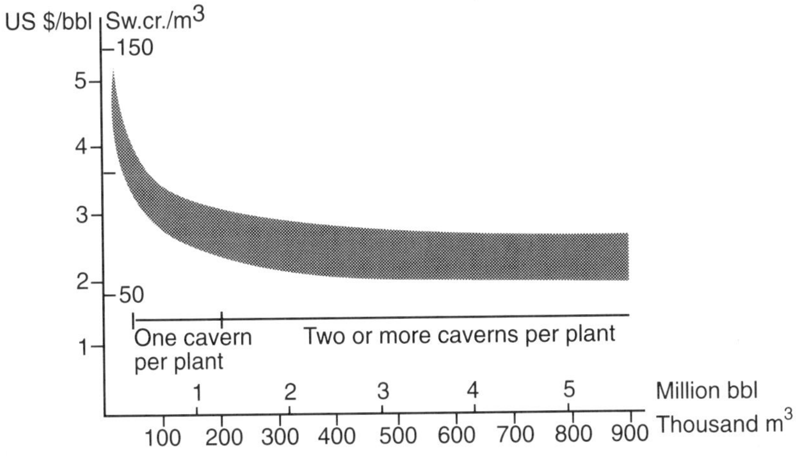

Figure 2-7: Cost comparisons for underground oil storage in Sweden – September 1977 price levels. (Source: Jansson in Bergman 1979)

also provide weather-independent construction which can offer some cost advantages in severe climates.

Sale of Excavated Material or Minerals

If the underground facility is excavated in a geologic material with an economic value, the sale of this material can be used to offset the excavation cost. If, as in the Kansas City, Missouri, USA, limestone mines, the excavation is part of a profitable mining operation, the space becomes a near-no-cost by-product of the mining. In Coober Pedy, Australia, the rewards are not as certain, but a resident excavating an underground home there can recoup costs if sufficient opals are found during the excavation. In most cases, however, a planned continuous supply of a mineral resource is required before a reasonable economic value can be developed. This limits the economic recovery for isolated, small projects even when the excavated material has value.

Savings in Specialized Design Features

The physical advantages of underground facilities may provide direct cost benefits when compared with a surface facility. For example, thermal isolation may reduce peak load demands for a facility's HVAC system, enabling a smaller, less expensive system to be installed (Setter, Leach & Lindstrom 1980, 1981, 1983). The same level of security and protection may be available at less cost than for an aboveground facility. The partial costs for providing low vibration, constant temperature, or clean room space may also be less underground than at the surface. For buildings that would have an expensive exterior finish aboveground, significant savings can be made below grade where such finishes are unnecessary. The architect who designed an addition to the Mutual of Omaha

Figure 2-8: Mining for limestone aggregate in Kansas City, USA. (Source: Underground Developers Association, Kansas City)

Figure 2-9: Reuse of limestone mines for warehousing in Kansas City. (Source: Underground Developers Association, Kansas City)

headquarters building in Omaha, Nebraska, USA, indicated that savings in the reduced use of the expensive facing stone used on the original building more than offset the increased costs of the construction of the underground addition (Savage 1979).

Operating Cost / Maintenance

The physical isolation of underground structures from the environmental effects that deteriorate building components can result in a low maintenance cost for underground structures. The reduced impact of temperature fluctuations, ultraviolet deterioration, freeze-thaw damage, and physical abrasion can reduce the rate of deterioration of underground structures. Other maintenance advantages may include the absence of snow removal problems in underground subways and the slow temperature change in storage facilities when equipment malfunctions.

Insurance

Physical isolation also can result in reduced insurance premiums for underground facilities. Reductions are not always available, however, even if theoretically warranted, because the insurance rating system depends either on an adequate historical loss record or a detailed risk assessment for the type of facility proposed. If a loss record is not available and the company is unwilling to distinguish a separate class of facility, no reduction may be available. The use of an insurance company with experience in insuring underground facilities along with care in planning to limit hazardous internal conditions offers the best possibility of rate reductions. For more complete discussions of insurance assessments for underground facilities, refer to de Saventhem (1977) and Muller and Taylor (1980).

Energy Use

The thermal advantages of underground structures usually translate into reduced energy costs to operate them. Although ventilation and lighting costs often increase, thermal benefits outweigh these in moderate to severe climates, particularly when a surface facility would be designed as a sealed, force-ventilated facility (Sterling and Carmody 1990). Savings in energy costs are rarely sufficient to justify building a facility underground for energy conservation reasons alone since there are also techniques for greatly reducing energy use in conventional buildings and the initial cost of an underground building may be high. The reduced operating cost and the stability of thermal conditions during energy outages become more important considerations as energy shortages develop and energy costs escalate.

Indirect Societal Benefits

These benefits can accrue on a large scale but are rarely important to an individual user.

Land Use Efficiency

The ability to place support facilities below grade and preserve the land surface for uses requiring the surface environment is an important benefit. With surface development, urban sprawl replaces farm land and recreational areas. Suburban factory development often covers large land areas with windowless buildings and parking lots. The sprawl itself requires more land area to be devoted to automobile and truck transportation because development densities are too low to support adequate urban mass transportation systems.

Figure 2-10: Varissuo civil defense shelter in Turku, Finland, is also used for recreational purposes. (Source: Saari 1988)

It is also possible to improve existing land use problems through underground construction by placing existing facilities below grade and reclaiming the surface for other uses. This is being done in some cities by moving railway lines underground and using the reclaimed land for recreational space, infrastructure facilities, or commercial development.

Transportation / Circulation Efficiency

The ability to infill buildings, provide underground connections, and improve urban densities contributes to compact development that can allow efficient transportation and circulation patterns to be developed.

Energy Conservation

Beyond the immediate financial impact to a building user or developer, energy conservation has implications for national security, economic development, and the balance of trade.

Environmental Benefits / Aesthetics

These are the regional impacts of underground construction that result in better land use. New development or redevelopment can occur but with a strong emphasis on preserving the environment.

Reduced Surface Disruption

The construction of new underground systems or facilities can be organized to disrupt the existing area less than equivalent surface construction. This is particularly true of facilities that can be excavated with only limited surface access. Cut-and-cover subway systems in urban areas have developed a reputation for very damaging interference with local businesses during their construction, but the effects can be mitigated with proper controls on excavation practices and the provision of temporary road surfaces (Walton 1978; Silver and Peters 1977). Tunneled subway system construction interferes less and may only be noticeable at station locations.

Disaster Readiness / National Security

National safety or security concerns provide the driving force for the construction of underground facilities in many countries. In Scandinavia, Switzerland, and several other countries, needed community facilities are constructed underground with the additional features necessary to provide adequate civil defense shelters. The national government provides for enhanced national security and the community obtains a needed local facility (Saari 1988; Winqvist and Mellgren 1988; Rygh 1990).

Potential Physical/Institutional Drawbacks

LOCATION

Locating facilities below grade requires a greater interaction with the local geological environment than for most surface construction. This geologic environment may be highly unfavorable for underground construction, and exact geologic conditions are difficult to predict prior to construction, which in turn increases project uncertainties. Some types of underground facilities are not restricted to a given area and can be located in a suitable geologic environment. However, for others such as service facilities for existing development, the geologic environment in which the construction must take place is already set. Due to their historical development on the estuaries of major river systems, many major urban areas of the world have rather unfavorable geologic conditions for underground construction.

ISOLATION

Climate

Although mostly a positive issue, the isolation of underground structures can provide thermal disadvantages for certain types of facilities. For example, it is difficult to reject excess heat production in underground facilities except through air-conditioning and/or high levels of forced ventilation. Similarly, the slow thermal response of underground structures and cool ground-contact surfaces can cause undesirable interior conditions. In warm, humid weather, non-air-conditioned buildings may experience high relative humidities and condensation. High thermal mass is also not well suited to short-term changes in desired interior conditions.

Flooding is a concern for many underground structures, and protection against the effects of surface floods, fire-fighting water, and water leakage from the ground must be provided.

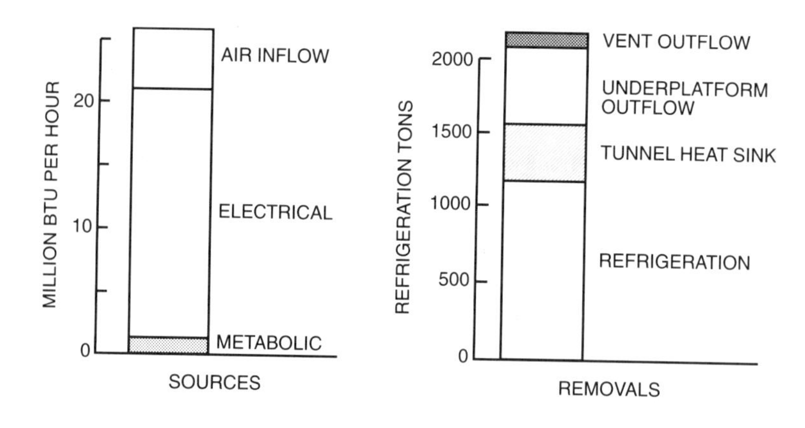

Figure 2-11: Example of the heat balance in a subway system with design temperatures below ambient levels. Only a small portion of the heat generated during subway operation can be dissipated to the ground. Refrigeration has been used to remove the excess heat produced. (Source: Associated Engineers 1976)

Communication

Communication within underground networks and between the surface and underground spaces may be impeded. Television, radio, and mobile communication systems will not operate in isolated underground spaces without antennas, cable systems, or special distributed signal repeater systems.

Human Occupancy

Probably the most pervasive drawback to the use of underground facilities for non-service functions is that a large majority of people express a strong dislike for working in underground or windowless spaces. Coupled to this psychological resistance are concerns for whether an underground environment is healthy for long periods of occupancy. Designing facilities to provide a pleasant and healthy human environment in underground space is the central issue in this book and is examined in detail in Part II. Only an indication of the problem areas is given here.

Psychology/Physiology. For most people, the idea of working or living underground elicits a negative reaction. Negative associations with underground space generally include darkness combined with humid, stale air. Among the most powerful associations are those related to death and burial, or fear of entrapment from structural collapse. Other negative associations arise in relation to feeling lost or disoriented since normal reference points such as the ground, sky, sun, and adjacent objects and spaces cannot be seen. Also, with no direct view of the outdoors there can be a loss of connection with the natural world and no stimulation from the variety of changing weather conditions and sunlight. Physiological concerns with the underground primarily focus on the lack of natural light and poor ventilation.

Continuing concern over placing people underground indicates that some of the historic images of dark, damp environments linger in our minds even though modern technology has overcome many of these concerns. The generally negative reaction to underground space has forced designers and researchers to attempt to overcome these perceptions.

Safety. Safety issues may also represent disadvantages for underground facilities. The ability to exit an underground facility in case of an interior fire or explosion is hampered in deeper underground facilities by the limited points of connection to the surface, the need for upward travel on exit stairs, and the difficulty of venting poisonous fumes from a fire. In ground containing dangerous chemicals or gases, these may potentially seep into the underground space, causing health problems. Heavier-than-air gases from the surface may also fall into underground structures to create higher concentrations than would exist on the surface.

Safety from personal attack can also be diminished in underground structures if public areas are isolated and provide areas for attackers to wait and act unseen. This has been a substantial drawback to some underground pedestrian connections in urban areas.

Resolving safety issues requires careful design and building operation, which translates into higher costs. The removal of all psychological resistance to underground facilities is not feasible despite the major improvements possible with careful design.

PRESERVATION

Aesthetics

The fact that facilities may be mostly or completely obscured below ground is not always desirable. Facilities that must attract attention for business such as retail stores and restaurants must maintain visibility to passers-by. Office buildings are often a symbol of the size, wealth, and profile of the corporations within them. Most architects who design buildings also like to make an architectural statement with their work in terms of its exterior appearance and are reluctant to consider placing their buildings out of sight.

In the design itself, underground building presents some aesthetic problems. First, even though the bulk of a facility or building may be placed below grade, entrances and building service facilities must still be provided. Unless such entrances and service facilities are provided through adjacent surface facilities, they can become the dominant visual image of the facility. Service facilities (which are normally rather unattractive) may thus have a strong impact on the exterior appearance of the facility. A more general problem for underground facilities, which has been noted in earth sheltered residential structures and large industrially oriented underground facilities, is that the aesthetic manipulation of earth forms, vegetation, and building layout to create a harmonious design can be very difficult for an inexperienced designer or one without architectural training. Poorly designed conventional facilities maintain many similarities to the normal building forms and do not stand out. A poorly designed underground building or its surface expression can quickly become an eyesore.

Environmental Disadvantages

Underground structures disturb the geologic environment in which they are placed. Sometimes this disturbance can degrade the ground environment and the surface environment. Open-pit excavation and trenching are the most immediately damaging to the existing topsoil and vegetation conditions. Mined or tunneled construction may cause surface settlement (altering surface drainage patterns and damaging existing buildings). Water leakage into the underground structure may drain the surrounding ground, causing long-term settlement in sensitive soils and again affect surface vegetation (Jansson and Winqvist 1977).

LAYOUT

Underground structures must maintain stability in the surrounding geologic environment. In some cases the ground can be self-supporting up to certain span limitations. In cases where

Figure 2-12: Surface settlement over a 3.7-meter diameter tunnel located 5 meters below ground level. (Source: USNCTT)

support is used, maximum opening sizes are limited by the increasing relative cost of supporting larger openings. Such support costs typically rise faster with clear span than for surface structures, and thus constrain the layout of underground facilities significantly by determining which opening sizes and shapes are economical. The layout must maintain the separation between adjacent openings necessary for ground stability and provide for the often substantial interior structure needed to withstand ground pressures in poor ground conditions or at great depth.

Although underground facilities may have a three-dimensional freedom not possible on the surface, the location of access points for fully underground facilities is limited by surface topography and existing surface uses, and their number is limited by the high costs of shafts.

The future expansion or adaptability of underground facilities is also a potential problem. Underground structures are usually expensive to modify and, if designed for a single use, opening sizes and arrangements may not be adaptable for a wide range of other uses.

Underground structures extending deeper than adjacent sewer services must provide for the collection and removal of sewage from the lower levels of the building using sewage lift stations.

INSTITUTIONAL

There are several broad impediments to the greater use of underground facilities—obtaining the rights to development, gaining permit approvals in unusual design circumstances, and obtaining financing approval for non-standard developments.

If the surface land is not owned, easements for the proposed underground use must be obtained. For long tunnel projects, this may involve hundreds or thousands of different landowners with different degrees of receptivity to the project and differing expectations as to the proper value of the easement. The delays and costs in solving these problems in some countries can terminate the project or lead a public agency to try to keep the tunnel entirely within public right-of-way even if this means a substantial cost increase or degradation of project performance.

The difficulty of obtaining zoning and building code permits varies substantially with the type of project and its location. It may be difficult to obtain code variances relating to safety even though existing provisions are not appropriate for the type of underground structure considered.

Finally, the geological and institutional uncertainties inherent in large underground projects discourage both public and private investors from committing their resources even if the cost/benefit analysis for the project is favorable.

Life Cycle Cost Drawbacks

These direct financial drawbacks are calculated by estimating the life cycle cost impacts of the disadvantages of an underground facility. These impacts may be in terms of initial cost or operating cost.

Initial Cost

There is often a substantial cost penalty for an underground facility compared with an equivalent surface facility. This depends on the type of facility and whether the location of the underground facility can be matched to favorable site conditions. The confined working conditions, the high ground support costs (both temporary and permanent), the limited construction access points, and the cost for excavation, transportation, and disposal of the ground removed to make the space all usually contribute to increased costs. High costs are exacerbated by the geological and institutional uncertainties, particularly when contractual practices attempt to place all financial risk on a contractor. This creates an adversarial relationship for the project that harms productivity and may result in unreasonably high legal costs. It also results in an owner paying for potential risk in the bid price even when no problems may actually occur (ITA 1988).

Operating Cost

Operating cost disadvantages relate primarily to the isolation of the facility. Personnel access to deep underground facilities may be time consuming and limited in capacity, shortening the effective working day. This effect may be particularly costly in heavily used facilities such as subway stations. Figures 2-13 and 2-14 illustrate the capacity and minimum travel times for typical forms of mechanized vertical transportation. It may also be difficult or time consuming to transfer large quantities of goods by elevator to an underground facility compared with the easy handling in a one-story surface facility with direct access (see Figure 2-15). Deep underground facilities without ramp access for trucks thus become less suitable for operations involving high rates of material transfer.

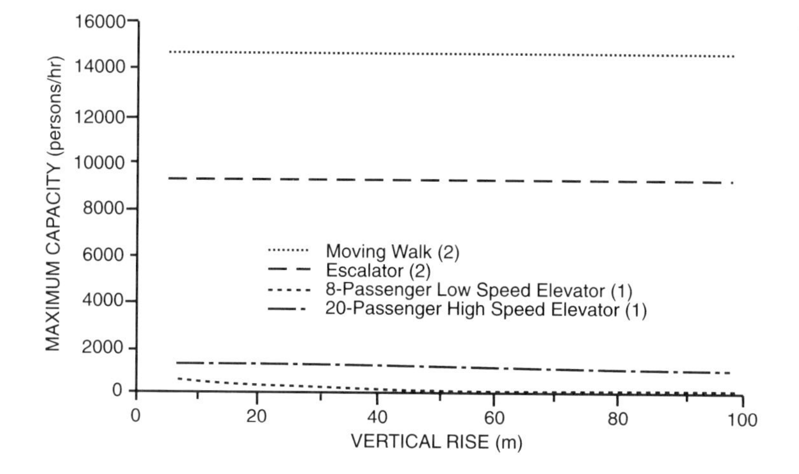

Figure 2-13: Maximum passenger capacity versus vertical rise for various forms of mechanized vertical transportation.

Notes:
1. One-way capacity, no dead time.
2. Observed capacity.
3. Capacity data from Strakosch (1983).

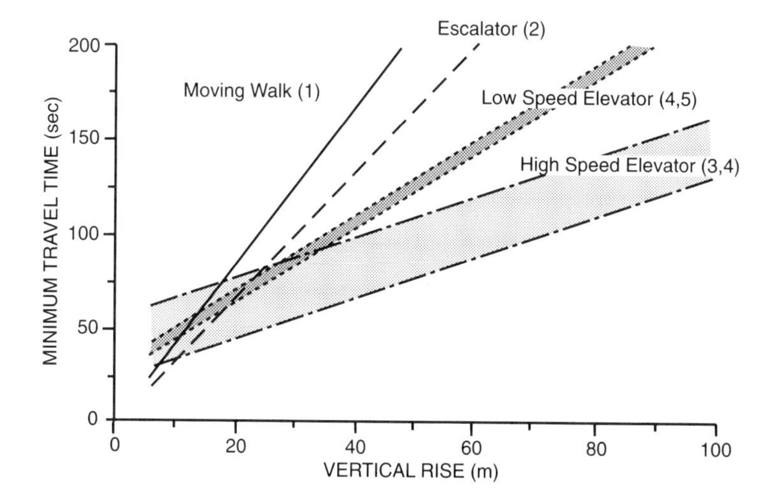

Figure 2-14: Minimum travel time versus vertical rise for various forms of mechanized vertical transportation.

Notes:
1. Based on 1.02-meter moving walls at 0.91 m/sec and 15 degrees incline.
2. Escalator operating at 0.61 m/sec.
3. Twenty-passenger elevator at 9.14 m/sec.
4. Minimum travel time based on door open/close, transfer in/out and travel time.
5. Eight-passenger elevator at 0.51 m/sec.

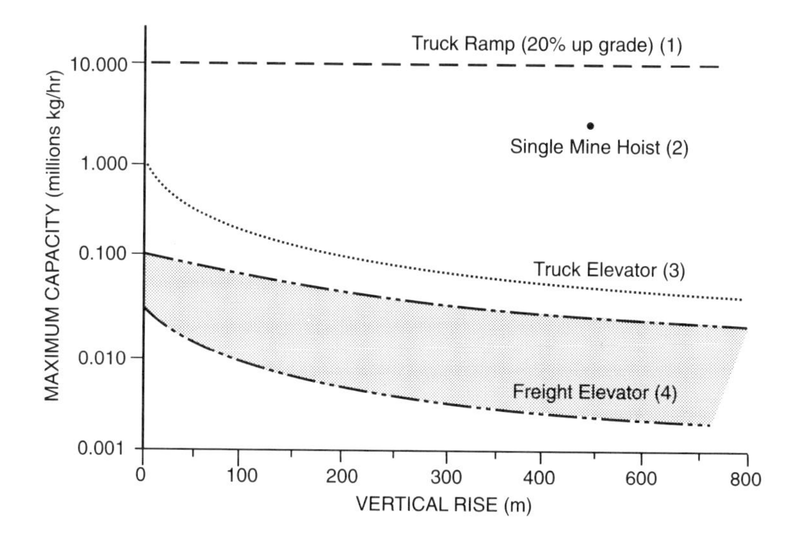

Figure 2-15: Comparison of material transport capacity for underground service options.

Notes:
1. Speed 3.6 m/sec, headway 30.5 m, truck capacity 22,700 kg.
2. Source: SME Mining Engineering Handbook 1973.
3. Capacity – 22,700 kg, speed – 0.5 m/sec, 60 seconds load/unload.
4. Capacity – 1135-3630 kg, speed – 0.5-2.0 m/sec, 110 seconds load/unload.

Adequate ventilation and lighting must be provided continuously in underground facilities whereas surface facilities may require far less (for example, an underground transit station versus a surface transit station).

Maintenance or repair of an underground structure may be very expensive due to the problems of accessing the point requiring repair. An example is the high cost of locating and repairing leaks in a waterproofing membrane on an underground building. Maintenance of plant materials above an underground building may also be more expensive than maintenance of a roof on a conventional building (Setter, Leach & Lindstrom 1981).

Potential Societal Drawbacks

These disadvantages may be important for large-scale underground space use or the long-term use of underground space even though they may have negligible impact on an individual user.

Environmental Degradation

The potential environmental problems of buried structures may not emerge for several years and may only be significant if the underground is widely used. Potential problems include drainage of groundwater through leakage into the facilities or watertable drawdown pumping (Jansson and Winqvist 1977); groundwater pollution from underground storage (Fairweather 1990) or waste disposal sites (National Research Council 1990); and chemical spills within underground facilities.

Permanent Changes

Underground structures permanently alter the ground conditions at a site, and the first underground facilities constructed may significantly deter or even preclude future uses. This places a burden of forward planning for competing underground space uses to a much greater degree than is required for surface structures, which are more easily adapted and renewed (Sterling et al. 1983; Jannson and Winqvist 1977).

Embodied Energy

One energy disadvantage of many underground structures is that they often constitute a higher level of "embodied" energy expended to create the facility than does a comparable surface facility. The embodied energy includes the energy for excavation, transport, and disposal of soil and rock to form the opening and the energy required to process, manufacture, transport, and install all the material used in the construction and finishing of the facility. The excavation process and the large quantities of concrete and steel used in most underground structures yield high energy investments in these structures (Hannon et al. 1977).

CHAPTER 3

by Raymond Sterling

Underground Space: Classifications and Configurations

Classification of Underground Space Uses

In the study of underground space utilization, it is useful to develop a classification or organization scheme that provides standardized terminology and an organizational basis for description, analysis, and research. Classification allows the most important attributes of an object to be described in a manner that others can understand without detailed examination. It also allows objects to be grouped into similar classes so that the characteristics of subgroups can be studied. Finally, it allows new objects to be readily fit into the context of prior knowledge.

Some classifications or taxonomies have previously been developed for underground space use, but they either are very broad concepts (Warnock 1978; Coogan 1979) or else have been developed with a subset of underground uses in mind (Baggs 1980; Labs 1976).

The difficulty in approaching this issue for underground space (as for many other interdisciplinary activities) is that the uses are very broad and major categorization may be desired from several different aspects. Uses range from utilities to churches, projects range from microtunnels to vast mining operations, and spaces range in size from the pore spaces in soil to citywide tunnel systems. A wide variety of practitioners are also involved—architects, planners, and several engineering specialties. Perceptions of the importance of physical location and layout vary greatly with the type of use considered and the design parameters of most importance. For example, "deep" underground space to an architect may be any space more than 8 to 10 stories (~30 meters) below grade, whereas deep underground space to a mining engineer may not be reached until depths exceed 1000 meters. The net result is that there appears to be no acceptable purely hierarchical classification scheme to fit all the varied potential uses.

In libraries that must classify all varieties of information, this problem has been dealt with in the past by assigning each work to a primary location in the cataloguing scheme and referencing other important attributes with keywords. Following this example, fast and widely available computerized databases have been developed featuring keywords that can be combined in various forms to rapidly select only those references desired. The use of such retrieval systems has greatly diminished the importance of the correct primary cataloguing identification.

Transferring this analogy to underground space uses suggests that trying to find a perfect, unified, hierarchical classification may be both impossible and unnecessary. The use of keyword attributes for each aspect of underground space considered important provides the necessary ingredients of a classification scheme:

- Terminology and descriptive elements can be standardized by specifying standard keywords and providing ranges of values for otherwise subjective descriptions such as size or depth.
- Projects or uses of underground space can be grouped by keyword combinations and/or ranges of selected values to allow study of particular types of uses or design features.

With the above rationale in mind, the Underground Space Center developed a database-style classification system that is intended to encompass all types of underground space use and

Table 3-1: Major classification groupings of underground space use.

MAJOR GROUPING	MAJOR SUBCATEGORIES
FUNCTION	Residential Nonresidential Infrastructure Military
GEOMETRY	Type of space Fenestration Relationship to surface Depth Dimensions Scale of project
ORIGIN	Natural Mined End use
SITE FEATURES	Geography Climate Land use Ground conditions Building relationships
PROJECT FEATURES	Rationale Design Construction Age

Table 3-2: Classification of underground space use by function.

MAJOR FUNCTIONS	SUBCATEGORIES OF USE	
	PEOPLE-ORIENTED USES	PRODUCT-ORIENTED USES
RESIDENTIAL	Single-family Multifamily	
NONRESIDENTIAL	Religious Recreational Institutional Commercial	Industrial Parking Storage Agriculture
INFRASTRUCTURE	Transportation of passengers	Transportation of goods Utilities Energy Disposal Mines
MILITARY	Civil defense	Military facilities

place them into a common framework. This database is described in detail in Appendix B. Only the principal elements involved in classifying underground space uses are introduced here.

Table 3-1 gives the major classification groupings chosen for underground space use: function, geometry, origin, site features, and project features. The major subcategories are listed under each category. These subcategories further organize the way underground uses are described, but must be supplemented by specific descriptors to classify individual uses.

CLASSIFICATION BY FUNCTION

The major functions to be placed in underground space together with subcategories of use are illustrated in Table 3-2. Uses that are principally people-oriented are separated from those that are not because of the importance of this distinction in determining the design approach. Design for people-oriented spaces will not be successful unless human acceptance factors are considered. For product-oriented uses, such factors are less important than satisfying the proper functional requirements, but they may still have an impact on the efficiency and well-being of any personnel operating or servicing the facility.

CLASSIFICATION BY GEOMETRY

Geometrical information is important in organizing underground space uses. The nature of the raw space utilized can be separated into uses involving underground caverns, uses developed by surface excavations, and aquifer storage involving the pore space in soil or rock.

Table 3-3 illustrates the basic geometric divisions chosen for describing types of space. The distinction between borehole and

Table 3-3: Classification of underground space use by type.

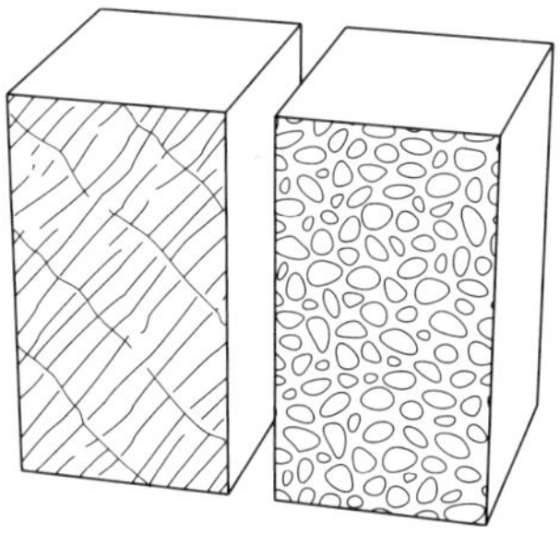

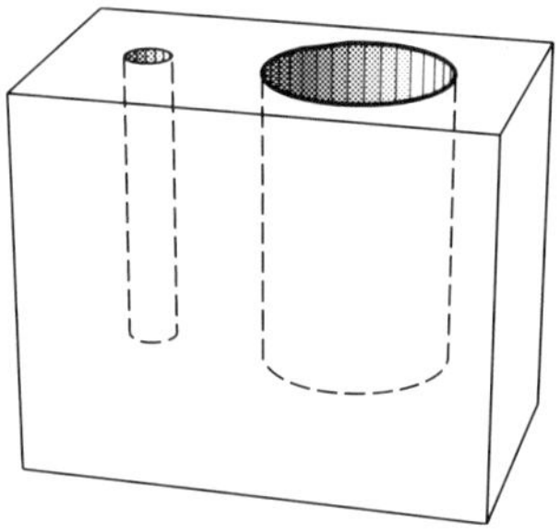

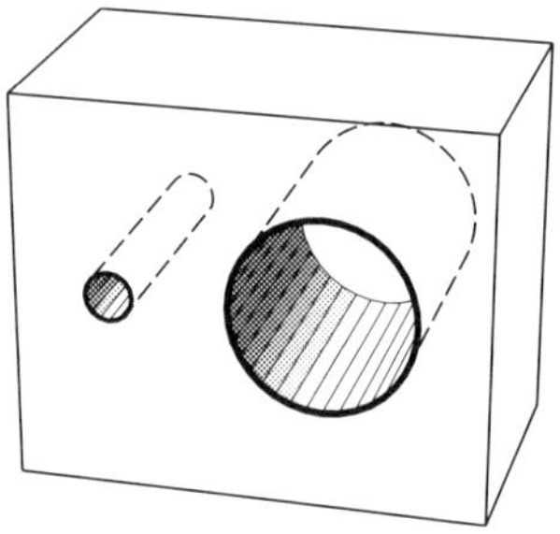

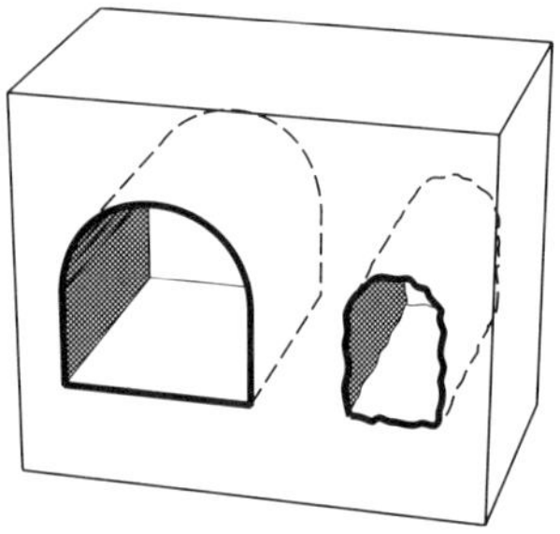

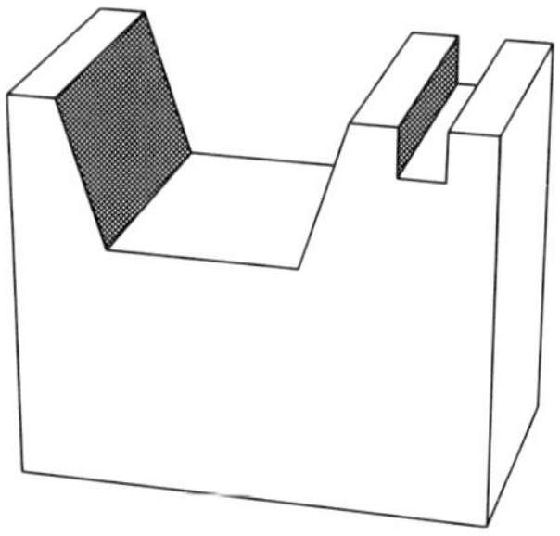

BASIC TYPE	REASON FOR OCCURRENCE	ORIENTATION OPTIONS
Pore Space Fissure	Natural Backfilled Fractured	
Borehole Shaft	Excavated	Vertical Inclined
Tunnel Microtunnel	Natural Excavated	Horizontal Inclined Spiral
Cave Cavern	Natural Excavated	
Trench Open Pit	Excavated	

shaft or between microtunnel and tunnel is most easily made on the basis of the possibility of personnel entry. Many uses, such as shafts, tunnels, and caverns, will obviously involve more than one type of space, but the existence of common elements among projects can be identified. The orientation of underground space elements also may be useful in classifying special uses if the orientation is non-standard, such as a spiral access tunnel.

The typical configurations of underground space either occurring naturally or resulting from mining or construction operations are discussed later in this chapter.

Fenestration

Table 3-4 illustrates a classification of the basic fenestration relationships for underground buildings together with the relationship of the building to the ground surface. The major elements of this classification scheme were presented by Labs (1976), and it is of most use for small near-surface buildings. Larger scale uses often involve several or all of the individual fenestration/ground relationships within the overall scheme.

Table 3-4: Classification of underground space use by fenestration and ground surface relationship. (Source: Labs 1976)

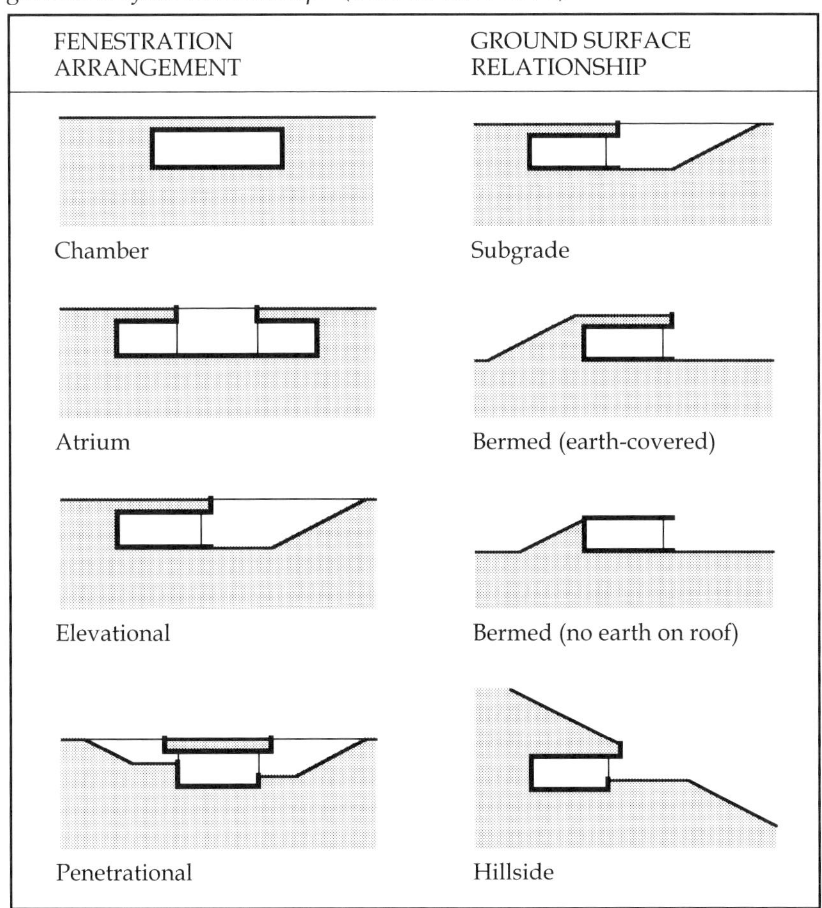

Table 3-5: Classification of underground space use by depth.

TERM	TYPICAL RANGE OF DEPTH IMPLIED ACCORDING TO USE (METERS)			
	Local Utilities	Buildings	Regional Utilities Urban Transit	Mines
SHALLOW – NEAR SURFACE	0-2	0-10	0-10	0-100
MODERATE DEPTH	2-4	10-30	10-50	100-1000
DEEP	More than 4	More than 30	More than 50	More than 1000

Depth

Table 3-5 illustrates the different uses of terminology associated with the depth of underground facilities. As explained earlier, the differences in physical depth associated with the terms shallow and deep are based on the differences in perspectives of the practitioners in the respective design fields. It is not necessary, even if it were possible, to resolve these terminology differences since keywords can be used easily to specify the actual depth, or range of depths, of a facility when there is confusion in interpretation.

Project Size

The size of a project may be important from two principal aspects. First, the size of individual spaces in terms of access and clear spans is important in terms of structural/geotechnical design and the construction systems utilized. This information is straightforwardly recorded as widths, heights, clear spans, diameters, etc. The other aspect that may be important is the scale of the project in terms of overall size and complexity. Projects of a large scale require major public or private investments, may have considerable societal impacts, and present much more difficult administrative problems than small projects. The separate classification of project scale allows a distinction to be made between a small local tunnel project and a major regional tunnel project even though the tunnel diameters and design features may be similar.

Building Type/Geographical Extent

Table 3-6 classifies underground uses by scale based on the area or volume of a building, facility, or storage use and the geographical extent of utilities, tunnels, or mines. District-scale pedestrian interconnection systems and regional use types are identified separately. Pedestrian interconnection systems may not involve the provision of much actual constructed space but can have a major impact on an urban area and can pose significant public policy issues. Likewise, a regional building type, such as cave dwellings in China, may be very small projects individually, but when large numbers exist in a region it may be useful to treat the use as a single entity to examine local or regional impacts.

OTHER CLASSIFICATION/GROUPINGS

The remaining classification groupings of origin, site features, and project features involve more straightforward descriptors of the key features of a particular use and its location. A fuller discussion is given in Appendix B.

Origin

Under origin, natural spaces are separated from spaces excavated for mining, military, or civil purposes. Mixed uses, adaptations, or reuses are also possible to identify.

Site Features

Classification by site features allows the collection of data concerning a wide range of factors that may affect the design of an underground facility—its economic, cultural, topographic, or climatic setting; local land use issues; and the ground conditions present. Identification of key features may be useful in understanding the regional or site influences that trigger a particular use and in grouping projects with similar site problems.

Project Features

The remaining grouping of project features allows the classification of underground space uses by specific project rationales, design features, construction features, or relationships to existing facilities. Such a classification permits projects with similar features to be identified for comparison. For instance, in occupied underground buildings, special natural lighting concepts may be of interest. In tunnels, the interest may lie in the type of excavating equipment used or the geotechnical design method. An initial list of keywords relating to the classification of project features is given

Table 3-6: Classification of underground space use by scale of use.

GENERAL FUNCTION	DESCRIPTION OF SCALE
RESIDENTIAL	Single family Small multifamily Large multifamily Settlement Widespread regional building type
NONRESIDENTIAL	Small storage or working chamber Medium-sized building scale Large building scale Block scale District scale
INFRASTRUCTURE (UTILITIES, TUNNELS, AND MINES)	Block scale District scale City scale Regional scale National scale

in Appendix B. Classification by age separates modern uses from vernacular traditional uses, historically recorded uses, and uses deduced from archaeological investigations.

Typical Configurations of Underground Openings

To understand the potential of underground spaces for meeting functional or aesthetic goals, it is helpful to understand the typical forms and configurations of underground openings available for use. These configurations may result from natural processes, remain from mining operations, or be constructed for specific underground facilities.

NATURAL CAVITIES

Small-scale Voids

The smallest natural cavities of interest for this discussion are the pore spaces between grains of soil. These spaces may be submicroscopic in clays, a few centimeters across in large gravels, and on the order of meters between large boulders. The pore spaces may be filled with gases such as air, natural gas, methane, radon, etc., and/or fluids such as water or oil.

Joints and fissures are typically planar or subplanar features in a rock mass caused by the natural structure of the rock type and/or the history of deformation of the rock mass. They fall into the following categories:

- **Open joints:** These are rock discontinuities in which the adjoining rock blocks are essentially detached from each other (or touch at limited irregularities).
- **Tight joints:** Tight joints are joints with no visible separation, although water and other fluids or gases may be able to pass along the joint.
- **Filled joints:** These are previously open joints that have been filled later with another material. This filling may be soft as in a clay filling or may be a precipitate that recements the joint surfaces together.
- **Fissures:** Although this term is often used interchangeably with joints, it may also imply wider rock features that cut across the normal rock structure and have been caused by substantial rock movement.
- **Faults:** These are zones along which large-scale rock movement has occurred. Faults are usually in-filled with a softer material called gouge.

The spacing of joints, fissures, and faults varies greatly with the type of rock and the geologic history of the area involved. Typically the spacing is greater for major discontinuities extending over a large area and smaller for minor discontinuities with less

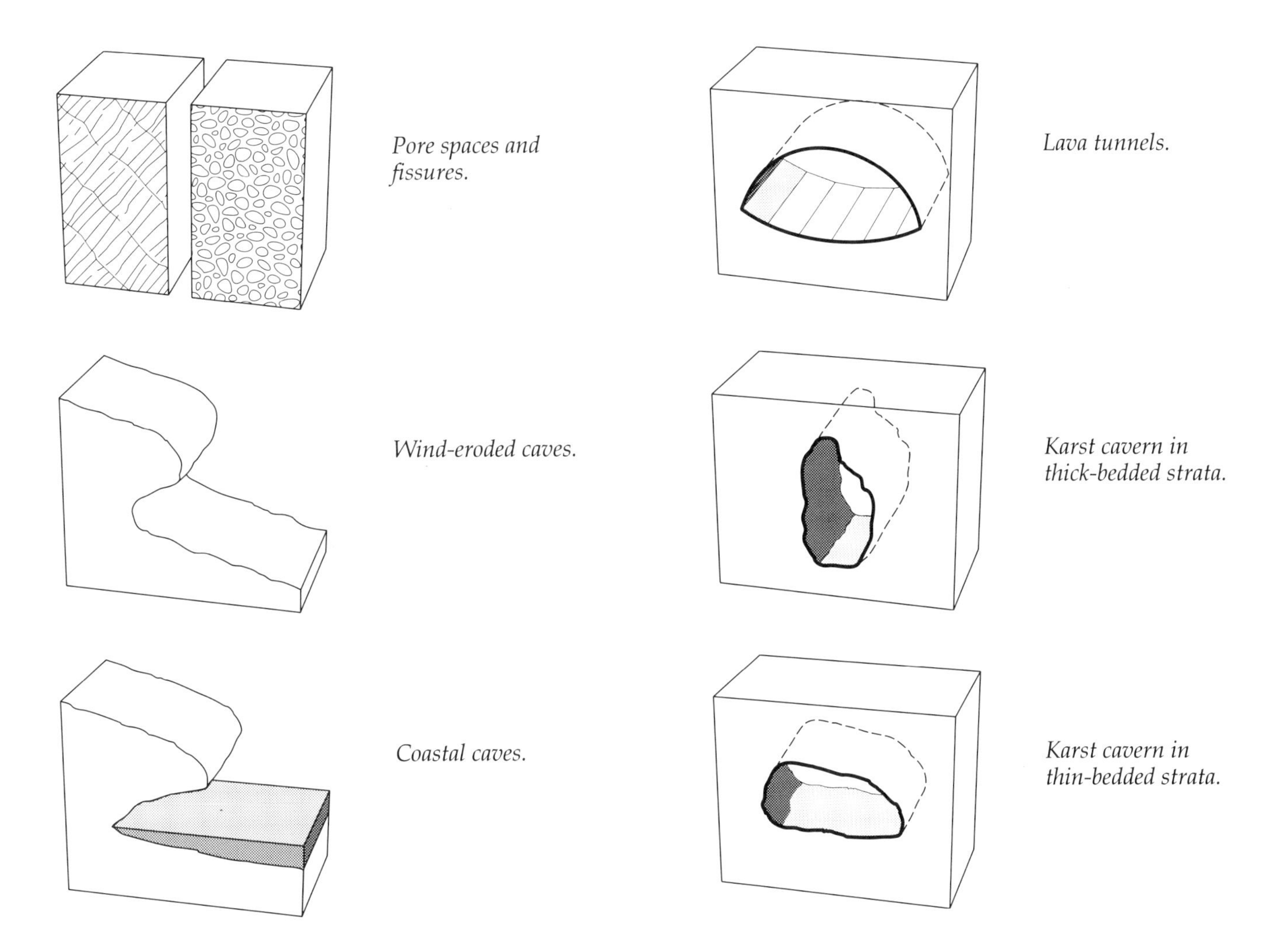

Figure 3-1: Shapes of natural cavities.

areal extent. Pore spaces, joints, and fissures are very important in the storage and flow of fluids below ground.

Caves and Caverns

Caves and caverns are natural cavities formed underground or in the sides of cliffs. The term cavern is usually reserved for underground cavities of particularly large dimensions. Caves may be formed by several natural processes:

- **Wind-eroded caves:** These are often high in elevation above the base of a cliff and relatively shallow in depth. Examples can be found at Mesa Verde, Colorado, USA, and in the Upper Nile Valley, Egypt.
- **Coastal caves:** These are water-eroded caves at the shoreline of large bodies of water. They may extend hundreds of meters from the shoreline. Because of the shift of the coastlines over geologic time, coastal caves may later be found well inland from the current coastline.

- **Lava tunnels:** These are tunnels formed during the cooling of lava flows from volcanic activity. While the surface of the lava flow cools and hardens, the hotter interior lava continues to flow, leaving systems of open tubes within the cooled lava flow. These tubes may be several meters across and several kilometers in length. For example, the lava tunnel at Kazimura Cave, Hawaii, USA, extends for more than 11 kilometers (Jackson 1982). Lava tunnels are expected to exist on the moon and are considered a potential form of shelter for a lunar base (Daga et al. 1990).

Karst Systems

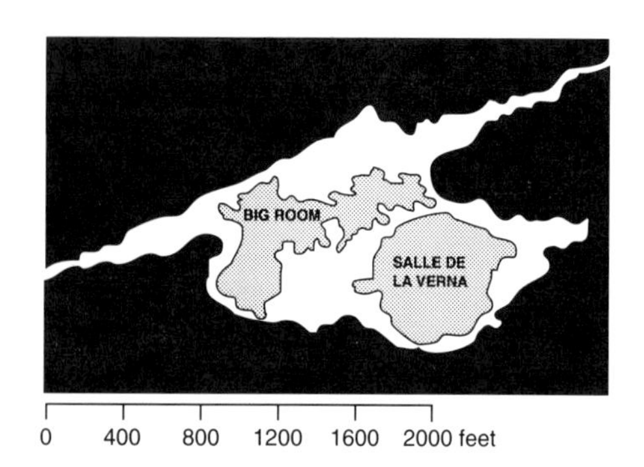

Figure 3-2: Good Luck Cave extends some 8,000 feet beneath the limestone mountains of Mulu National Park in Borneo. Its Sarawak Chamber (dark area above) is so enormous that the world's second- and third-largest underground chambers – Carlsbad Caverns' Big Room and Pierre St. Martin's Salle de la Verna – both could fit in it with room to spare. By contrast, the largest manmade cavern – an ice hockey arena in Norway – spans less than 200 feet, which is approximately one-tenth of the length of the Sarawak Chamber.

Karst systems, the most widespread form of large natural cavity, are formed when flowing water dissolves limestone and dolomite. The water dissolves calcium carbonate in the presence of oxygen, and as the water flows along systems of joints it gradually widens the joints into large cavities. The term "Karst" originates from a limestone region in Slovenia that was systematically explored for caves in the late 1600s. It has been estimated that Karst areas cover 5 to 10 percent of the land surface in the world (Jackson 1982).

In a Karstic region, the main erosion takes place above the water table where both oxygen and water are present. Surface water flows downward along vertical fissures, widening them and connecting into a horizontal flow system at the water table. As the river cuts deeper into the rock, previously eroded caves are left above the water table. When calcium-rich water flows into these voids from joints and fissures, some of the calcium may be precipitated, forming the flow structures, stalactites, and stalagmites that decorate such caves.

The largest systems of underground space and the largest known underground cavities are formed in such Karst systems. Karst caverns may be over a hundred meters wide, thousands of meters long, and over a hundred meters high. The Flint-Mammoth-Joppa system in Kentucky, USA, is the largest interconnected system of openings discovered to date. It has approximately 370 kilometers of caverns, caves, and passages large enough for human entry.

The largest known individual cavern is the Sarawak Chamber in northern Borneo, discovered in January 1981. The chamber is 396 meters wide, 700 meters long, and nowhere less than 70 meters high. The next two largest caverns are the Big Room at Carlsbad Caverns, New Mexico, USA, and the Salle de la Verna at Pierre St. Martin in France. A comparison of the sizes of these caverns with the size of one of the largest span underground caverns designed for civil use is shown in Figure 3-2. Although these enormous natural caverns are the result of very unusual conditions, they do indicate that a potential exists in favorable geologies for significantly larger underground spaces than are currently being constructed.

SURFACE MINING CONFIGURATIONS

When rock deposits containing useful minerals or building stone are at or near the surface, the least expensive method of mining is usually to create an open pit or quarry. In rock quarries, the face of the quarry typically advances horizontally into the surrounding ground (see Figures 3-3 and 3-4). Quarrying may stop for economic reasons (such as a downturn in prices or demand) or if the deposit is exhausted. Quarrying also may shift to an underground mining operation if the overburden depth becomes too large to remove economically, if the adjacent surface land is occupied, or if environmental regulations on dust or noise production hamper surface operations.

Open-pit mines may be in soil (e.g., gravel pits) or in rock (e.g., iron ore mines or coal mines). The decision on whether to mine a deposit as an open pit again hinges on economics, the depth of the deposit, and environmental regulations. The range of sizes of open-pit excavations is large, from a small gravel pit to massive excavations conducted over decades. The largest iron ore open-pit mines in northern Minnesota, USA, cover as much as 930 hectare and are over 150 meters deep.

Unreclaimed surface mine pits are usually considered unacceptable eyesores, but with imaginative pre-planning and restoration, the potential for development or recreation in a region can be improved. For instance, in the Appalachian Mountains of the eastern United States, surface mining reclamation has been proposed as a means for creating much-needed flat land for development (Gilbert 1981). The Belchatow brown coal mine in central Poland, when production is finished early next century, is planned to have excavated an area 13 kilometers by 3 kilometers to a depth of 300 to 500 meters to produce approximately 1 billion tons of coal. The re-landscaping of the site will create a permanent ski hill 150 meters high and a recreation lake that will significantly improve the recreational possibilities in the region (Aughenbaugh 1978).

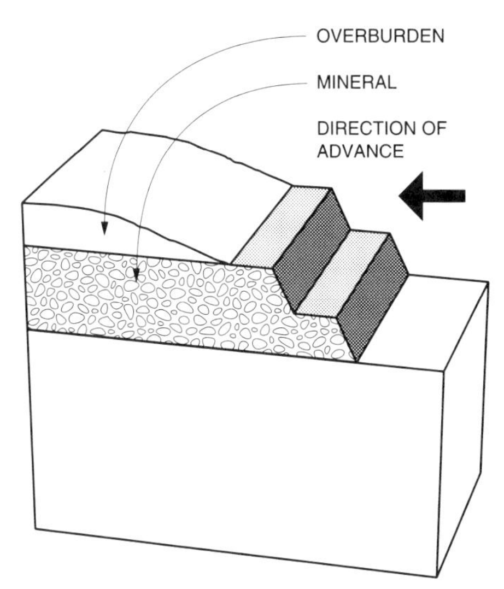

Figure 3-3: Rock quarry.

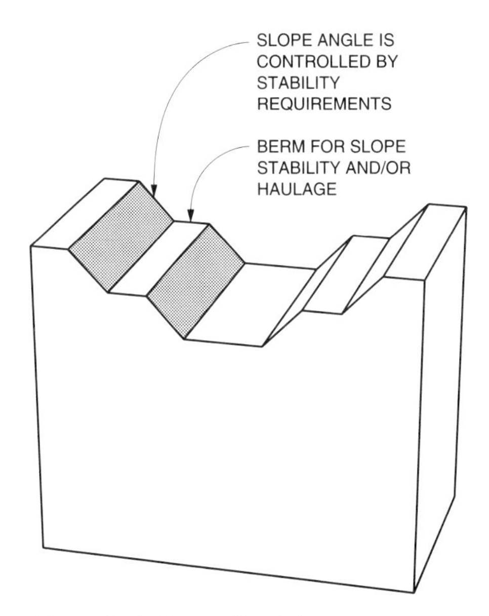

Figure 3-4: Open-pit mining.

UNDERGROUND MINING CONFIGURATIONS

Traditional methods of underground mining generally involved small shafts or tunnels supported by timber frames ("sets") and planks ("lagging") that could be erected by hand. Larger openings were only made in self-supporting ground, and the mining chambers were developed in formations designed to optimize the existing rock structure and strength. Figures 3-5 through 3-12 illustrate some traditional shapes and layouts of mining chambers.

Many other types of underground mining configurations are also feasible, with wide variations in the amount of mined space left behind. For example, on a hillside a mine may open directly from the surface with a horizontal tunnel ("adit"). When the ore-bearing zone is inaccessible from the surface, an inclined tunnel or shaft and tunnel system is used for access.

Since ore-bearing zones may be inclined at any angle (dip) to the horizontal, and may occur in rock types of widely varying strength and degree of jointing, a variety of mining methods have evolved to remove the ore in the most economical fashion. These result in very different characteristics of the space left behind by the mining operation. Also, since removal of the ore as cheaply as possible is the normal goal of the mining engineer, the stability of mine openings is considered principally in terms of the working life of the mine. The eventual collapse of mine openings is either accepted or made an active part of the mining operation.

When a mine cavity collapses, the state of the surrounding rock alters drastically, and ground settlements usually occur on the surface above the mine. The prediction of the ground settlement

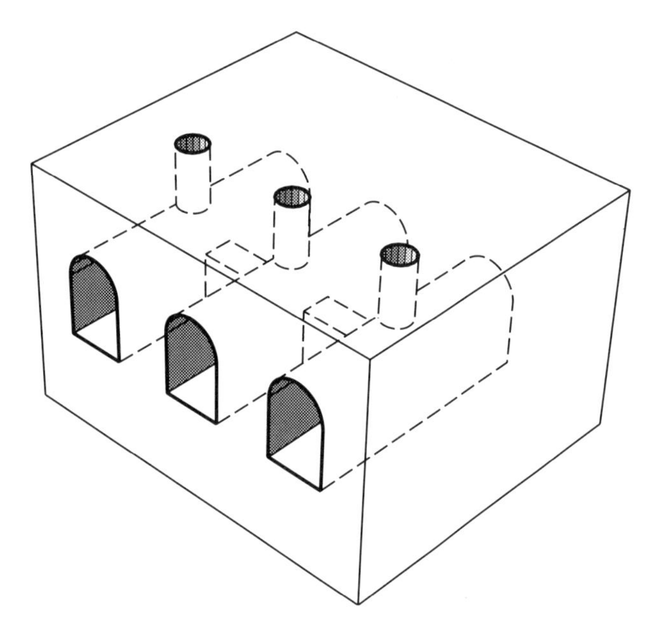

Figure 3-5: Traditional chamber mine.

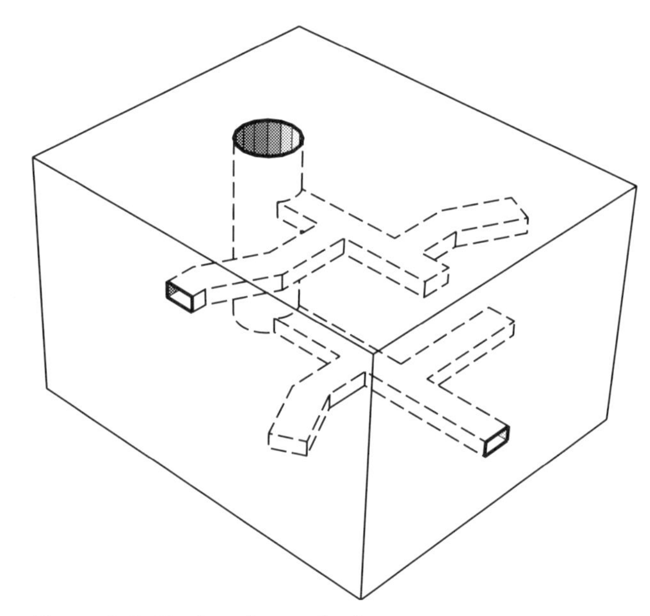

Figure 3-6: Shaft and tunnel mine.

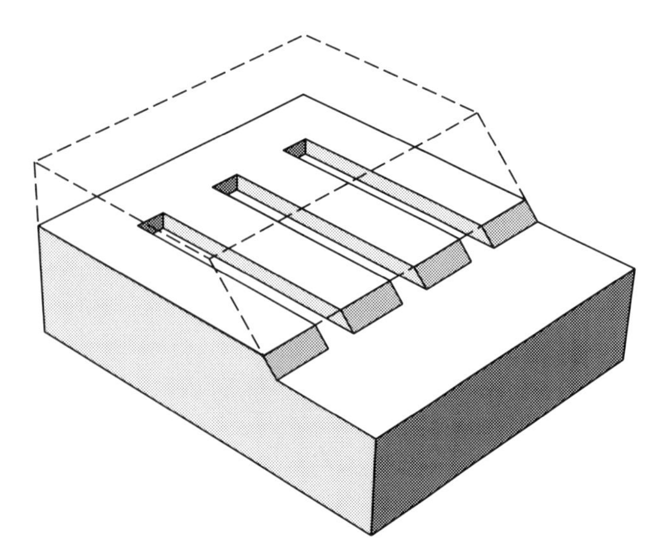

Figure 3-7: Horizontal adit mine.

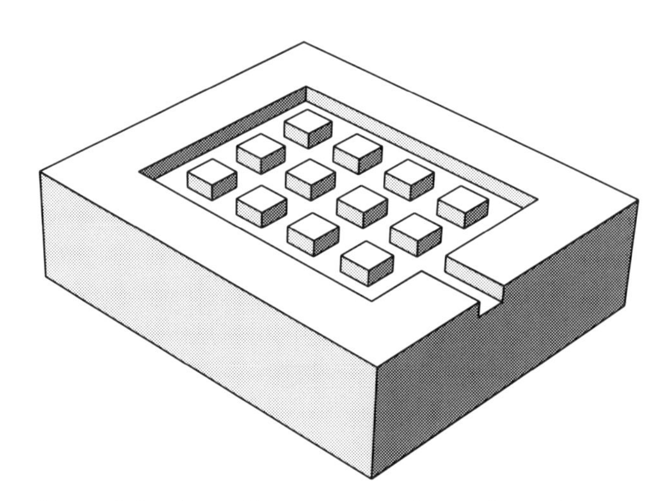

Figure 3-8: Mine with room-and-pillar configuration.

from mining activities is an important part of the mining operation when mining under existing surface facilities. Surface facilities must be designed to resist settlement-induced damage or be repaired after the settlement has occurred. Many old mines originally designed to remain open are now structurally unsafe, and the gradual collapse of these mines must be anticipated in the planning of surface works above suspect mine workings.

In shallow ore bodies, it is possible to leave a series of pillars within the ore body to support the surrounding ground. At greater depths, the size of the pillars becomes too large to economically allow the ore to remain in the pillars. In some mines, a room-and-

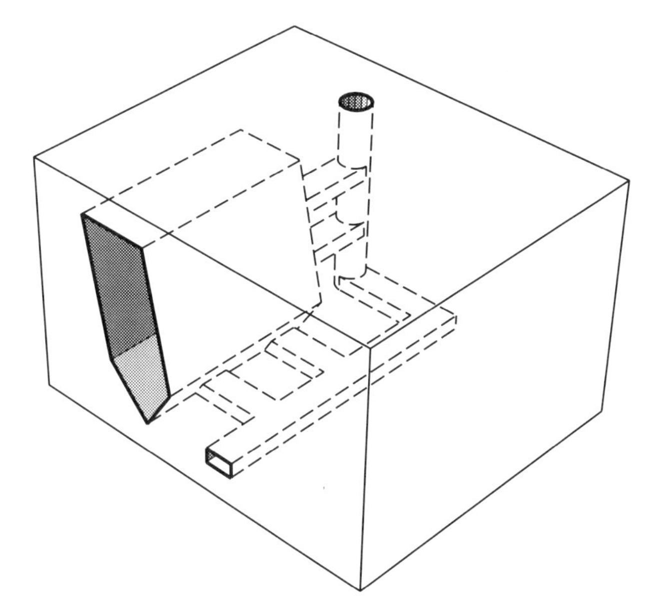

Figure 3-9: Open stope mine.

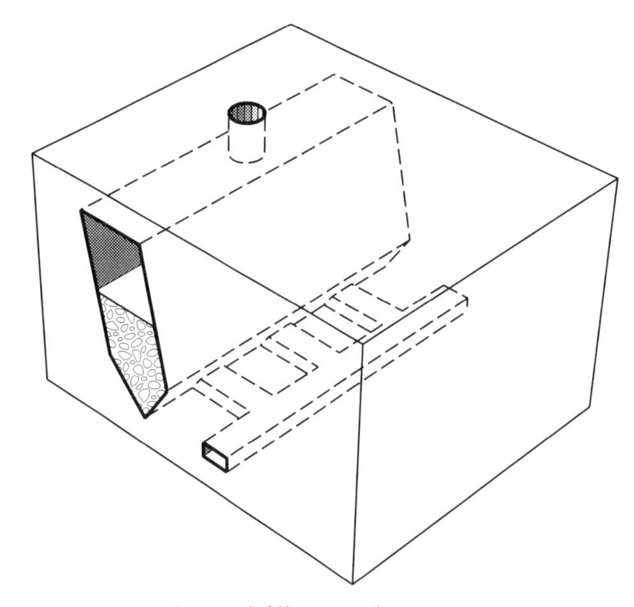

Figure 3-10: Cut-and-fill stope mine.

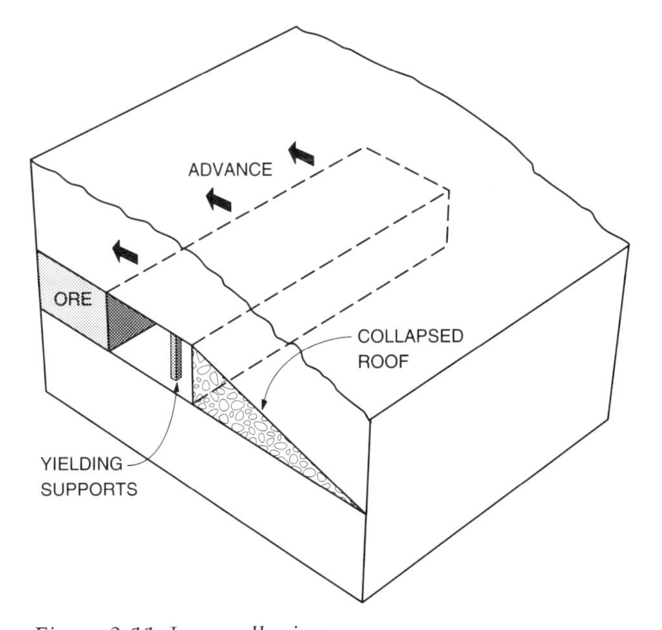

Figure 3-11: Longwall mine.

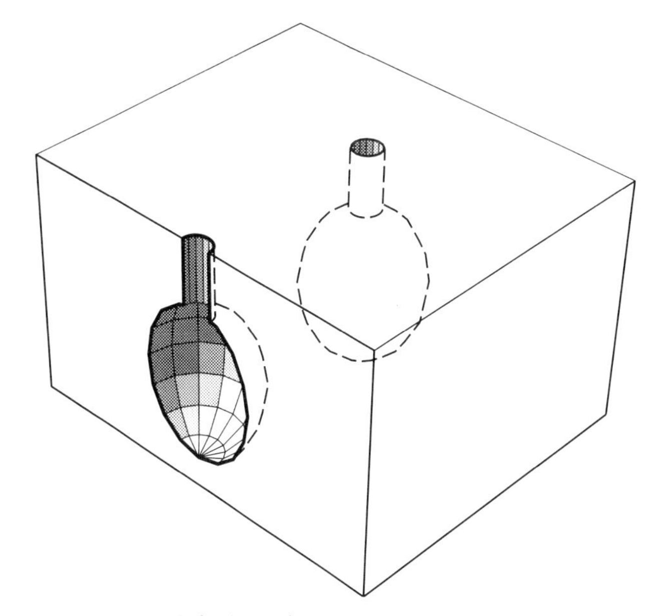

Figure 3-12: Solution mine.

pillar system is used to open a mine, and when the extent of the ore body has been reached, the pillars are removed during a retreat mining operation and the ground is allowed to collapse to fill the mined opening. Other mines using a room-and-pillar system may leave behind usable space after mining is finished if the design provides for long-term stability. The extensive underground facilities in worked-out limestone mines in the Kansas City area of the United States are perhaps the best known example (see Chapter 4).

Usable mined space may also be created after other types of mining. Systematic mining operations in steeper ore bodies generally utilize the gravity flow of the rock after fragmentation by explosives. Tunnels are driven beneath the area to be mined, and rock from the ore body falls into these tunnels to be removed as the excavation proceeds. The excavation may proceed laterally or up the dip of the ore body. The operation may leave rock pillars to prevent the cavity (stope) from closing (open stoping), fill the cavity with waste rock to limit closure of the cavity (cut-and-fill stoping), or allow the cavity to collapse to fill the void. If the rock when blasted flows naturally to removal points in the tunnel(s) below, the mining process is called caving.

Other mining methods leave no usable space behind. In longwall mining, an ore body of wide areal extent is fully mined (except for haulage and shaft zones). The rock behind the advancing face is temporarily supported using yielding supports that control the collapse of the ground behind the excavation face. A wave of surface settlement follows the movement of the excavation face, and no usable cavity is left by the mining operation.

The mining of steeply dipping ore bodies generally does not result in underground space that is useful except for bulk storage of liquids. Both stable and caved zones of such mines may be useful for liquid storage depending on the permeability of the caved rock zone, the nature of the fluid stored, and the ability to confine the fluid within a storage zone.

A type of mining that is quite separate from the methods previously described is solution mining. For instance, in salt, large cavities may be created remotely by pumping water through a pipe in a borehole into the salt and recovering the water through a separate pipe. The recovered water contains dissolved salt that is reclaimed or disposed of, and the dissolution process gradually creates a cavity within the salt deposit. The shape of the cavity is controlled by the positioning of the inlet and outlet pipes and the pumping rates.

CONFIGURATIONS FOR SPECIFIC USES

The most important class of shapes available for underground facilities are those that can both be excavated and supported economically for a specific end use. The range of cross-sectional shapes commonly used for underground facilities is quite small because of the nature of the excavating equipment available and the optimization of structural support for the opening. Figures 3-13 through 3-15 illustrate many of the commonly used configurations

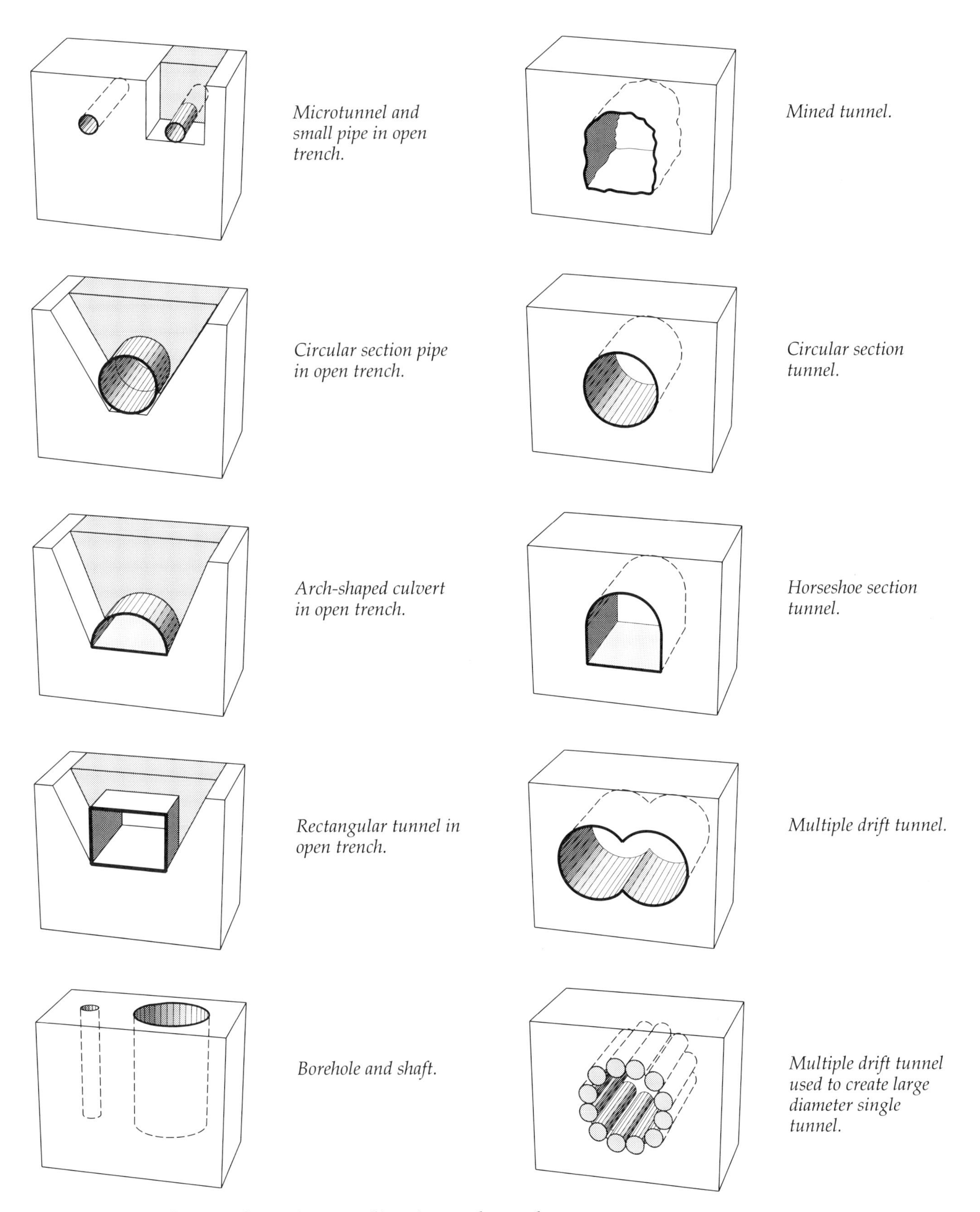

Figure 3-13: End use configurations – utility pipes and tunnels.

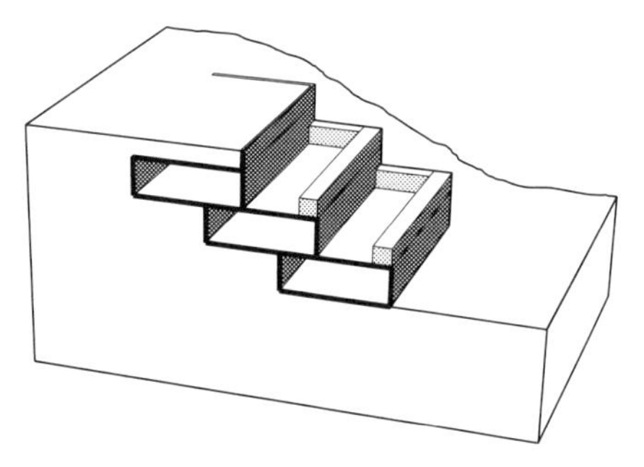

Terraced or hillside structure.

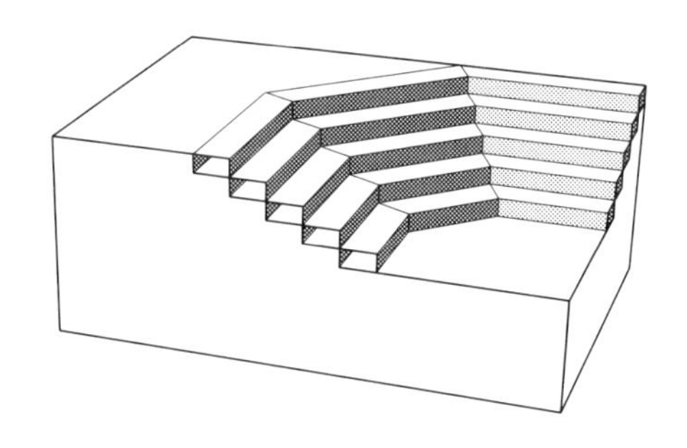

Large-scale terraced structure.

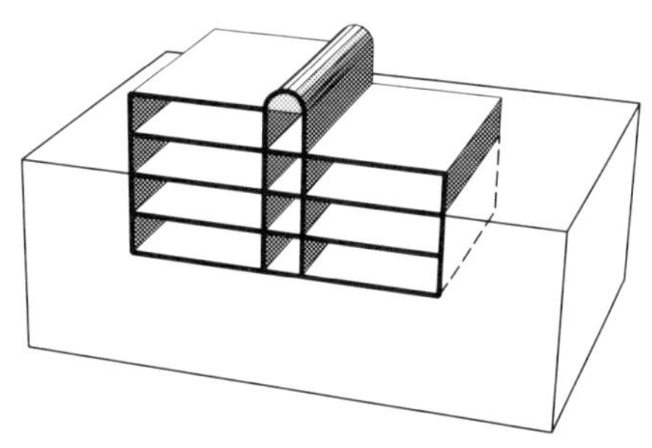

Shallow basement.

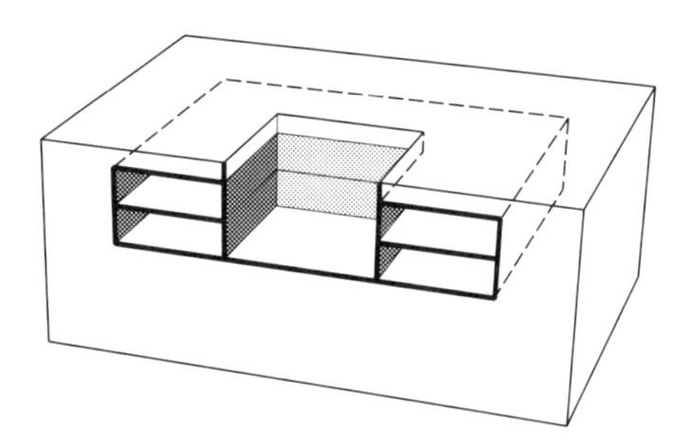

Shallow atrium (courtyard).

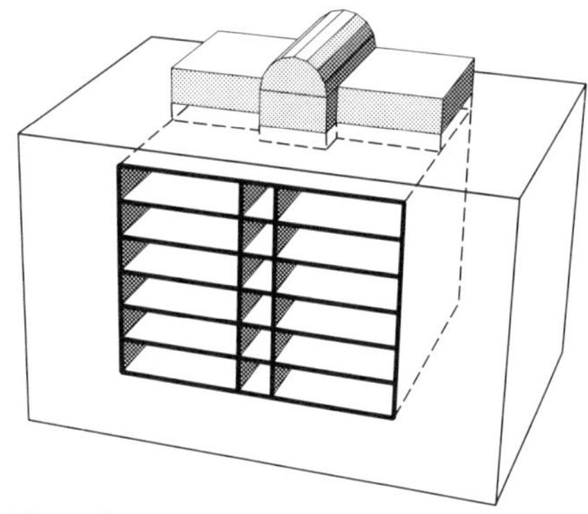

Deep basement.

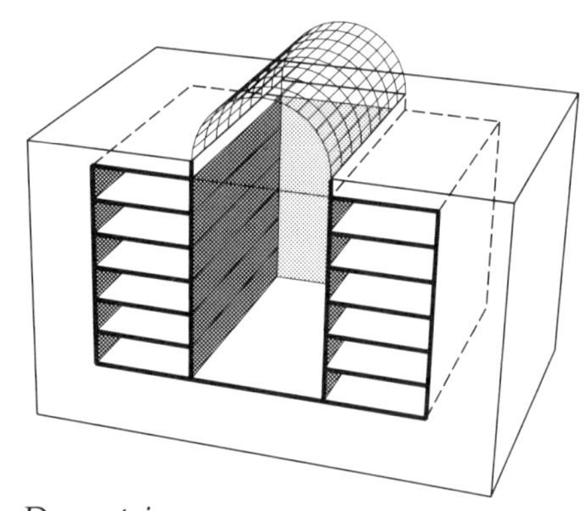

Deep atrium.

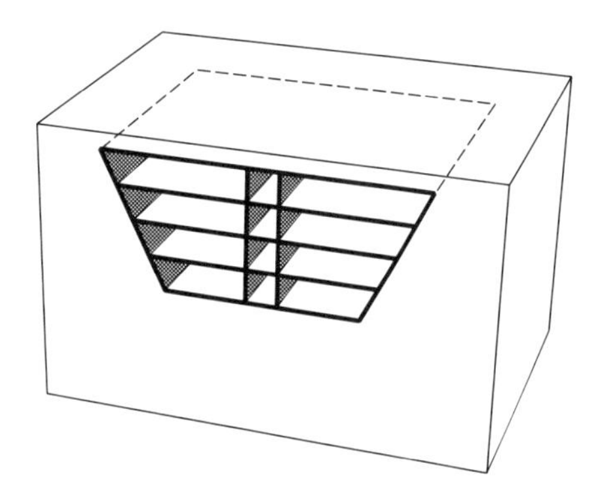

Cut-and-cover structure with sloped sides.

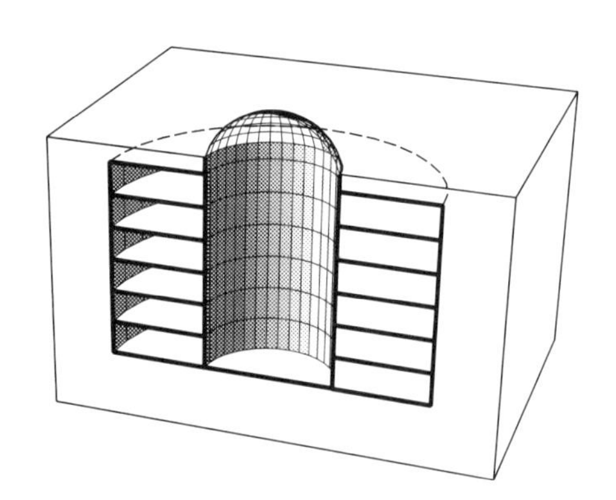

Cylindrical deep atrium.

Figure 3-14: End use configurations – cut-and-cover structures.

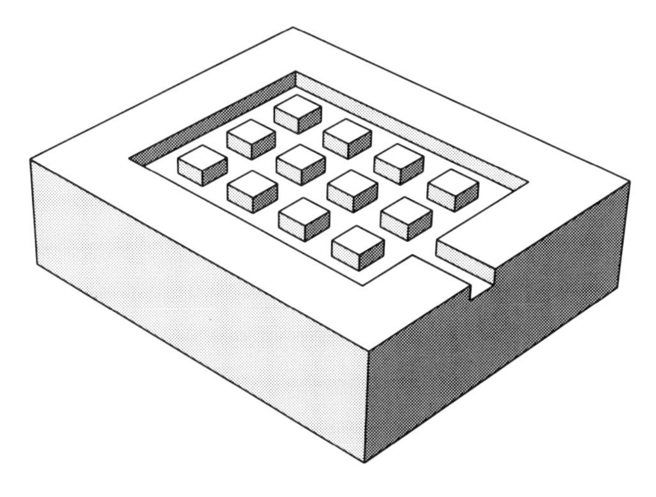

Caverns arranged in a room-and-pillar configuration. This approach maximizes the amount of excavated material and minimizes the pillar size. In this illustration, the space is shown in a flat-bedded geology with the flat roof and overburden removed. Access is shown through a tunnel, but may also occur through a shaft.

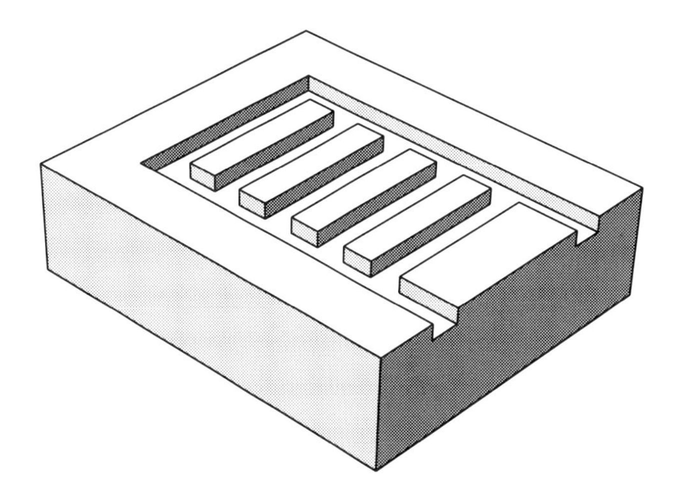

Caverns arranged in a rib configuration. This approach results in long, continuous openings and maximizes the span length between pillars. Similar to the room-and-pillar layout, this illustration shows the rib system in a flat-bedded geology with the flat roof and overburden removed.

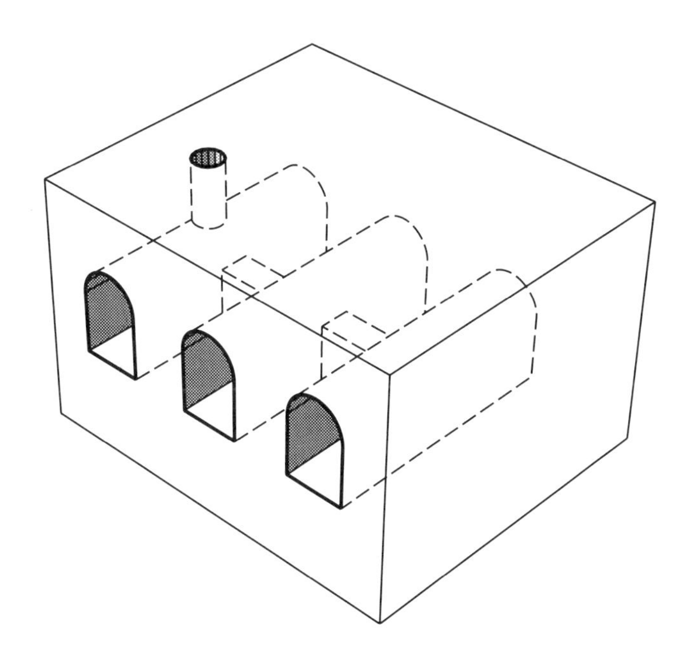

Cavern roofs are vaulted in many geological conditions. In this illustration, a series of parallel openings are shown resulting in a plan similar to the rib system. As shown here, access can occur through shafts as well as through tunnels.

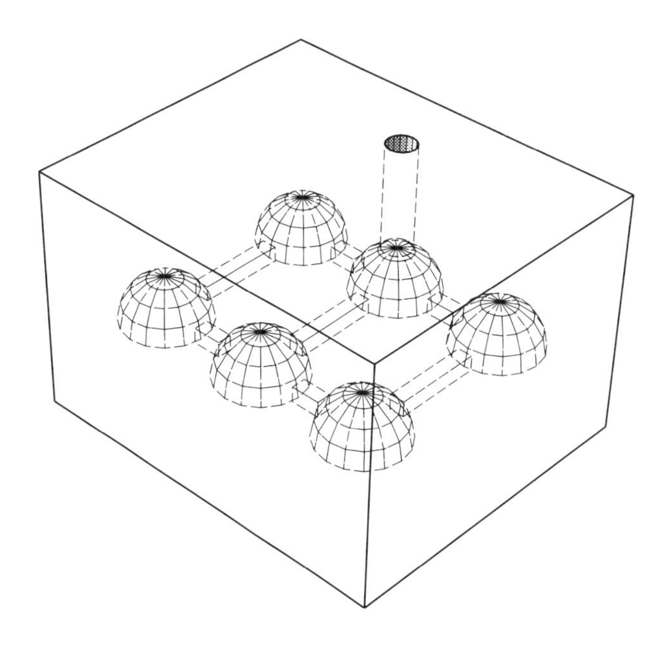

Dome-shaped caverns may be appropriate in some geological settings. In this illustration, a series of these openings are shown with interconnecting tunnels. In this case, access is shown through a shaft. Hemispherical or spherical caverns may be created.

Figure 3-15: End use configurations – caverns.

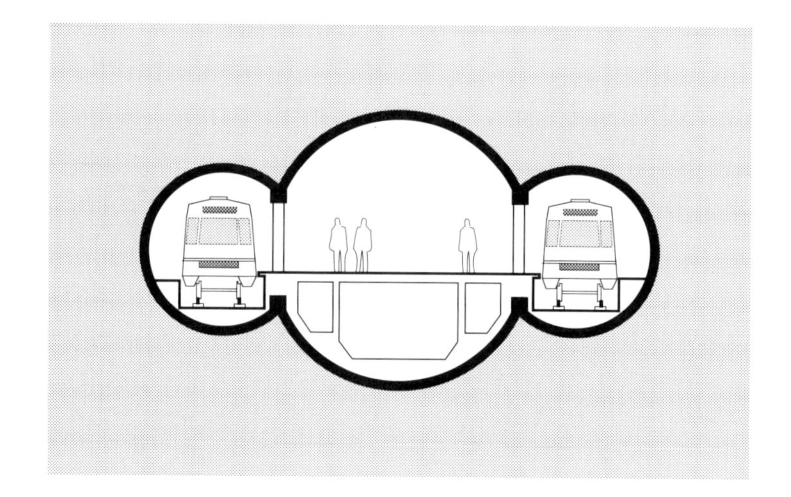

Figure 3-16: Section of a rail transit station illustrating the use of a multiple shield tunnel.

of underground openings. Variations in the shape of an opening may be required by the specific end use application, or to take advantage of local geologic features.

Because much of our utility service infrastructure is located in the ground, the majority of cavities beneath the ground are small cross-section, linear systems of pipes and tunnels. Larger tunnels are used for major water tunnels, interceptor sewers, railway/ transit tunnels, and highway tunnels. The next most common uses are the basements of surface buildings and cut-and-cover shallow underground buildings. Large-scale, purpose-built underground chambers are not commonplace but are increasingly being used for specialized applications. The shapes of large caverns are controlled primarily by the end use and rock support considerations. These considerations typically result in arched cavern roofs, except in some competent bedded rock formations, where the roofs may be flat.

Other specific uses include culverts and boreholes. Culverts are short tunnel sections built to provide a crossing beneath a highway or railway line. They may be erected and covered during embankment construction, placed by cut-and-cover construction on flat sites, or tunneled or pipe-jacked beneath existing transportation routes. The shapes and materials are chosen on the basis of cost, longevity, and any particular requirements of the end use (for example, the flatter section shapes provide larger capacity flow even at low water levels when compared with a circular section). Boreholes are drilled into the ground to explore sites, to recover liquid or gaseous natural resources (e.g., water, oil, and gas), and for some thermal energy extraction or storage projects. The number of boreholes existing in an old urban area or mining region may be large and, unless the boreholes were properly abandoned (by fully grouting the hole), they may interfere with future underground construction.

Underground cavities may be created in several ways: excavation from the surface; construction of a structure and backfilling above the structure (cut-and-cover construction); or mining or tunneling completely below ground with only limited surface access points. When excavating soil or rock for a specific end use, it is usually best to excavate the minimum volume needed to house the function adequately and at the same time fit an economical method of construction. The trend towards the use of tunnel boring machines (TBMs) in both hard and soft ground often makes a circular cross-section the most economical section for tunnels even if not optimized for the end use. To increase space utilization efficiency while retaining the advantages of TBMs, the Japanese have developed multiface machines that construct, in a single pass, two or three overlapping circular sections (see Figure 3-16). When very large cross-section tunnels are required in poor ground, the tunnel may need to be constructed using a partial or full ring of small pilot tunnels which provide the eventual support of the full opening.

The desire for a greater utilization of subsurface space in poorly suited geologic regions is spurring the development of both new shapes for underground spaces and the new design and construction technology necessary to construct such spaces economically. For example, deep spherical structures and cylindrical shapes extending deep underground have been proposed in Tokyo.

Most underground uses involve several combinations of underground forms, sometimes in elaborate complexes that are only possible in the three-dimensional freedom an underground environment provides. As an example, Figure 3-17 illustrates the complicated layout of chambers and tunnels in an underground powerhouse complex.

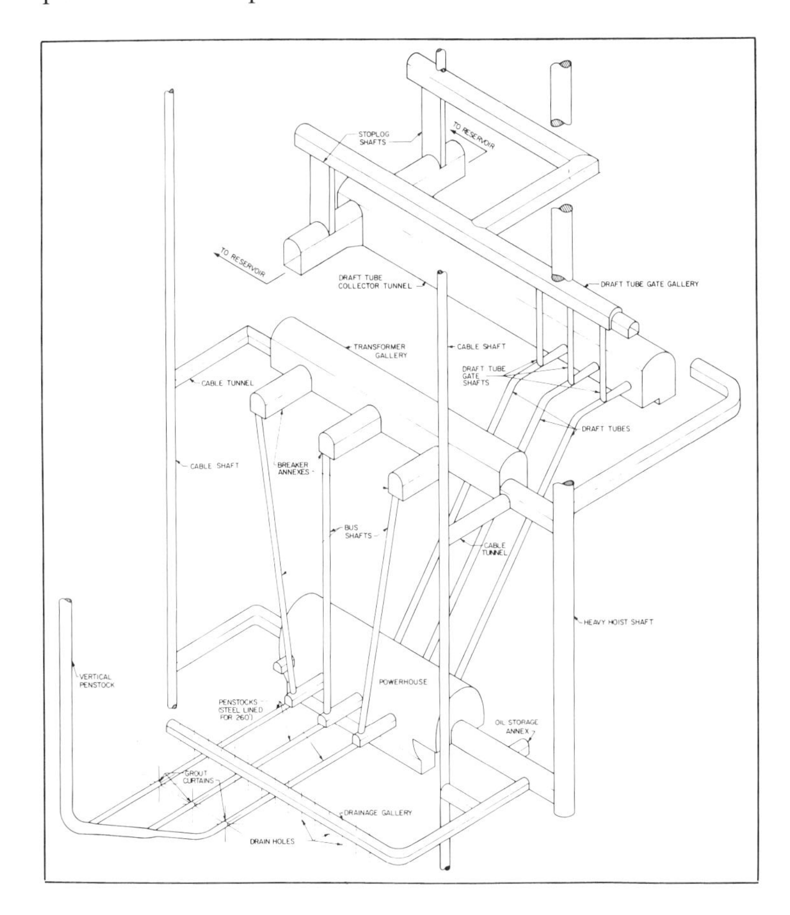

Figure 3-17: A complex combination of caverns, tunnels, and shafts forms this underground pumped hydro facility (Willett and Warnock 1983).

Configurations Applied to Urban Design

Under a given set of geological conditions, certain types of cut-and-cover as well as mined (or tunneled) configurations may be created. When these are developed in the context of an existing urban environment, they can take many forms reflecting different scales of development and relationships to the surface, as well as land use patterns above and below grade. Figures 3-18 through 3-25 illustrate a range of urban design concepts utilizing underground space.

The first set of drawings (Figures 3-18 through 3-20) primarily illustrates cut-and-cover spaces. Figure 3-18 shows a minimal level of underground utilization found in many modern cities—utilities under streets and a few isolated basements. The next level of underground development, as shown in Figure 3-19, is characterized by more intensive use of shallow subsurface space, often for commercial and other pedestrian-oriented functions. This shallow development creates opportunities for increased surface open space as well as connections between underground structures resulting in below-grade pedestrian networks. In Figure 3-20, more extensive underground development is shown by the use of deep cut structures extending several levels below the surface. In this case, a significant proportion of the overall space in a city may be placed underground. This creates the opportunity for increasingly dense development and a more efficient utilization of valuable urban land. It also provides the option of creating a more desirable, less dense surface environment by creating more open space. Since they form the foundation for the surface structures and spaces above, these cut-and-cover approaches to underground development by nature must correspond closely to the pattern of surface development.

The second set of illustrations (Figures 3-21 through 3-23) reflects the use of mined caverns beneath existing surface development. Figure 3-21 illustrates mined space in a flat-bedded geology that permits the creation of a layer of space in a room-and-pillar configuration. The exposed bluff permits horizontal entry to the space through a tunnel. In this case, housing is shown on the surface with no direct vertical connection to the space below. This approach permits complete separation of incompatible functions (i.e., housing and manufacturing) while utilizing land efficiently. Figure 3-22 illustrates a similar mined space development with the horizontal access through a bluff. In this case, however, the surface development is nonresidential with direct vertical connection to the mined space below. This approach is suitable for functions that may require a direct relationship between the above- and below-grade spaces. Example include offices above and manufacturing below, a library above with archives below, or secure research laboratories and computer facilities beneath offices on the surface. Figure 3-23 illustrates a similar concept with a few variations. The mined space in this case is a series of interconnected arched caverns rather than a flat-roofed continuous space. Also, there is no horizontal access through a tunnel, only vertical connections to the surface. This approach can be used to create direct relationships between above- and below-grade functions, or the below grade can

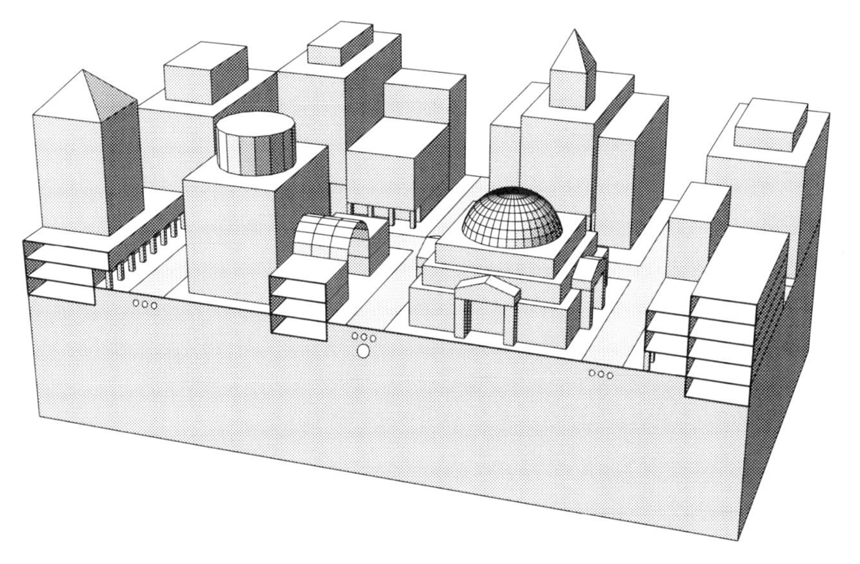

Figure 3-18: In most urban settings, underground space is utilized to a minimal degree. Utilities are placed under streets and some isolated basements are beneath buildings.

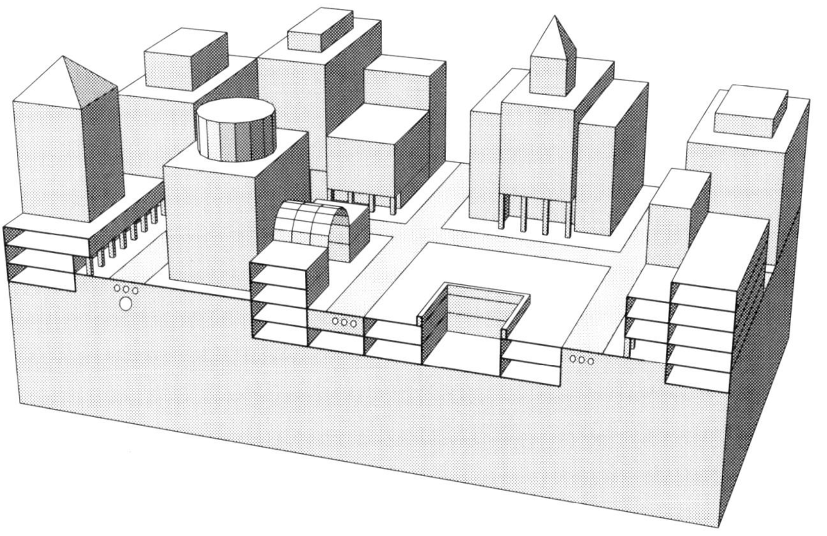

Figure 3-19: Use of shallow underground space creates opportunities for increased surface open space. Connections between underground structures and below-grade levels of buildings can create a pedestrian network.

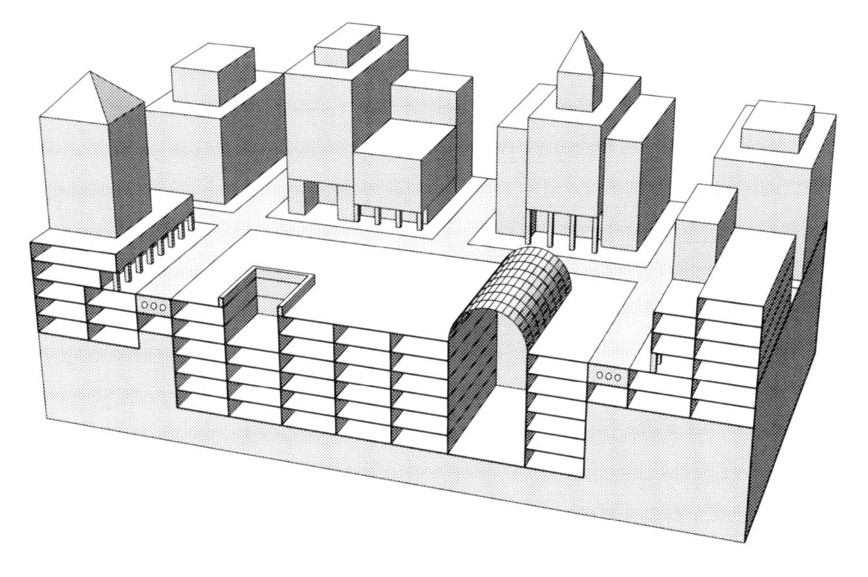

Figure 3-20: Deep cut structures extending several levels below grade provide opportunities to increase the density of urban development, and/or to improve the surface environment by creating open space.

Figure 3-21: Mined space in flat-bedded geology can provide space beneath existing surface development. In this illustration, the mined space is completely isolated from housing on the surface. Access to the underground occurs through a horizontal tunnel in the bluff.

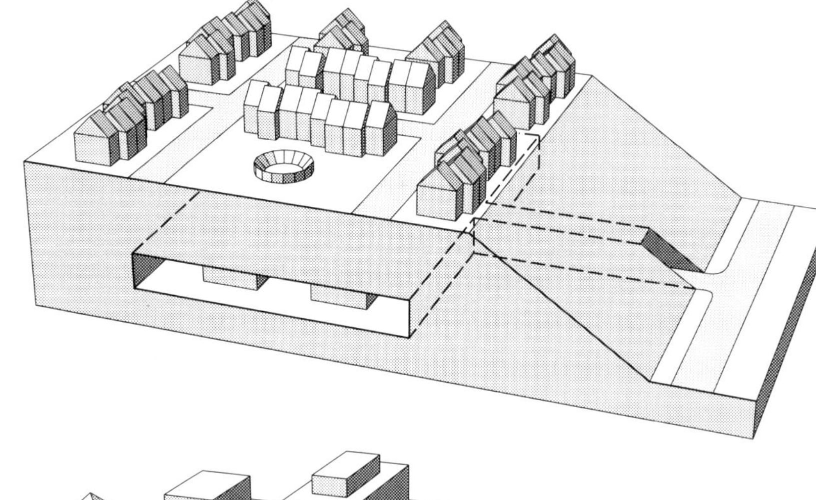

Figure 3-22: Access to mined space can be provided through vertical shafts as well as horizontal tunnels. A direct connection is shown here between office or commercial functions on the surface and the manufacturing/storage functions in the mined space below.

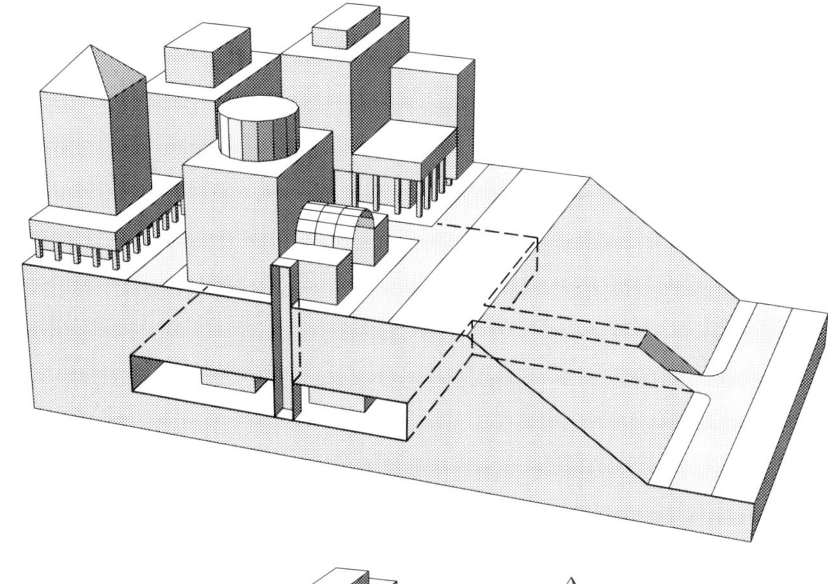

Figure 3-23: The mined space in this illustration consists of a series of interconnected caverns. Vertical shafts provide the only access to the underground space.

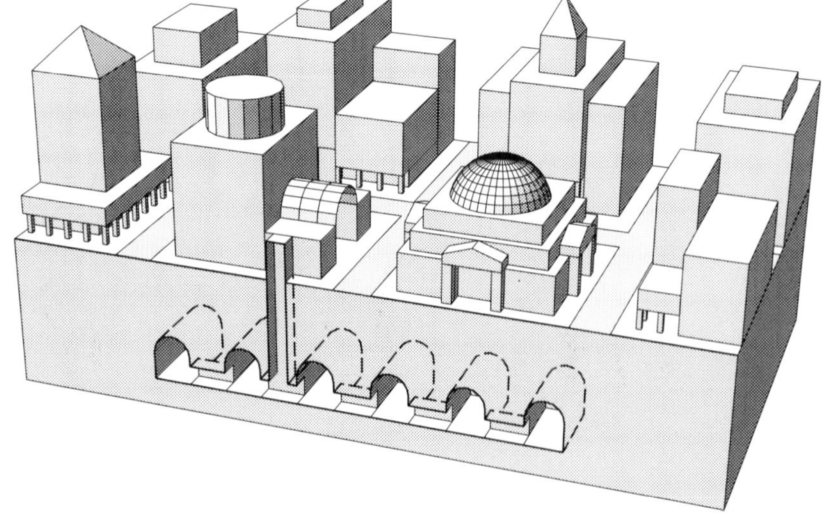

be substantially separated and isolated from the surface facilities except for limited points of access. Compared with cut-and-cover facilities, mined space provides the opportunity to build beneath existing structures in a manner that does not have to correspond to the geometry or land use patterns of the surface.

The final set of drawings in this section (Figures 3-24 and 3-25) illustrates the use of underground space on a larger scale—that of a district or citywide system. Figure 3-24 illustrates the concept of a large deep tunnel beneath an urban area that consolidates traditional utilities and transportation functions and also may provide solid waste removal, energy supply, and other services. Deeper tunnels can be placed beneath existing urban areas with minimal disruption of the surface, and can be designed as a citywide network.

Another large-scale underground design concept is the creation of cut-and-cover corridors in an urban environment. These long trenches could contain traditional utility and transportation

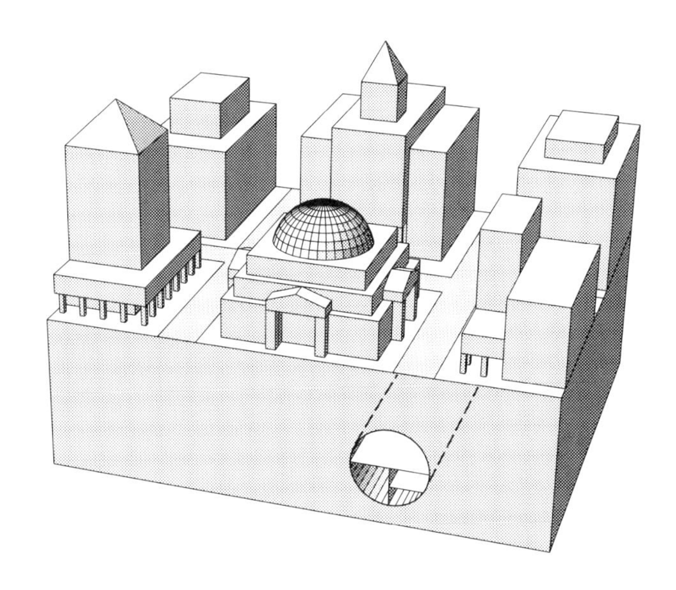

Figure 3-24: Large tunnel systems beneath existing urban areas can be used to consolidate traditional utilities and transportation. A network of tunnels may also provide energy supply, waste removal, and other services.

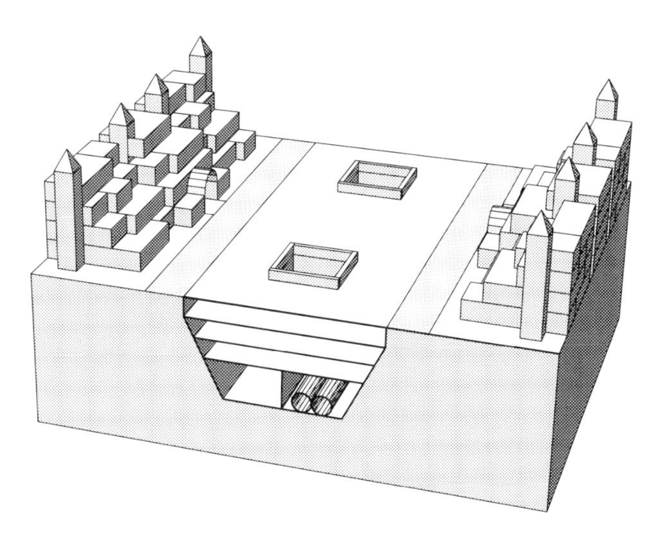

Figure 3-25: Cut-and-cover corridors may be used to contain utilities and transportation as well as commercial, industrial, and storage functions. Higher density housing combined with open space can occur along these corridors. This concept could be used to revitalize existing urban areas and utilize land more efficiently.

functions, but might be enlarged to include commercial manufacturing and storage spaces as well. As shown in Figure 3-25, one application of this corridor concept is to place medium to high density housing above grade with open space just above the underground development. These cut-and-cover spines could extend out from a dense city center in a radial pattern. Such corridors could be used as a major technique for revitalizing and configuring existing urban environments in a more efficient manner (Birkerts 1974).

The urban design concepts illustrated in this section are intended to suggest a range of possibilities, not to represent a comprehensive set of solutions. While these large-scale approaches have the potential to solve a number of urban problems, they could only be developed with effective long-range planning. Unfortunately, the overall configuration of underground spaces and systems in urban settings tends to develop haphazardly due to uncoordinated decisions on individual projects.

CHAPTER 4

by Raymond Sterling

Historical Development and Current Use of Underground Space

There are many examples of both historical and current uses of underground space. This chapter describes the major types and uses of underground space and provides examples from around the world. These uses are organized by the functional classification system described in Chapter 3. The discussion is intended to be comprehensive and cover all types of uses, but in keeping with the thrust of this volume, the emphasis is on facilities that involve significant human occupation.

Because of the vast number of underground facilities throughout the world and their diverse histories and uses, it is impossible to present a complete listing or a detailed map indicating worldwide underground utilization. There are, however, some notable patterns of underground utilization, both historically and in recent times. In an attempt to identify some of these more significant use patterns, the world map in Figure 4-1 was created. Continents, regions, or individual countries are highlighted where notable underground use patterns exist.

Residential Uses

Residential uses probably represent the oldest use of underground space by humankind. Archaeological and anthropological research has revealed much about our early ancestors. Many of the sites where fossil remains have been discovered in various parts of the world are cave sites. Some of the oldest discoveries of caves inhabited by modern Homo sapiens are at the Qatzeh cave in Israel, dated to 92,000 years ago, and at Klasies River Mouth in South Africa, where it has been theorized that anatomically modern humans lived from 120,000 to 60,000 years ago. Some findings are still in dispute, but it is relatively

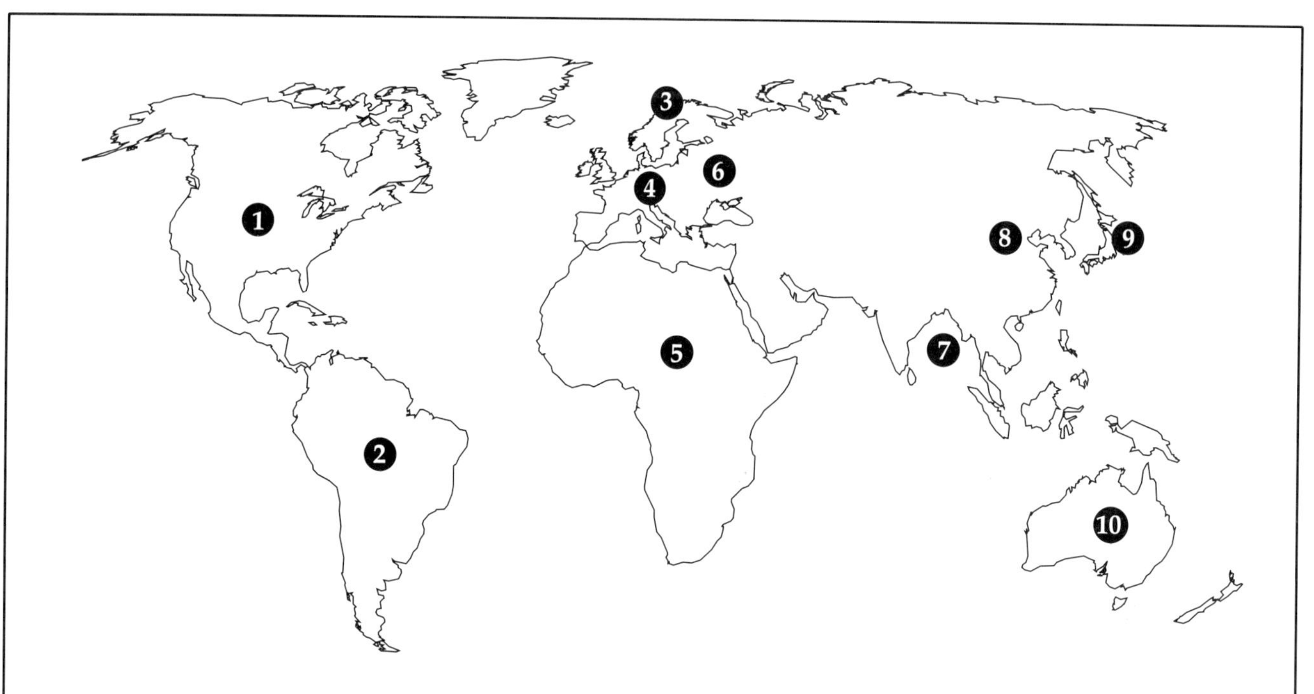

1. **NORTH AMERICA**
   - Indigenous housing utilized earth and rock structures. Examples include Indian cliffside dwellings.
   - Many examples of modern earth sheltered housing and nonresidential buildings such as libraries and museums.
   - Subway systems in some larger urban areas including some with related underground commercial development (Montreal and Toronto, Canada).
   - Scattered examples of mined space use. Examples include the limestone mines in Kansas City, USA.

2. **SOUTH AMERICA**
   - Limited number of uses outside of mining excavations.
   - Subway systems in some large cities.
   - Hydroelectric schemes under development in mountain areas.
   - Some experience with underground food storage.

3. **SCANDINAVIA**
   - Large variety of uses mostly in hard rock. Examples include churches, concert halls, sports facilities, and archives.
   - Many uses are dual-purpose civil defense/community facilities.
   - Large number of underground hydropower facilities.
   - Extensive oil storage caverns and other energy storage systems.
   - Subway systems in capital cities.

4. **OTHER WESTERN EUROPEAN COUNTRIES**
   - Variety of urban uses including multipurpose commercial centers, parking facilities.
   - Many interurban road and rail tunnels crossing natural barriers. Examples are the English Channel Tunnel, alpine tunnels, and German high speed rail network.
   - Many underground portions of transit systems in major cities.
   - Indigenous underground housing found in France, Spain, Italy and Greece.

5. **AFRICA**
   - Indigenous food storage in North Africa—notably Morocco.
   - Extensive mining activities and some hydropower.
   - Indigenous housing in North Africa (both current and historical). Examples include Matmata and Bulla Regia, Tunisia.

6. **EASTERN EUROPE AND WESTERN ASIA**
   - Extensive metro systems in major cities.
   - Use of utilidors for some urban utilities.
   - Civil defense facilities.
   - Indigenous housing and religious structures—mostly historical. Examples found in Cappadocia in central Turkey.

7. **SOUTHERN AND SOUTHEASTERN ASIA**
   - Cave temples such as Ajanta and Ellora in India.
   - A few urban underground facilities including pedestrian underpasses and short road tunnels.
   - Subway systems in some major cities including Calcutta and Hong Kong.
   - Hydropower facilities in mountainous regions.

8. **EASTERN ASIA**
   - Approximately 30 million people living in cave dwellings in north-central China.
   - Extensive civil defense works in cities in China.
   - Extensive interurban road and rail tunnels.
   - Metro systems in some cities such as Beijing, Novosibirsk.

9. **JAPAN**
   - Large metro systems in major cities.
   - Extensive underground shopping centers connected to transit facilities.
   - Urban uses for infrastructure purposes.
   - Extensive interurban road and rail tunnels.
   - Intense interest in a wide range of future uses.

10. **AUSTRALIA**
    - Housing and other building uses in outback mining communities.
    - Building applications for environmental preservation in sensitive areas.
    - Hydroelectric facilities in mountainous areas.
    - Limited underground urban road and rail facilities.

Figure 4-1: World map indicating notable patterns of underground utilization.

clear from fossil records that Homo sapiens (Neanderthal) and Homo sapiens (modern) used caves as a dwelling place beginning more than 50,000 years ago (National Geographic Society 1988). The use of caves by Homo erectus has been assessed as occurring as early as the middle Pleistocene, some 700,000 to 200,000 years ago (Yip 1983). Caves are assumed to have provided shelter from the weather and to have been more easily defended against intruders.

One of the earliest records of constructed semi-underground shelters is at a site near Kostenki in Russia where remains of partly underground shelters built with a structure of large mammoth bones were discovered. This site was estimated to be 23,000 years old and was similar to more than a dozen other sites discovered on the East European plain (National Geographic Society 1988).

In China, the 6,000-year-old Banpo site near Xian discovered in 1953 records a village of semi-underground pit homes with floor levels up to 1 meter below ground level. The superstructures were either square or round and used branches and sod cover supported by posts set in rammed earth (Sterling 1981). These pit homes are similar to other deep or shallow pit dwellings constructed in China and Russia in the Paleolithic and Neolithic ages.

Extensive underground settlements have existed in China since the earliest historical records. The easily excavated loess soil that covers much of central and north central China can be excavated by hand to form underground chambers 2 to 3 meters wide. Chambers 5 to 10 meters long are either dug from a central courtyard excavated on flat sites (see Figure 4-3) or directly into the side of a hill (Li 1985; Aoki et al. 1985). The ability to provide shelter with a minimum of materials and the protection the underground location provides against the severe heat and cold of

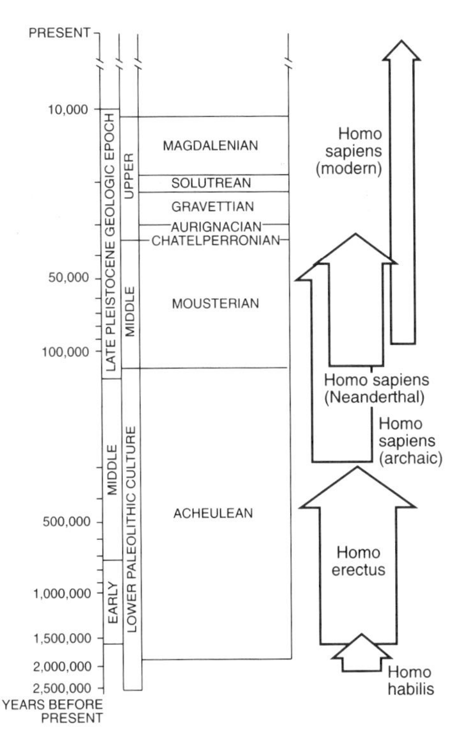

Figure 4-2: Time scale of human evolution. (Source: National Geographic Society 1988)

Figure 4-3: Underground courtyard houses in China mined out of loess soil.

the region are the principal reasons why more than 30 million people are estimated to live in such structures in China today. Cave dwellings at Yan'an in Northern Shaanxi Province were the headquarters of the Chinese Communist Party for nearly 10 years after the Long March of 1934-35.

Figure 4-4: Underground atrium dwellings built by the Romans at Bulla Regia in northern Tunisia. (Photographer: R. Kennedy)

Many other countries and regions can point to at least a few examples of historical or archaeological underground settlements. The principal causes for underground use appear to be the climate, the availability of conventional building materials, the availability of a suitable geology, topography, or landscape for construction, the need for protection from intruders, and the existence of previous examples.

The Romans, for example, are only known to have constructed housing underground at their settlements in northern Africa. One significant settlement called Bulla Regia is located in present-day northern Tunisia. The hot climate, together with the example of existing underground settlements constructed by the local Berber inhabitants, is thought to have influenced the Roman settlers. Their housing design retained the conventional atrium style built in other areas, but the floor level of many houses was sunk up to 5 meters below grade (Figure 4-4). High ceiling heights were used with 0.5 to 1 meter of earth cover on the roof of the structure. The combination of the central atrium and small perimeter openings provided light and ventilation to all living spaces (Golany 1988). Traditional underground settlements still exist today in southern Tunisia in atrium-style dwellings in towns such as Matmata (Figure 4-5) and in hillside-style dwellings in villages such as Chenini, Guermessa, and Douiret (Golany 1988).

Other significant underground settlements have included the rock-cut dwellings, churches, and towns in Cappadocia, Turkey, which reached their peak during the tenth and eleventh centuries of the Byzantine period. Two of the best-known examples of the underground towns are Kaymakli and Derinkuyu in central Anatolia. They reached depths of 8 to 10 floors below ground and comprised several kilometers of tunnels leading to rooms of varying sizes excavated into the volcanic tuff. The excavations included ventilation shafts and wells to provide fresh water to the town. Space was also included for livestock, food storage, and wine storage. The tunnels could be sealed by large round slabs housed in cavities adjacent to the tunnels. The towns were used as a refuge during Arab raids into the region, although this may not have been the primary reason for their existence (Hazer 1975).

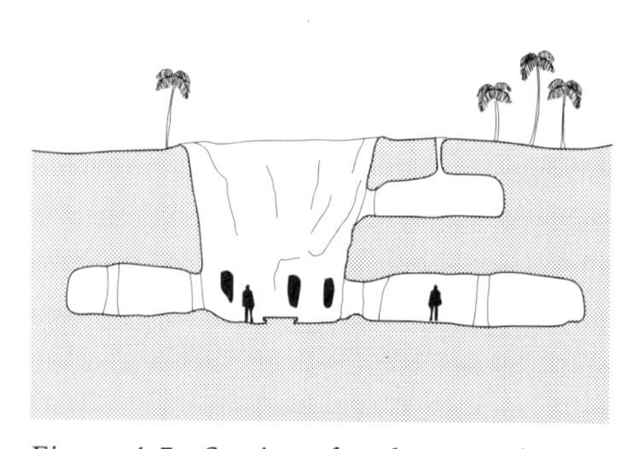

Figure 4-5: Section of underground dwelling, Matmata, Tunisia.

In Spain, underground settlements still exist today in the southern Andalusia region. A 1985 survey recorded 8,639 inhabited caves in the region. Early Iberian civilizations inhabited caves and painted them up to 25,000 years ago. The caverns near Guadix in Granada province have been occupied since the sixteenth century, but most of the caves in use today have been occupied only in the last 100 years. The caves are hewn mostly out of soft rock, and many include natural ventilation towers and adjacent aboveground structures. In Spain as a whole, it is estimated that approximately 80,000 people live in caves. A survey has indicated that while there are cases of severe poverty, many cave-dwellers are house-proud, contented, and prosperous (Mooney 1985; Flores and Bravo 1984).

In France, there are many sites of troglodytic settlements (see Figures 4-6 and 4-7). Some important sites were inhabited throughout prehistoric times, initially using overhanging rocks and natural caves but later incorporating excavated rooms in the sides of the cliffs. In the Middle Ages many underground chambers were used principally as defensive shelters near villages. In the seventeenth and eighteenth centuries, especially in the valley of the Loire, the use of cave dwellings expanded and caves were used as single-family houses. At the peak of their use in the eighteenth century, hundreds of thousands of cave-dwellers lived in France. By the beginning of the twentieth century it was estimated that 20,000 French citizens still lived in caves (Charneau and Trebbi 1981). In the last two decades, there has been a renewed interest in the cave dwellings both for use as holiday cottages for Parisians and for their historical and cultural importance in France.

Other countries with an ancient tradition of underground dwellings include Italy (especially Sicily; see Di Cristofalo et al. 1989); Greece (especially Santorini; see Andreadaki-Chronaki 1983); and Jordan, Israel, and Egypt (Labs 1976; LaNier 1971; Goldfinger 1969; Allen 1971).

The use of residential basements in northern climates is an important residential use of the underground for storage,

Figure 4-6: Facade of a house dug into the hillside in the Loire Valley, France. (Photographer: E. Revault)

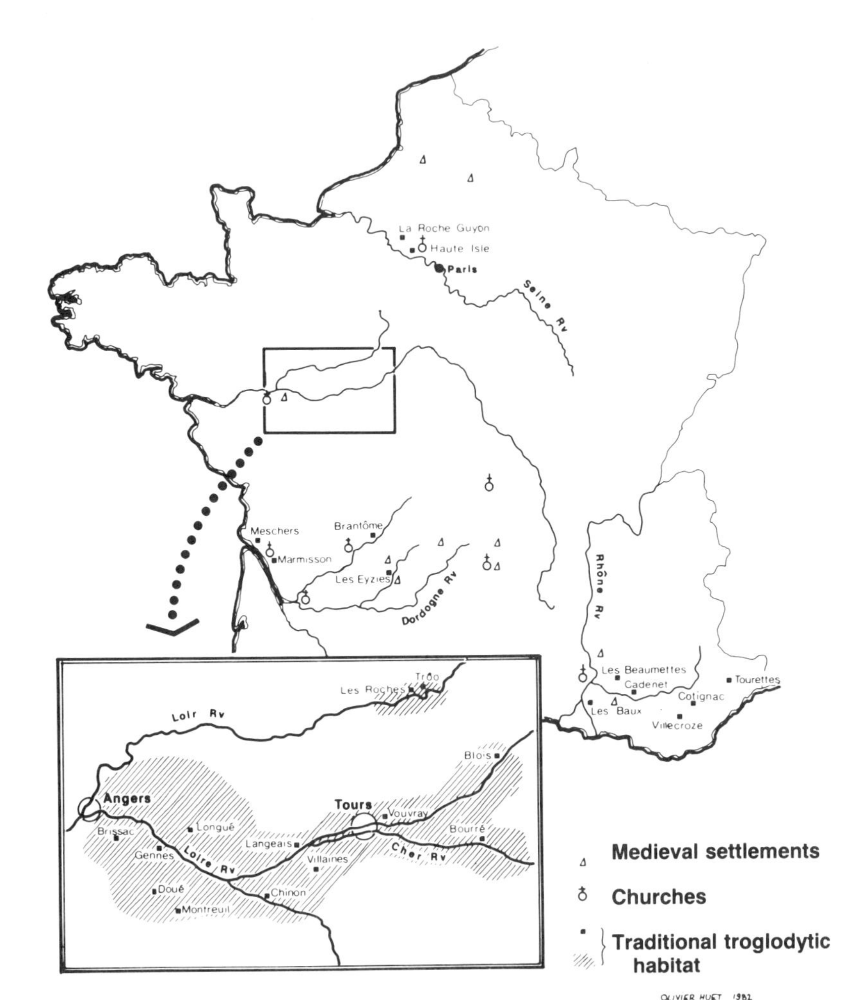

Figure 4-7: Map of troglodytism in France. (Source: Huet 1982)

Figure 4-8: Conceptual design for an underground house with minimum environmental and aesthetic impact. (Architect: Malcolm Wells)

Figure 4-9: Winston House, Lyme, New Hampshire, USA. (Architect: Don Metz)

mechanical equipment, and ancillary living space. It is not clear at present, however, what the trends in single-family residential basement construction will be (Labs et al. 1988).

Recent developments in residential uses of underground space have occurred in a few countries of the world, most notably the United States and Australia. In Australia, several mining towns in the outback have placed a large percentage of the dwellings and community buildings underground to escape the severe heat. These examples include the opal mining towns of Coober Pedy (Medway), White Cliffs, and Andamooka, and the now abandoned riverside dugouts of Burra, once an important copper mining town (Auhl and Finch 1979).

In the United States, Native Americans used semi-underground structures for habitation (for example, Anasazi tribe cliff dwellings and Mandan tribe earth-bermed structures). In the absence of readily available building materials, the early European settlers also used dugouts and sod houses for protection from the severe climate in the plains of the Midwest. These settlers also may have echoed the use of sod-roofed houses in Scandinavia from where many settlers had originated during this period.

U.S. examples of the development of earth-integrated design can be found in some of the work of Frank Lloyd Wright in the 1930s and 1940s, the development of Cold War-inspired fallout shelter houses in the 1960s (Swayze 1980), and the emergence of an environmental and natural aesthetic concern in the middle-to-late 1960s (Wells 1977). With the advent of the energy crises of the 1970s a strong public interest in the coupled environmental and energy conservation advantages of earth sheltered houses emerged, and the number of residential earth sheltered structures grew from a handful to several thousand. In the 1980s public interest in energy conservation dwindled again and interest in earth sheltered construction for housing likewise decreased. Problems of initial cost, waterproofing, and poor architectural design in many of the residential structures built in the 1970s and 1980s contributed to this drop in interest. For a full discussion of earth sheltered housing design, see Carmody and Sterling (1985).

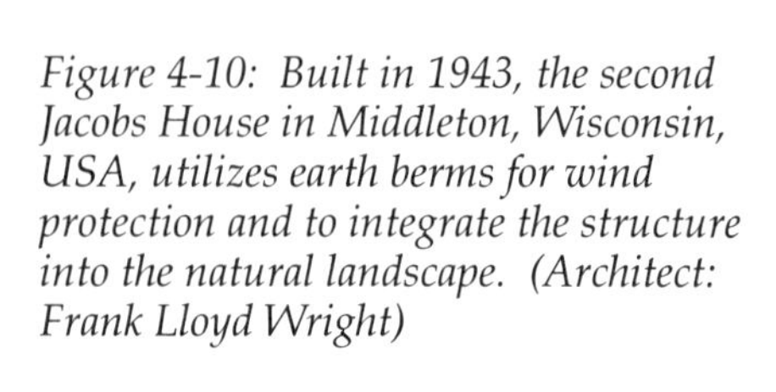

Figure 4-10: Built in 1943, the second Jacobs House in Middleton, Wisconsin, USA, utilizes earth berms for wind protection and to integrate the structure into the natural landscape. (Architect: Frank Lloyd Wright)

Figure 4-11: Terraced housing in Innsbruck, Austria. (Photographer: Edmund Burke)

Most of the residential earth sheltered structures built in the past 20 to 30 years have been single-family dwellings. There have been a few multifamily developments, however, such as along a freeway in Minneapolis and on steep hillsides in southern Europe (Sterling et al. 1981). These multiple-unit designs allow a greater control over the site integration of the housing in medium density developments and also permit an effective use of steeply sloping ground for housing.

Religious Uses

It is not clear if the religious significance attached to many underground uses and sites implies a special relationship of underground space with the spiritual essence of religious activities. The preservation afforded by the underground location of religious artifacts found in caves, underground temples, or catacombs may provide a distorted impression of the relative importance of such spaces in everyday religious life in prior civilizations. In fact, the underground location of many religious sites may be due as much to practical considerations as the mystery of the netherworld. Carved images and paintings were better preserved underground, and the use of burial for preservation and sanitary reasons has contributed to strong religious connotations. Religious history has also been marked by many persecutions that caused religious sects literally to go underground to survive.

Despite the importance of these external pressures, there is still a special character of unadorned underground spaces—silent, dark, and somewhat foreboding—that provides a separation from the normal world and an opportunity for spiritual reflection. In salt mines, for instance, in widely separate places—Poland and Colombia (Figure 4-12)—miners converted large chambers into underground cathedrals (Pinzon-Isaza 1983; Bieniawski 1984). The Anasazi Indians of the southwestern United States are also known to have constructed underground kivas specifically for religious ceremonies (Labs 1976).

Figure 4-12: Entrance to the underground salt cathedral of Zipaquira, Colombia. (Source: Pinzon-Isaza 1983)

Some 15,000 to 20,000 years ago, caves had already become more than mere shelter—they had also become a place for the expression of artistry in painting, engraving, and sculpting. The stunning paintings in the Lascaux cave in southwest France dating from 17,000 years ago, and clay statues in the Grotto of Montespan in the French Pyrenees dating from approximately 20,000 years ago, are examples of the use of the deeper recesses of a cave for these artistic endeavors (Rigaud 1988). Whether they have religious significance or were mere expressions of visual images recorded by the inhabitants, the difficulty of working in these dark interior spaces implies a strong motivation in seeking out these remote places for the creation of their art.

Underground burial has been common in much of the world from the ancient barrows in Great Britain to the grand tombs of Egyptian kings and Chinese emperors. The Egyptian, Greek, Roman, and Chinese civilizations all left behind important records of their civilizations attached to underground religious sites and tombs. During the Roman empire, Roman gods were consulted at underground oracles, and persecuted Christians hid underground and excavated the network of catacombs in Rome. The persecution of Christians also bolstered the development of the large excavated complexes in the wind-eroded volcanic tuff of central Turkey described earlier. The Byzantine Christians who settled there in the ninth century built many places of worship in addition to the residential chambers.

The rise of Buddhism in India and Southeast Asia led to the excavation and carving of many rock-cut temples and grottos containing carved and painted Buddhist images. Some of the largest sites are the Longmen, Dazu, and YünKang grottos in

Figure 4-13: Buddhist temples cut into the rock at Ellora, India.

central China, the Thousand Buddha Caves in Xinjiang Province in northwest China, and the Ajanta and Ellora sites in India (Nicoletti 1980).

Modern-day underground churches do exist, but there are only a few examples. Two churches in Coober Pedy in central Australia constructed in 1967 and 1977 were built underground in order to escape the heat in a town with a substantial proportion of its other buildings already below ground (Medway). The Temppeliaukio Church in Helsinki, Finland, constructed in 1968-69, was also built underground but primarily for aesthetic reasons and to preserve the existing open space in Temppeliaukio Square near the city center (Saari 1988).

Many semi-religious, anti-religious, and paranormal uses or manifestations are also assigned to the underground. The view of hell, or its equivalent, as an underground location is quite prevalent in many regions and religions of the world. Perhaps from this, devil worship has often been practiced in secret underground locations. Some people also believe in special paranormal effects attributable to certain locations or directed lines in the ground. These "lay lines" are part of an interest area termed "geomancy" which can also be related to the traditional methods of building layout and orientation in Asia (known as Feng sui in China).

Recreation

NATURAL CAVE EXPLORATION AND TOURISM

The grandeur, intrigue, and beauty of natural caves has always made them fascinating sites for exploration and, when made accessible to the public, popular tourist attractions. Until the end of the seventeenth century, cave exploration was an eccentric hit or miss pursuit, but in the 1670s and 1680s John Beaumont in England and Baron Johann Valvasor in Slovenia began to record systematic cave explorations. Baron Valvasor documented visits to 70 caves in the Karst region of Slovenia, which became the namesake for all similar limestone regions.

In 1747, Joseph Nagel was ordered by court officials in Vienna to explore and map the major caves in the Austro-Hungarian empire. Among these was the Adelsberg Cave (now called Postojna Jama), which became the most famous cavern of its time and perhaps the first to be developed and controlled as a profitable tourist business in the early 1800s.

Figure 4-14: Tourist boat ride through the Machocha Cave, Czechoslovakia.

In 1866, a seven-year-old French boy named Edward-Alfred Martel visited a cave and became so fascinated with cave exploration that he continued to explore caves for the next 48 years. He became known as the father of speleology. He was succeeded in this interest in France by Norbert Castaret, born in 1897, who discovered and explored more than 2,000 caverns.

In the United States, major cave finds were made in the 1790s when the Mammoth Cave in Kentucky was found, and in 1901 when the Carlsbad Caverns were discovered. These caves were exploited both for the mining of bat guano, which produces a nitrate-rich soil, and for public tours of the spectacular chambers and rock formations. In Kentucky in the Mammoth Cave region, competition over attracting tourists to rival caves led to the local "cave wars" of the 1920s.

In 1925, cave exploration in Kentucky turned into a tragedy of national dimensions when Floyd Collins, discoverer of the Great Crystal Cave in Kentucky, was trapped while exploring another nearby cave. For two weeks he was pinned by a fallen rock in a narrow passage, unable to move or to be freed by others. His plight and attempted rescue became the subject of front page headlines across the country, but a separate shaft and tunnel sunk to save him arrived too late.

Today, cave tours can be a large recreational business in almost any area of the world. For example, in the United States the Carlsbad Caverns alone attract approximately 800,000 visitors a year (Jackson 1982).

The attraction of natural caves also encouraged the development of artificial caves and grottos on the estates of large mansions in Europe. Rowlinson (1984) writes: "By the early nineteenth century many country houses could boast grottos and tunnels in their parks, designed to lend a little horror and romance to an afternoon walk." A series of passages and caves on the estate of Sir Francis Dashwood at West Wycombe in England became the site of meetings of a secret society often known as the Monks of Medmenham or the Hell-Fire Club. The object of the society was to hold sensual orgies in the spirit of the Gothic delight in medievalism. The society had a membership of approximately 50 drawn from the highest levels of the government and aristocracy. It had previously met in London and at the ruined abbey of Medmenham but moved to the underground chambers for greater privacy (Rowlinson et al. 1983).

SPORTS FACILITIES AND COMMUNITY CENTERS

Modern recreational facilities constructed in the underground principally include sports facilities and community centers. Many such facilities have been constructed in Scandinavia as dual-purpose facilities available for civil defense (Saari 1988; Winqvist and Mellgren 1988; NSREA 1982). The types of facilities in use include swimming pools, gymnasia, running tracks, ice hockey rinks, and multipurpose facilities. The community swimming pool at Gjorvik in Norway (Figure 4-15) and the gymnasium of the Kannusillanmaki underground sports center in Helsinki, Finland, are good examples of the potential for valuable yet unobtrusive community facilities. At Georgetown University, Washington, D.C., in the United States, a sports facility was expanded beneath an existing football playing field site and an artificial turf playing surface was restored above the underground building (Figure 4-16) (Carmody and Sterling 1983).

In China, another community use has been for amusement centers in cities and recreational areas. The city of Hanzhou, for example, has coffee shops, a dance hall, and many amusement rooms for children in various rock caverns (Golany 1989).

Auditoria and concert halls have also been built in rock caverns. The city of Hangzhou contains an 1,800-seat theater in a

Figure 4-15: Underground swimming pool, Gjorvik, Norway.

rock cavern that doubles as a defense shelter. The Retretti concert hall in Finland is popular for many types of artistic performance. In some cases, existing rock caverns may become the setting for temporary exhibitions or events. The rock caverns of the Ohya Building Stone Mine in Japan, for example, have been used for a number of performances and exhibitions.

The inward focus of many court sports and the enclosed nature of many sports facility buildings aboveground make them a natural candidate for underground construction when surface space is limited. The principal limitations are related to the maximum clear spans possible in mined facilities in rock, and the cost of providing large clear spans in near-surface facilities in soil. The largest clear span in rock for a sports facility is currently approximately 32 meters for underground ice hockey halls in Finland (although a 60-meter span Olympic ice hockey arena is being planned in Norway). At the Yates Fieldhouse at Georgetown University mentioned above, hypar roofs provide unobstructed floor areas of 20 meters by 40 meters.

An increase in the number of recreational underground facilities is expected in crowded urban areas. This is especially so in developing cities, where the combination of increasing affluence and congestion creates demand for more sources of recreation.

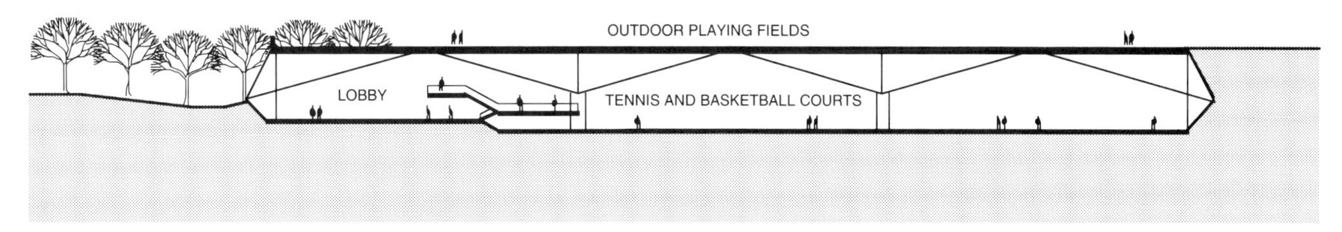

Figure 4-16: Section of the Yates Fieldhouse, George Washington University, Washington D.C., USA. (Architect: Daniel F. Tully Associates)

When surface land is not available or is too expensive, these recreational facilities often move to the rooftops or to underground facilities. The rooftop golf driving ranges in Tokyo and rooftop tennis courts or swimming pools in many countries are examples of these trends.

PARKS

There is strong interest in Japan at present for a significant further increase in recreational space, including areas suitable as parks as well as spaces for structured sports or community activities. One possibility for satisfying this demand is the use of underground parks. Although at first a seeming oxymoron, cities with severe climates already have indoor spaces that function as public parks in inclement weather. In Edina, Minnesota, in the United States, a fully indoor city-operated public park is attached to senior citizen high-rise apartments to provide a snow-free, climate-controlled park for wintertime use. Park facilities include an open playing area, a small ice-skating rink, an amphitheater, children's playground, and a landscaped strolling area. Many indoor conservatories, building atria, and shopping malls can fulfill a similar function.

Commercial and Institutional Uses

Commercial and institutional uses are a relatively late development in the history of underground space use. They are spurred most often by the constraints of high land prices, aesthetic considerations, or by an advantageous proximity to important existing facilities or large volumes of pedestrian traffic.

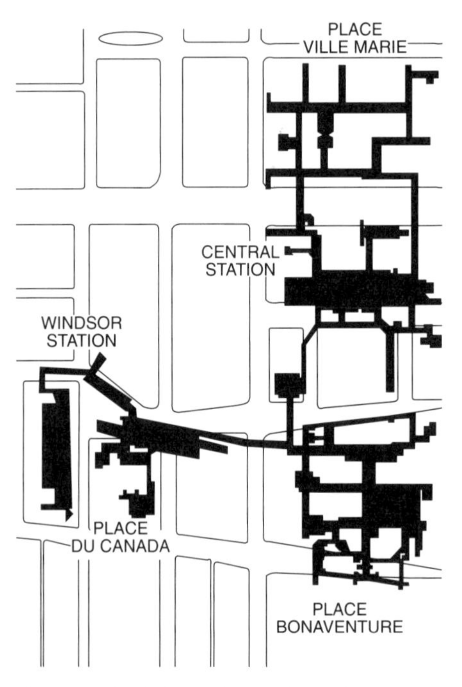

Figure 4-17: Map of a portion of the underground pedestrian network in Montreal, Canada.

INTEGRATED URBAN DEVELOPMENTS

Integrated underground commercial, institutional, and transportation centers have been envisaged in several futuristic development concepts (for example, the plan for an underground city beneath the Seine in Paris developed in 1963) and already exist in a few cities in the world. The present-day systems in both Montreal and Toronto, for example, are large interconnected underground pedestrian, commercial, and shopping systems that permit movement throughout much of the downtown area without exposure to severe weather or street traffic (Figure 4-17). These underground shopping centers contain some of the most fashionable and expensive shops in the city and are a far cry from the small booths and shops in underground transit stations that previously exemplified underground shops. Toronto's underground pedestrian network, for example, began at the turn of the century when the T. Eaton Company, Canada's largest department store complex, connected several of its buildings with tunnels. By 1917 there were five under-street tunnels, and in 1929 the bi-level Union Station was connected to the Royal York Hotel. No further development occurred, however, until 1954, when a

Figure 4-18: Underground Les Halles development in Paris, France, preserves open space and the historic character of the city.

downtown subway loop was constructed that offered opportunities for developing a more continuous and integrated system (Barker 1986). Starting in 1956, Montreal redeveloped Place Ville Marie and Place Bonaventure by constructing in and over a large railway cutting at the Central Railway Station. This stimulated a rapid private investment in the extension of these hubs of the underground connection system. The commercial success of the Montreal development, in turn, further stimulated the system development in Toronto (Besner 1990).

Growth of grade-separated pedestrian systems (aboveground or underground) appears to be natural once a critical mass is created in a city center. This in turn encourages the appropriate level(s) of adjoining buildings to be upgraded to serve the new pedestrian activity. The greatest reinforcing effect for development naturally comes when transit stations are linked to this pedestrian level. Thus in cities with established subway systems, most pedestrian links are underground, whereas in cities with elevated or surface transit systems, "skyway" connection systems may develop as in Minneapolis, Minnesota, USA.

One of the largest examples of an underground commercial and institutional complex tied to urban transit is the redevelopment of the Les Halles site in Paris (Figure 4-18). This site was made available when the Halles market was moved to Rungis. The complex covers 100,000 square meters on the surface and extends four levels below grade while preserving most of the surface as a park surrounded by beautiful historic structures. Les Halles is notable for the diversity of systems and uses it contains. These include a major subway station, roadways, car parking facilities, a shopping arcade, and community recreational facilities including a swimming pool. This complex is an excellent model of enhancing the total human environment by utilizing underground space, but proved to be an extremely difficult project on which to gain political agreement (Pilon 1980; Heim de Balsac 1980).

Figure 4-19: Underground shopping center, Osaka, Japan.

An interesting alternative to the underground connection or the skyway connection is the concept of creating a false ground level or "platform" above the original ground level. This idea was explored in some detail in *Traffic in Towns* (Buchanan Report 1963) as one of the few possible solutions to traffic problems and pedestrian comfort in major cities. An example of the use of a "platform" as the principal public service level for a development is the La Defense district in Paris. This massive redevelopment district with more than 2.5 million square meters of office space adopted this concept at an early stage, and it has been cited as a major reason for its success (Lecomte 1990). Underground excavation for new services is reduced, and vehicular and pedestrian traffic are more naturally separated.

Figure 4-20: Underground shopping center, Kawasaki, Japan.

Japan has had a long history of development of underground urban shopping centers. Two enormous underground shopping complexes were built adjacent to subway and rail stations in Osaka in 1957 (Figure 4-19). They were designed to relieve pedestrian traffic on Osaka's crowded streets and quickly became profitable ventures. After numerous expansions, they now cover more than 127,000 square meters and include over 1,000 shops and restaurants. More than 20 Japanese cities from Sapporo on the northern island of Hokkaido to Fukuoka in the south now have underground shopping complexes along their subway lines. In 1980, a fire and explosion at the Shizuoka underground shopping center killed 20 people, prompting the Japanese government to enact extremely restrictive laws governing underground commercial development. Only a few underground shopping centers have been built since then, with one of the newest being the Azalea underground shopping center in Kawasaki, which opened in October 1987 (Figure 4-20). The immense land pressures in major Japanese cities and the high land prices are today again spurring interest in more commercial underground uses as well as infrastructure service uses.

COMMERCIAL AND INSTITUTIONAL BUILDINGS

Many individual commercial/institutional buildings are also placed underground. Aesthetic concerns and preservation of open space are usually the critical reasons cited for their construction.

The uses of such underground buildings are very diverse since it is the site rather than the use that drives the decision to build underground. Some of the more common types of commercial/institutional underground buildings are discussed below. For a discussion of underground building design issues and a description of 20 U.S. examples, see *Underground Building Design* (Carmody and Sterling 1983). Although examples are not discussed specifically here, the commercial/industrial use of basement space underground is important and widespread.

Visitor/Interpretive Centers and Museums

One class of institutional facility is the "interpretive" center that acts as a small museum or visitor building for an important historical or natural site. The building is placed underground to allow the site to remain the focus of attention—not the building. Examples of this type of facility exist in many countries of the world.

An example of a major underground interpretive center is that at the Gateway Arch in St. Louis, Missouri, USA, where the entire visitor center is located beneath the surface so that the dramatic lines of the arch remain uncluttered by surface structures. A much smaller example is the interpretive center for the Oliver Kelly farm in Minnesota—the birthplace of the Democratic Farmer-Labor movement in the United States. The underground location of the center at this rural site preserves the view of the farmhouse across its surrounding fields and provides the needed visitor services at a short distance from the farm itself.

In Sweden, the new National Archives were excavated in rock in Marieberg near the center of Stockholm. These archives are used frequently and require both a secure and a readily accessible location. A proposal has also been made by Swedish architects to house and display the Pharaoh's funeral ship underground near the pyramids. The current museum of glass and concrete has been severely criticized in Egypt and abroad as providing a poor environment for the preservation of this important artifact.

Libraries

Additions to existing aboveground commercial or institutional buildings may be placed underground to retain proximity to existing facilities and to preserve the aesthetics of existing open spaces. Examples of this type of facility primarily include library additions on university campuses or urban sites.

There are many excellent examples of underground library facilities. Some notable examples are the Nathan Marsh Pusey Library built in the famous Harvard Yard at Harvard University in Cambridge, Massachusetts (Figure 4-21); the Radcliffe Science Library at Oxford University, Oxford, U.K.; and the seven-story deep addition to the National Diet Library in Tokyo, Japan.

Figure 4-21: Pusey Library, Harvard University. (Architect: Hugh Stubbins and Associates; photograph: © Steve Rosenthal)

When a new library at the University of Illinois, Champaign-Urbana campus was constructed approximately 20 years ago, designers were faced with an unusual site restriction. The nation's oldest agricultural test plot was situated immediately to the west of the library site. The solution was to place a two-story building with a central courtyard under the site rather than above, thus avoiding the casting of building shadows on the test plot (Labs 1976).

At Park College in Kansas City, Missouri, the solution to the need for a new library was to hire a mining company to excavate the library beneath the campus. The limestone rock is extensively mined elsewhere in the Kansas City area for use as aggregate and hence the cost of the excavation was offset by the sale of the aggregate produced.

Office Buildings

An example of an office building addition is the Mutual of Omaha Company's building expansion in Omaha, Nebraska, USA (Figure 4-22). This was placed underground to preserve the much-televised image of their corporate headquarters. As a side benefit, it was found to be cheaper than an aboveground addition due to the high cost of the facing stone required to match the existing building aboveground (Savage 1979).

For the Monsanto Company's world headquarters, existing site conditions and building relationships were not an issue since a new corporate campus was being designed from scratch. It was still decided, however, to place the company cafeteria underground in the center of the campus so that it conveniently could serve all the office buildings and still permit a large central open space on the surface (Labs 1976).

Government buildings often must occupy a central position in a

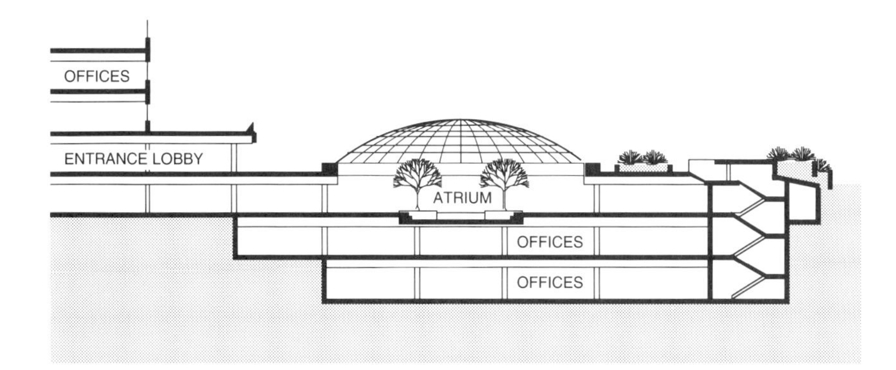

Figure 4-22: Mutual of Omaha building addition, Omaha, Nebraska, USA. (Architect: Leo A. Daly)

city and may be important symbols for the city or region. Additions to existing government buildings in historic settings are often placed largely underground to minimize their site impact (and sometimes for civil defense purposes). An example of such an extension is in the Kremlin in Moscow, a building which reportedly extends many stories below ground (Aughenbaugh 1978). The California State Office Building in Sacramento, California, USA, is an example of open space preservation on a central two-block site in the city as well as a demonstration of energy conservation techniques (Figure 4-23). The building is designed for solar collection on the exposed office tower and maximum daylighting through the use of sunken light courts for the portion of the building beneath the park (Carmody and Sterling 1983).

Office spaces are not common in rock caverns except as ancillary office spaces to a large storage or industrial facility. There are, however, many offices in converted Kansas City limestone mines in the United States.

Figure 4-23: California State Office Building, Sacramento, California, USA. (Architect: The Benham Group, Oklahoma City)

Figure 4-24: Wildwood Elementary School, Aspen, Colorado, USA. (Architect: David F. Gibson and William N. Gardner, Associated Architects; Photographer: David Marlow)

Educational Institutions

Educational buildings are an important class of underground structure. They are usually shallow cut-and-cover structures to facilitate fire exit requirements. For example, the Terraset and Terra Centre elementary schools in Fairfax County, Virginia, USA, were designed to provide low energy consumption and retain play areas on the roof of the building. The Wildwood School in Aspen, Colorado, was designed to provide an intriguing, naturalistic learning environment for elementary children (Figure 4-24). The Civil and Mineral Engineering Building at the University of Minnesota, was built in response to the lack of open space on campus and the severe Minnesota climate, and demonstrates the potential for mined space development in the Minneapolis-St. Paul geology. The 15,000-square-meter building houses classrooms, offices, and research laboratories. Part of the building is a cut-and-cover structure in soil but approximately 2,000 square meters was mined from two vertical shafts in a soft sandstone at a depth of 25 to 35 meters below ground level. The building was named the Outstanding Civil Engineering Achievement of 1983 in the United States (American Society of Civil Engineers 1983). At the Technical Research Center of Finland, a new underground research laboratory comprising several large rock caverns was recently completed. Slightly over 50 people normally work in the laboratory but it is designed to accommodate 6,000 persons for emergency shelter use (Saari 1988).

Special Use Facilities

Some unusual special-purpose facilities constructed underground have included the Moscone Convention Center in San Francisco, California, which was placed mostly underground in response to neighborhood objections to the scale of the project. To allow the project to proceed, the floor of the convention/exhibition space was placed 5 to 9 meters below grade on the sloping site, and massive arches providing a 85-meter clear span were designed to allow a landscaped park or a three-story building to be placed above the convention center (Figure 4-25).

Public perception of a building was also largely behind the placement of a high security prison partially underground in Oak Park Heights, Minnesota. The prison is arranged around a sunken courtyard in a shallow valley with the exterior walls of the prison almost completely below the surrounding grade level (Figure 4-26). Security is maintained without the imposing and often frightening visage of high perimeter walls and watch towers.

National research facilities are also being developed in rock caverns and tunnels for major particle physics experiments. Several deep underground chambers are being used around the world for proton decay experiments in which it is advantageous to shield the laboratory from as many sources of extraneous radiation as possible. Countries in which such facilities already exist include France, India, Italy, Japan, and the United States. The large particle collider experiments are also placed underground to provide safety against stray radiation and the consequences of losing the accelerated beam from its magnetic confinement (for example, the Cern facility in Switzerland and the Superconducting Supercollider in Texas).

Finally, there are medical facilities and emergency response facilities located underground in cities around the world. These usually fulfill civil defense roles as well as peacetime operations. In Shanghai, China, for example, a 430-bed hospital is located underground for civil defense purposes (Sterling 1981). In another example in Los Angeles, California, the emergency response center in the city hall is located at the deepest basement levels of the building.

Figure 4-25: Moscone Convention Center, San Francisco, California. (Architect: Hellmuth, Obata and Kassabaum; photograph: © Peter Henricks)

Figure 4-26: Minnesota Correctional Facility, Oak Park Heights, Minnesota. (Architect; Windsor Faricy; photographer: Saari and Forrai Photography)

Parking

Parking is a common use of underground facilities in major urban areas. The need to place parking adjacent to activity sites without spoiling the aboveground environment often forces an underground solution even when the costs of underground parking are several times that of a surface parking ramp. Many seemingly unused open spaces in city centers are underlain by parking facilities with unobtrusive entrances (Figure 4-27).

Figure 4-27: Entrance to underground parking, Paris, France.

Because of the cost of excavation on crowded urban sites, car parking is usually made as dense as possible. In drive-in ramps, two-level parking machinery may be used to increase density. Automatic parking facilities have also been used in Europe to increase density and remove a major operational cost of conventional underground parking—forced ventilation for the enclosed structure.

In Scandinavia, underground parking structures may be combined with civil defense facilities in rock-cut parking structures.

Industrial Facilities

There are three principal reasons why industrial facilities may be placed underground: (1) protection, (2) special attributes of the underground environment, and (3) use of available or low-cost underground space.

The advent of aerial bombing in the early part of the twentieth century created the ability to destroy the industrial capacity necessary to sustain a war effort. During World War II many industrial facilities were moved underground either to escape aerial detection or to provide protection from bombing. In England, a section of the London underground system was converted to a top secret factory. In Germany, an order was issued in May 1942 for the general dispersal of the entire German aircraft industry. This was amended in February 1944 to have factories placed underground; 9 million square meters were programmed but only 1.3 million square meters were actually in use by the end of the war, with 5.6 million square meters in various stages of construction. The working conditions were not considered very effective but the protection was excellent, and there was no effective bombing of these installations. Large earth covered shell structures were used with spans of approximately 200 meters (Kommendant 1978).

Japan also constructed more than 280,00 square meters of underground industrial plants in World War II for its production of aircraft parts. In the United States, the mines in Kansas City were first used for extensive warehousing during the same period. Since World War II, new underground factories have been constructed in Sweden, and working conditions have been considered acceptable for ongoing use.

In addition to protection, there are other potential special attributes available underground that are favorable for certain kinds of development. These include a stable thermal environment; a typically lower vibration level than surface sites; close control of ventilation air and low infiltration levels (which permit clean environments to be created more easily); high floor load capacities for excavations in rock; and the high security afforded critical industrial uses. The growth of high technology industries is requiring more specialized industrial environments incorporating these attributes. These environments can be created aboveground but at much higher costs than normal surface facilities. The same attributes require less additional cost for an underground facility on a suitable site, and hence direct initial cost advantages may be available, even if already excavated underground space (such as in mines) is not available.

Figure 4-28: Use of underground factories and warehouses to improve land use in Kansas City, Missouri. (Photograph: Underground Developers Association)

Many uses of underground spaces for industrial purposes are most effective if the space has been designed specifically to accommodate the nature of the industrial process. If the reuse of mined or constructed space becomes important, this has a large impact in terms of the layout of new mining or construction. This has happened both in China, in the development of dual-purpose facilities, and in Kansas City, in the alteration of mining plans to suit future utilization of the space created rather than solely to optimize mining efficiency (see section on mining uses at the end of this chapter).

Additionally, the more general aesthetic implications have caused some industrial facilities to be built fully or partly underground. Major industrial facilities are often buildings with large, imposing outlines and are resented by neighboring residential communities. Reducing the aboveground height of the building by full or partial placement underground can significantly ease placement of facilities in sensitive locations.

Military and Civil Defense Facilities

Security, defense, and military uses have always been associated with the use of the underground. Underground facilities can provide a secure refuge with limited points of entry and protection from shelling and bombing. Specialists in tunneling and explosives (called sappers) were used by armies in historical times to tunnel beneath the walls of cities to place explosives to blow up the fortifications. Defenders in turn would try to tunnel beneath the incoming tunnels to destroy them with explosives before they could reach the walls.

Figure 4-29: Entrance to NORAD Strategic Air Command, Colorado.

Many lines of fortification contained tunnels that provided refuge and protected access along the defenses. Perhaps the most elaborate of such systems was the Maginot Line built in France between the first and second world wars. It was an outgrowth of the trench-style warfare of World War I, but was rendered obsolete by the airplane and rapid military outflanking movements such as the "blitzkrieg."

The nuclear age brought new demands for defense protection and for the ability to provide a sure retaliation against an initial attack. Explosion and fallout shelters have been developed around the world to provide a measure of protection against this threat, but the nature and extent of the development has varied widely from country to country.

In the United States, major military command centers are built deep underground—the NORAD facility in Colorado, for example—but many other less critical military facilities are instead rendered less vulnerable by dispersal, i.e., reducing the likelihood of a significant portion of the facilities being destroyed by a single attack. Civil defense shelters for radiation protection in the United States were stressed in the 1950s, and many families constructed backyard fallout shelters. Few purpose-built public facilities were constructed in the United States, however, and during the 1960s there was a backlash of public opinion against the cost and perceived futility of such shelters.

Figure 4-30: Swedish submarine base constructed in a rock cavern.

In several other countries—notably Switzerland and the Scandinavian countries—a steady interest has been maintained in both military and civil defense structures underground. Civil defense uses include the creation of underground telecommunication centers (Stockholm), underground national archives (Norway), and underground oil storage caverns (Scandinavia), as well as public shelter facilities. The most radical difference in the development of these uses is, however, in the planned relationship of civil defense shelters to the community. Instead of solely being shelter facilities, they are planned as facilities fulfilling a valid community purpose such as sports halls, swimming pools, and community centers. The extra costs of the shelter aspects of the facility are borne by the national government, while the community has help in constructing a useful facility with minimal surface impact.

Such integrated development contrasts with the shelter facilities constructed in China in the 1960s. Tunnels were excavated under large cities in China under an urgent directive from Mao Zedong. The tunnels were mostly of small cross-section and constructed primarily with non-specialist labor. Beijing, for example, has approximately 5,000 kilometers of such tunnels that provide local shelter and underground escape routes from the city center to the outer suburbs (Sterling 1981). The investment in these tunnels was enormous, but most of the civil defense space constructed during that period is very poorly suited for other uses despite the pressing urban space needs in China. Recognizing this problem, China now adopts a strategy to combine civil defense needs with public facility needs (Sterling 1981).

Figure 4-31: Employee dining and meeting facility connected to underground factories in China. These spaces represent a reutilization of the networks of small tunnels beneath major Chinese cities that were created for civil defense purposes.

More specific military underground facilities include missile silos, underground submarine bases, ammunition stores, and a wide variety of specialized facilities. The protection afforded and the difficulty of detecting military hardware or facilities underground make such facilities desirable, but the cost and fears concerning the vulnerability of any fixed facility are drawbacks. Proposed developments to combat such deficiencies have included long underground tunnels connecting multiple missile silos (thus disguising the exact positioning of the missiles themselves) and deep relatively self-contained underground caverns containing missiles and the excavation equipment necessary to rapidly create a shaft to the surface for a retaliatory strike (the U.S. "deep basing" concept).

Military uses of the underground also include testing major new weapons. Extensive underground nuclear weapon testing has been carried out in the several countries with nuclear capability. This use of the underground has required large site areas to be placed off-limits for other uses because of the remaining radioactive contamination of the site.

Storage

BULK STORAGE OF FOOD

The practice of storing food underground has typically been due to three factors: (1) environmental conditions are well suited for food preservation; (2) rodent and insect infestation is easier to repel; and (3) food supplies are more secure against pilferage or attack by invaders.

It is much easier to maintain a closed environmental condition for grain stored underground. Respiration of the grain, along with that of any insects or fungi present, lowers the oxygen levels and raises the carbon dioxide levels of the atmosphere within the storage. This kills or anesthetizes the insects and prevents the

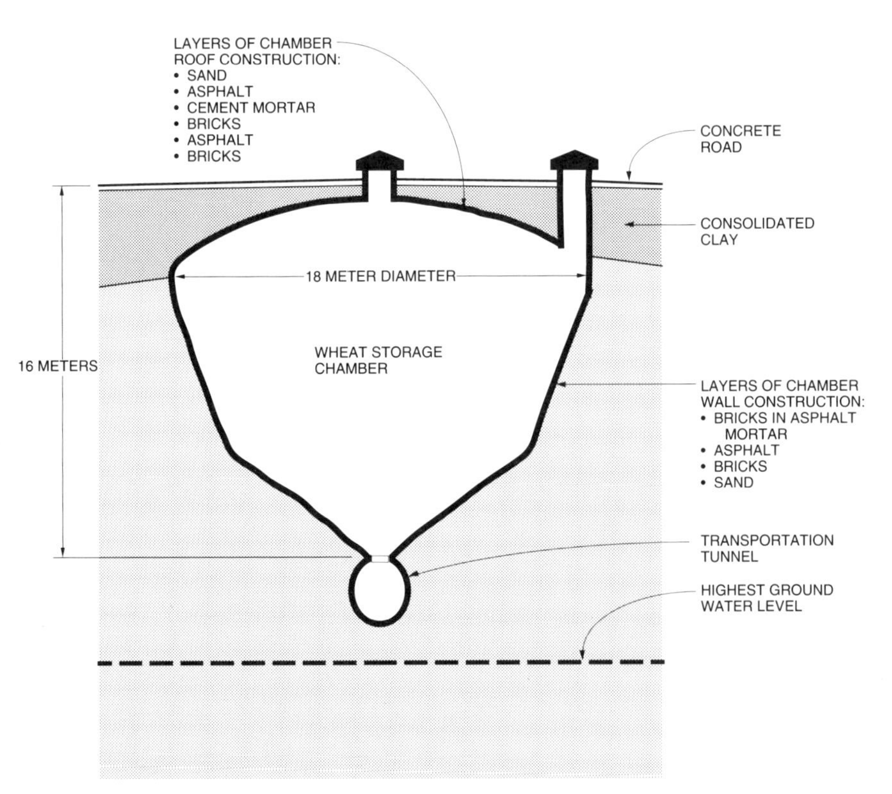

Figure 4-32: An underground wheat storage facility in China with a capacity of 1500 tons. (Source: Lundström 1983)

growth of aerobic fungi, providing a natural control without the use of pesticides. Also, the relatively constant temperature conditions below grade reduce moisture movement within the stored grain toward cold surfaces where the moisture may condense and cause rotting of the grain or development of anaerobic fungi (Dunkel et al. 1987; Sterling et al. 1983).

The drawbacks of underground storage have always been the initial cost of the storage compared with aboveground storage, the difficulty in grain handling during emptying, and the prevention of groundwater infiltration that could damage the grain. France was the first country to carry out a systematic study of controlled-atmosphere storage below ground in the 1800s, but today China is the leading exponent of such storage with several purpose-designed facilities that address the drawbacks very effectively (see Figure 4-32).

Despite drawbacks, underground storage of food has been practiced in many regions of the world. Major historical examples include the underground grain silos discovered in Luoyang, China, dating from the Sui and Tang dynasties (sixth to seventh centuries A.D.). A total of 287 storage bins were discovered ranging in size from 7 to 11.8 meters in depth and from 8 to 18 meters in diameter. Rice, wheat, and millet were stored in these bins, and many bins still had grain in them when discovered. The grain was 48.8 percent carbonized and, even after 1300 years, the husks could be removed from the millet (Sterling 1981). Marco Polo, in his account of his travels to China, noted the existence of these underground food stores, reporting their advantage in remaining undetected by an invading army (Komroff 1982).

Figure 4-33: Unloading a "matmora" – a traditional grain storage pit in Morocco.

Traditional underground storage structures called matmoras are still in common use today in North Africa in countries such as Morocco and Sudan (Figure 4-33). Cylindrical jar-shaped openings about 2 meters deep are filled with grain and then sealed until the grain is removed for later use. Research is currently underway to improve the efficiency of the traditional storage methods using modern materials such as plastic linings without losing the natural advantages of the storage method (Bartali 1987; Sartori 1987).

During the Second World War Argentina was faced with a huge oversupply of grain caused by disrupted commerce. The grain was deposited into specially constructed, large concrete-lined trenches and then sealed. The grain was stored for several years and remained in excellent condition. Temporary disruptions of grain transport in Australia have also led to the at-surface storage sealing of approximately 2,000 tons of grain covered by approximately 1 meter of soil. Test storages were made in 1975-76 (6-month storage) and 1977-79 (21-month storage). Grain was sealed in a plastic membrane before covering with soil (Dunkel 1985).

Grains are not the only candidates for underground storage. The natural conditions in dark, cool, humid underground chambers provide an excellent storage environment for pulses such as potatoes and some varieties of fruits. Wine cellars are a traditional underground use that is regaining popularity. The use of caverns for aging wine has been in continuous use in many wine-producing regions such as France. In newer wine-producing regions such as California which did not have the traditional caverns, new facilities are being excavated using tunnel boring machines to provide a cost-effective alternative to climate-controlled surface warehouses.

The special climatic conditions can also be of benefit in the preparation or aging of other foodstuffs. In Japan, the large Ohya Stone Caverns are being developed for a number of food-related projects: the preparation of Prosciutto hams, the storage of rice, and research into the storage of a variety of other products. The aging of certain kinds of cheeses is also suited to the use of rock caverns. In Minnesota, blue cheese has been aged in purpose-excavated caverns in a soft sandstone for several decades, and the caverns were extended in the 1980s when additional storage was required.

Processed and packaged food also requires storage prior to final distribution and sale. The temperature conditions for such storage vary with the type of product, but an underground location provides a high degree of economy and safety in maintaining those conditions because of the slow thermal response of the surrounding ground (Sterling et al. 1983).

The largest freezer storage warehouses in the world are located in Kansas City, Missouri, created as a reuse of the space left by room-and-pillar limestone mining operations. Backup refrigeration equipment is not necessary because the temperature only rises by 0.5°C per day following a power outage or equipment breakdown. The temperature in a conventional store may rise by 0.5°C per hour.

A final example is an ice cream storage and distribution center in Stockholm, Sweden, which uses its inexpensive underground freezer storage costs and product security to permit an extended production period to meet the summer peak demand. The central location of the warehouse also cuts distribution costs (Winqvist and Mellgren 1988).

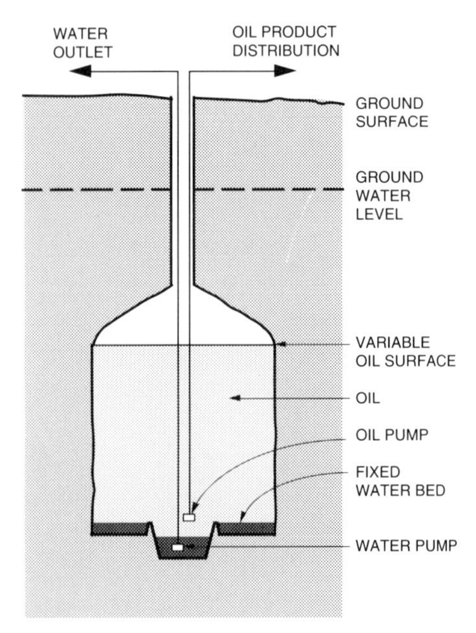

Figure 4-34: Section of oil storage cavern in rock. The surrounding groundwater forms a barrier that prevents the oil from leaking out into the rock joints. (Source: Winqvist and Mellgren 1988)

OIL AND GAS STORAGE

Oil and gas are critical elements in the fuel supply of all industrialized countries, both economically and militarily. To insulate the domestic supply from seasonal supply problems, international shortages, or acts of aggression, a large number of oil and gas storage facilities have been constructed around the world. Many of the largest stores have been constructed underground in recent years due principally to a lower cost (for large facilities), higher security, and a reduced potential for environmental damage.

The first underground storage schemes were essentially conventional tanks in an underground cavern. The Scandinavians, however, developed the use of unlined rock caverns below the water table for storing oil, which provided much lower costs. The oil floats on a water bed and is contained by the depressed surface of the groundwater around the cavern. Recharge systems were later developed to allow storage above the natural groundwater level by controlled water injection to create an artificial containment (Winqvist and Mellgren 1988; Saari 1988; Lien and Løset 1982).

In the United States, a national strategic oil storage facility is being created in purpose-mined solution caverns in salt. Oil can

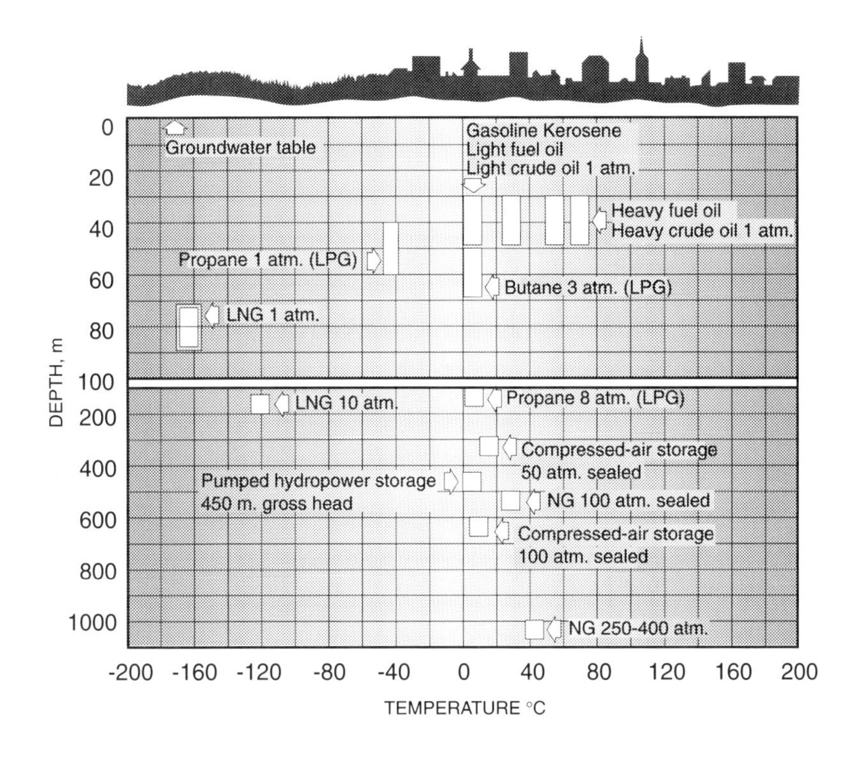

Figure 4-35: Temperature and depth requirements for various forms of energy storage. (Source: Winqvist and Mellgren 1988)

also be stored in abandoned mines, but layout and flow difficulties often prevent such use (Bergman 1979).

Natural gas or petroleum gas may be stored at ambient temperature under high confining pressures or at ambient pressure in a liquefied form. Surface pressure tanks are unsightly and potentially dangerous, and the refrigeration costs for surface liquefied storage are very high. Underground pressurized storages utilize either caverns or the natural pore space in a porous rock layer, and are situated at such a depth that the water pressure and/or rock confinement is sufficient to confine the natural or petroleum gas at the storage temperature desired (see Figure 4-35).

The temperature for liquefied storage can cause significant thermally induced stress changes in the rock or soil and lining surrounding the storage. Early storage facilities had significant cracking and leakage problems.

SECURE STORAGE

Many countries and large companies pay great attention to the secure storage of archival records and essential operating records for continued functioning in case of a natural disaster or act of war. A series of facilities have been developed around the world to provide a maximum level of security. In the United States, for example, records of the Mormon religion are kept in a deep underground chamber near Salt Lake City, Utah. In addition, facilities for records storage for companies exist in various limestone mines near Kansas City, Missouri, and in a converted mine near Boston, Massachusetts. During the Second World War national treasures were evacuated from London to a large system of worked-out mines in the western part of the country and, as mentioned earlier, the Norwegian national archives are now located in a shock-protected building constructed within a rock cavern. The most complete commercial facilities not only store records but also duplicate computer systems and records that would permit virtually uninterrupted company operation after a disaster at the main facility.

Transportation

Underground space has long been important to the development and advancement of transportation systems. Transportation-related underground space uses are principally in the form of tunnels for canals, railways, subways, or roads. Tunnels provide convenient routes past natural and artificial obstacles for a variety of transportation and utility purposes. Other transportation components, such as transit stations, can also be placed underground.

TUNNELING FOR TRANSPORTATION USES

The earliest evidence of tunneling dates from about 15,000 years ago when picks made of deer antlers and horse bones were used to dig tunnels for mining flint (*World Book* 1988). With the development of gunpowder in the 1600s, the speed of tunneling in rock increased greatly and permitted a wider range of uses. The rise of railroad systems in the 1800s necessitated a large increase in tunneling activity to reduce track grades and route lengths. In 1882 the first of the major railroad tunnels through the Swiss Alps was completed – the 15-kilometer St. Gotthard railroad tunnel.

Tunneling in soft ground and for underwater crossings was significantly advanced by the invention of the tunnel shield in 1825 by Marc Isambard Brunel (Figure 4-36). The shield was used for building a railroad tunnel under the River Thames in London.

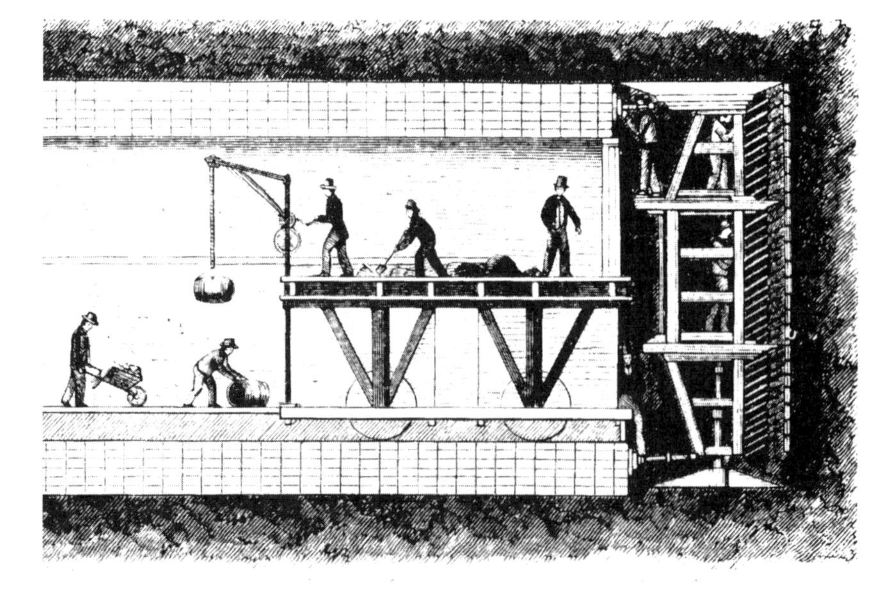

Figure 4-36: Brunel's shield used to dig the first underwater crossing of the Thames in London, England. The tunnel was completed in 1843. (Source: Bobrick 1981)

Despite many setbacks in tunnel progress, including two major in-rushes of water, the tunnel completed in 1843 was the first railroad tunnel built under a navigable river.

Undersea tunnels were begun as early as 1882 when a tunnel boring machine was developed to tunnel in the soft chalk beneath the English Channel. The work was stopped by the British government after 2,400 meters of progress because of fears of a surprise attack by foreign armies. After a century of speculation about an eventual crossing, a railroad tunnel is again under construction and is due to be completed by 1993. The tunnel will cross a 40-kilometer width of the channel and consist of two 7.6-meter diameter railway tunnels with a third 4.8-meter diameter pilot tunnel between them to provide emergency and other services (Kirkland 1986).

As cities have expanded, tunnels have been used for urban transportation systems such as subways, motor traffic tunnels, and utility tunnels. The first subway line was opened in London in 1863; today the system has 273 stations and a track length totaling 404 kilometers. Subway systems are now used in approximately 70 cities worldwide (Table 4-1). Urban motor traffic tunnels were used initially to alleviate specific sites of congestion, create underpasses for through traffic, or to provide alternatives to bridge or ferry crossings of rivers. More recently, however, tunnels are used to lessen the impact of motor traffic on surrounding neighborhoods and to allow the planning of new citywide routes that would be impossible on the surface. The LASER proposal for Paris (Lemperiare et al. 1989) and a new underground freeway proposal for Tokyo are examples of such proposed schemes.

Figure 4-37: Underground subway station in Washington, D.C.

There are many important advantages in using tunnels. The use of tunnels for canal networks in hilly regions allows shorter routes, fewer locks, and easier control of canal water. Early tunnels were usually only wide enough for one canal boat to pass through at a time. Tunnels also were important in the growth of railways in the 1800s because the available traction of steel wheels on steel rails and the power required to pull heavy trains up steep grades limited the grades of most rail lines to a few percent. Tunnels can provide shorter routes, flatter grades, and hence increased speed of operation. For example, rail line development in China, from 1891 to the end of 1984, involved 4,676 tunnels with a total length of 2,162 kilometers (Zhang and Jing 1989). In mountainous regions tunnels also reduce the problems of snow clearance.

Subways in major urban areas are not built underground so much to avoid topographical problems but to allow fast, high-capacity metro systems to be installed in an existing urban area with as little impact on the existing surface conditions as possible. In addition to the cities around the world that now have metro systems, there are others that have basically aboveground urban commuter systems, but with tunneled sections in the city center.

The need for road tunnels did not become widespread until the advent of the automobile. Although cars and trucks can negotiate very steep grades (up to 30 percent), the congestion and slow travel times caused by steep grades and long surface routes encourage tunneling in areas with a rugged topography. In many mountainous regions roads are closed in winter due to snowfall, thus cutting off important routes for commerce. Road tunnels face

Table 4-1: Subways throughout the world in 1987.

Nation	City	Inaugural Year	Total Operating (km)	Underground Operating (km)	Number of Routes	Stations	Annual Passengers (millions)	Cars
Argentina	Buenos Aires	1913	34.0	34.0	5	57	207	414
Austria	Vienna	1976	21.7	19.1	3	27	--	240
Belgium	Brussels	1976	13.7	10.6	1	21	35.3	90
Brazil	Sao Paulo	1974	20.0	15.0	2	23	209	306
	Rio de Janeiro	1979	12.3	11.0	2	13	20.4	96
Canada	Toronto	1954	59.9	44.5	2	59	--	632
	Montreal	1966	41.3	41.3	3	46	170	759
China	Peking	1971	23.6	23.6	1	17	45	64
	Tientsin	1980	23.8	1.3	1	18	34	29
Czechoslovakia	Prague	1974	19.3	18.8	2	23	207.4	187
Federal Republic of Germany*	West Berlin	1902	100.9	83.4	8	111	346	340
	Hamburg	1912	89.5	32.0	3	80	180.2	849
	München	1971	32.0	28.5	3	38	101.4	250
	Nuremberg	1972	12.3	8.9	1	19	35	74
France	Paris (M)	1900	190.2	175.4	15	358	1093.9	3496
	Paris (R)	1938	100.2	26.9	2	63	205.1	561
	Marseilles	1977	9.0	6.0	1	12	27.8	63
	Lyon	1978	11.8	11.8	3	17	47.7	66
German Democ. Republic	East Berlin	1902	15.8	13.6	2	23	75	340
Greece	Athens	1925	25.7	2.9	1	21	85	135
Hong Kong	Hong Kong	1979	15.6	12.8	1	15	166	210
Hungary	Budapest	1970	24.2	21.2	3	33	330	256
Italy	Rome	1955	25.1	18.5	2	33	114	208
	Milan	1964	47.1	29.4	2	57	205.8	361
Japan	Tokyo (TRTA)	1927	131.8	107.6	7	124	1603.4	1738
		1960	54.9	49.3	3	60	371.9	440
		1977	9.4	8.6	1	7	123.9	216
		1968	1.2	0.8	9	--	--	--
	Osaka	1933	89.1	77.8	6	87	796.8	792
	Nagoya	1957	54.4	51.8	4	60	323.9	429
	Kobe	1968	7.6	6.8	2	10	104.4	
		1977	5.7	5.2	1	4	16.5	32
	Sapporo	1971	31.6	19.6	2	32	180.4	320
	Yokohama	1972	11.5	11.2	2	12	46.2	70
	Kyoto	1981	6.6	6.6	1	8	--	36
	Fukuoka	1981	5.8	5.8	1	7	--	48
Korea	Seoul	1974	23.8	13.6	2	20	248	140
Mexico	Mexico City	1969	51.6	38.8	3	57	909.6	882
Netherlands	Rotterdam	1968	17.1	3.3	1	12	38	83
	Amsterdam	1977	16.2	3.7	1	18	33	88
Norway	Oslo	1966	35.5	10.7	1	44	39.4	162
Portugal	Lisbon	1959	12.0	12.0	1	20	120.5	80
Spain	Madrid	1919	86.0	80.5	10	124	391	768
	Barcelona	1924	48.2	47.2	5	72	239	412
Sweden	Stockholm	1950	103.6	56.6	3	94	195	885
United Kingdom	London	1863	387.9	163.6	9	248	559	4087
	Glasgow	1896	10.5	10.5	1	15	6.8	33
	New Castle	1980	23.8	1.3	1	18	34	29
United States of America	New York	1868	371.1	220.5	23	456	1040	6328
		1908	22.4	12.7	1	13	35.9	291
	Chicago	1892	143.2	16.1	5	140	150.7	1100
	Boston	1897	55.1	21.1	3	51	95	354
	Philadelphia	1907	39.2	25.3	2	54	65	419
		1969	23.3	4.6	1	14	11.3	121
	Cleveland	1955	30.5	0.5	1	18	11	108
	San Francisco	1972	114.0	30.5	1	34	45.3	440
	San Diego	1975	25.3	18.7	2	35	95	195
	Washington	1976	59.8	35.8	3	41	75.6	300
	Atlanta	1979	19.0		1	13	20	120
USSR	Moscow	1935	184.0	166	8	115	2318.2	2807
	St. Petersburg	1955	61.8	61.2	3	38	717.4	937
	Baku	1967	18.7	16.8	2	12	140.8	108
	Kiev	1960	26.2	20.4	2	17	255.2	299
	Tashikent	1977	15.4	15.4	1	12	74.3	105
	Tbilisi	1966	18.8	16.4	2	16	142.5	125
	Kharkov	1975	17.3	17.3	1	13	174.8	187
	Yerevan	1981	7.5	7.5	1	5	--	--

* Additionally, 16 cities in the FRG have light-rail systems that include significant portions of underground operations (source: ITA 1987).

more difficult problems than other transportation tunnels because of the need for ventilation systems in all but the shortest road tunnels, and because of the problems posed by tunnel fires involving the gasoline or diesel fuel in cars and trucks and any hazardous materials carried by trucks using the tunnel.

In modern times, the longest railroad or motor traffic tunnel is the Seikan tunnel, which connects the island of Hokkaido with the main island of Honshu in Japan. The tunnel was constructed in extremely adverse geologic conditions and was opened in 1988. The tunnel is 53.9 kilometers long with 23.3 kilometers below the sea and a maximum depth below sea level of 240 meters (Matsuo 1986). The world's longest railroad and motor traffic tunnels are listed in Tables 4-2 and 4-3.

Tunneling for transportation uses is increasing significantly due to the drive to build higher speed rail lines, with straighter alignments and flatter grades; the need to reduce urban congestion; and the construction of intercity freeways. Not only are tunnels longer and/or more frequent—capacity requirements, stricter

Table 4-2: World's longest railroad tunnels in 1988.

Tunnel	Location	Length (miles)	Length (km)	Year Opened
Seikan	Japan	33.5	53.9	1988
Ooshimizu	Japan	13.8	22.2	1982
Simplon I,II	Italy-Switzerland	12.3	19.8	1906 1922
Shin Kanmon	Japan	11.6	18.7	1975
Apennine	Italy	11.5	18.5	1934
Rokko	Japan	10.1	16.3	1972
Furka	Switzerland	9.5	15.3	*
St. Gotthard	Switzerland	9.3	15.0	1882
Nakayama	Japan	9.1	14.6	*
Lotschberg	Switzerland	9.1	14.6	1913

* Under construction (*World Book* 1988).
Note: The Channel Tunnel is not included in this table but has an overall length of approximately 50 km.

Table 4-3: World's longest motor traffic tunnels in 1988.

Tunnel	Location	Length (miles)	Length (km)	Year Opened
St. Gotthard Road	Switzerland	10.1	16,3	1980
Arlberg	Austria	8.7	14.0	1978
Frejus	France-Italy	8.1	13.0	1980
Mt. Blanc	France-Italy	7.3	11.7	1965
Gran Sasso	Italy	6.2	10.0	1976
Seelisberg	Switzerland	5.8	9.3	*
Ena	Japan	5.3	8.5	1976
Rokko II	Japan	4.3	6.9	1974
San Bernardino	Switzerland	4.1	6.6	1967
Tauern	Austria	4.0	6.4	1974

* Under construction (*World Book* 1988).

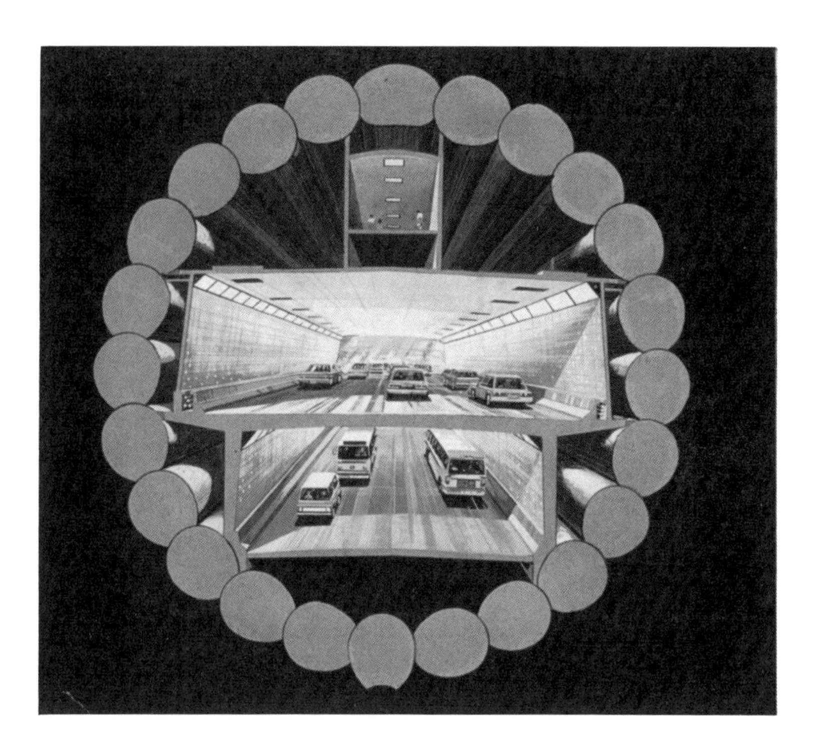

Figure 4-38: Mt. Baker Ridge Tunnel (19.5-meter inside diameter), Seattle, Washington, USA. (Source: Shannon and Wilson)

safety measures, and overhead electrification are making tunnel cross-sections larger. The largest soft ground transportation tunnel built to date is the Mt. Baker Ridge Highway tunnel with an inside diameter of 19.5 meters and an outside diameter of 25.4 meters (Figure 4-38).

Another trend evident in transportation facilities is the "undergrounding" of existing surface transportation facilities. Railway stations in major cities have been built over to provide new development "land" above the existing station. Urban freeways have had sight and sound barriers added to reduce the environmental degradation they cause to residential neighborhoods. The most extreme cases have involved the creation of a complete box enclosing the freeway (in Tokyo, for example) or the relocation of a freeway in a tunnel underground (now underway in downtown Boston, Massachusetts, USA).

OTHER UNDERGROUND SYSTEMS

Not all transportation-related uses are tunnels. Many transportation facilities may be built below grade, and the underground stations that serve subway systems and underground rail lines are important uses in their own right. Underground subway or rail stations, for example, serve as important focal points for development and often provide below-grade pedestrian connections into surrounding buildings or for crossing busy intersections. In cities such as Montreal, Toronto, Tokyo, and Paris, the stations are part of large underground shopping centers and pedestrian networks, which were discussed earlier.

Less visible underground transportation facilities may include facilities for ventilation, emergency rescue, equipment servicing, or system control. In the United States, several buildings for highway rest areas have been built partly underground for aesthetic reasons, and also for a decreased dependence on continuity of fuel supplies in remote areas with severe climates (Figure 4-39).

Utility Services

Figure 4-39: Highway rest area building, Enfield, Minnesota, USA.

The use of underground space for urban utility systems is by far the most extensive use of the underground. The expansion and replacement of utilities is a multibillion dollar annual market worldwide. For example, U.S. expenditures for the construction of gas, water supply, and sewer facilities were estimated to be $8.4 billion in 1984 according to the U.S. Chamber of Commerce. It has been estimated that the total market in the developed Western world for all types of utility installation is approximately 500,000 kilometers per year, with an approximate market value of US$25 billion annually (Jason Consultants 1987).

Although utility systems are a relatively recent development in the history of humankind, life in developed areas today would be unthinkable without them. The ancient Babylonians constructed water supply tunnels in about 2500 B.C. in the Indus Valley, and the Romans had a well-developed water supply system and sewage disposal system. A long period of neglect followed in almost all parts of the world except for the provision of water supply. Until the 1800s sewer systems in urban areas consisted principally of open ditches, but since this time utility systems have developed rapidly in urban areas around the world. Water and sewer systems were followed by electricity and telephone systems, district heating systems, mass transit systems, and communications systems. Some utility tunnels today combine several services, and are termed *utilidors*. Utilidors have long been a goal of municipal engineers because they provide accessible and adaptable utilities, but only countries with strong central planning seem to have been able to arrange the individual utility investments in a timely manner to support the large initial cost of such a tunnel.

Water and sewer systems are placed underground for frost protection, maintenance of utility slope (sewers), and because of the large pipe sizes required. Electricity and telephone systems are not so constrained, and the traditional practice outside of major downtown areas has been to use overhead systems. Aesthetic pressures today force such utilities in most new developments to be placed underground. New reasons for urban tunnels include the need to separate storm and sanitary sewers and to provide increased storage capacity for waste water prior to treatment.

UTILITY TUNNELING TECHNIQUES

The increase in the number and type of utilities being placed underground together with the need to replace and upgrade existing utilities has raised serious concerns about the traditional methods of locating and constructing underground utilities. Most utility systems are buried at shallow depth and are constructed by trenching. Although this installation method is relatively simple and is currently the cheapest method in most circumstances, it has significant disadvantages in terms of traffic interference, pavement damage, and the congestion of utilities in the shallow underground beneath streets.

These disadvantages, together with a greater realization of the nonproject economic costs associated with trenching (for example, economic damage to neighboring businesses), have led to an increasing interest in tunneling techniques for utility placement even at relatively shallow depths. Tunnels have historically required personnel entry to permit tunnel advancement, and the minimum size of such tunnels has limited the use of tunneling to larger utilities or groupings of utilities. In the last decade the technology for remotely operated "microtunneling," pipe-jacking, and drilling operations has improved dramatically. Because of the size of the utility construction and replacement market and the market share that microtunneling and small diameter tunneling could achieve, this technology is expected to become an important factor in the development of small diameter tunnels in the future.

In terms of length of utility installed, the overwhelming majority of utilities are small diameter utilities where personnel entry is not possible. Larger diameter utilities are required later in the development of an urban area to provide increased capacity for the main branches of supply systems and perhaps to upgrade the performance of sewage systems by separating storm and sanitary sewage. Large diameter sewer tunnels also can provide storage capacity within the system to avoid the release of untreated water during heavy rainfalls. The public investment required for such upgrading is very significant because large new citywide tunnel systems may be required to be built over a period of only a few years. For example, the Tunnel and Reservoir Plan (TARP system) in Chicago was designed to prevent the pollution of Lake Michigan, eliminate pollution caused by combined sewer overflows, and provide an outlet for flood water. The cost of Phase I of the project (completed in 1986) was US$1.2 billion, and the cost of all phases is estimated to be over US$3 billion (Engineering News Record 1986).

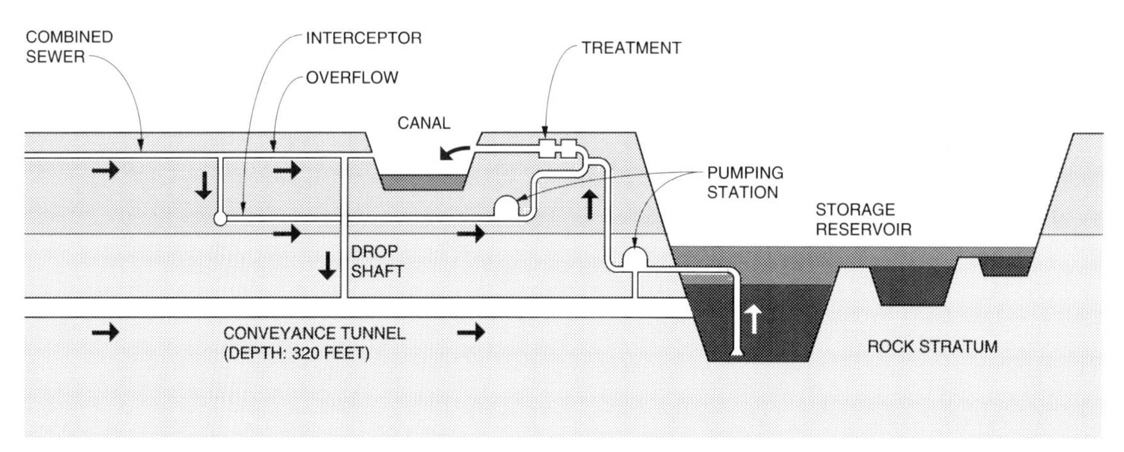

Figure 4-40: Schematic section of the Tunnel and Reservoir Plan (TARP), Chicago, Illinois, USA.

The urgent need to repair aging utility infrastructure systems and improve their quality is leading to major investments around the world. Cairo, for example, embarked on a major sewerage system upgrade in 1983 which is expected to be finished in the early 1990s at a cost of US$2.6 billion (Engineering News Record 1986). Tokyo has several schemes in progress or under consideration to reduce flooding, provide more complete sewage treatment, and increase the capacity of communication links (Tokyo Metropolitan Government 1989). The congestion near the surface under existing streets is forcing new utility systems to be constructed at a greater depth, often by tunneling rather than trenching methods. Remote tunneling procedures will provide powerful technological advances but, because of their reduced operational constraints, will increase pressure on city administrators to provide an orderly rationale for satisfying competing demands for the underground space beneath a city.

Water Supply and Sewage Treatment

The provision of a clean water supply and the proper treatment and discharge of waste water are becoming increasingly important applications of underground space. Long water supply tunnels may be used to bring water to cities and towns from remote reservoirs and lakes. The Bolinen project in Sweden involves transporting water through a rock tunnel to communities 100 kilometers from a large upland lake (Winqvist and Mellgren 1988).

Water treatment facilities can be located in underground plants where they offer less aesthetic impact and some operational advantages due to constant temperature conditions, security, and protection. For example, water from the city of Oslo's main source is treated at the Oset water treatment and pumping plant located in rock at Lake Maridalsvann. The lake and surrounding watershed function as a natural recreation area for the city, and preserving the surface environment was an important design consideration. The excavated volume of the plant is approximately 400,000 cubic meters (Saetersmoen 1982).

Figure 4-41: Entrance to an underground water treatment plant, Oslo, Norway.

Improving the treatment and discharge of waste water is also a critical task facing urban communities. As mentioned above, interceptor sewers may be used to redirect sewage from old systems to new treatment plants, to separate storm and sanitary sewage, and to provide temporary storage for storm water to reduce the release of untreated water.

Sewage treatment plants can also be located underground to reduce surface land requirements, lessen odor and visual pollution problems, and improve the purification processes affected by extreme cold or strong sunlight. In Sweden, 15 water purification plants have been constructed in rock caverns, accounting for 30 percent of all waste water purification in that country (Winqvist and Mellgren 1988). The largest plant in Sweden—Henriksdal—in the Stockholm area, has even had a residential complex constructed on land overlapping the plant.

The final stage of the urban water cycle is the release of the treated waste water into watercourses or the sea. Because of past

Figure 4-42: Henriksdal sewage treatment plant, Stockholm, Sweden.

contamination and stricter regulations on the release of waste water in coastal areas, there has been an increase in the use of outfall tunnels to allow the discharge of waste water further out from the coast or in less damaging locations.

Waste Disposal

One of the urgent problems in the world today is the management of society's waste products. The conveyance, treatment, and release of sewage was discussed in the previous section. This section discusses the disposal of other types of waste that interact with underground space use—solid waste, radioactive waste, and other hazardous waste materials.

The burial of unsightly or unwanted refuse dates back to prehistoric times, but because of the low population density and the preponderant use of only naturally occurring materials, this practice did not cause problems. Only a few years ago unprotected landfill sites were regularly used to store urban waste. However, the pollution of groundwater supplies due to toxic chemicals leaching from landfill sites, combined with the increasing volume of garbage and the reduced availability of suitable landfill sites, has caused fundamental shifts in the way wastes are handled. The poor practices of the past have also introduced a need for caution when excavations are made at existing urban sites where industrial or landfill activity may have occurred.

Apart from the steps taken to recycle as much solid waste as possible and to incinerate suitable solid waste, there has been an increase in the attention paid to separating waste into various categories of hazard, and diverting each category to a landfill or disposal facility engineered to contain the waste with little probability of damage to the environment. Final disposal of the solid residue of waste disposal processes is usually underground either by the eventual covering of an open landfill site or by the placement of wastes in purpose-constructed underground chambers.

The construction and expansion of waste disposal facilities is a contentious public issue that is not necessarily eased by the location of waste sites below ground. The history of poorly controlled waste disposal sites polluting area groundwater supplies and surface waters adds to public concern. Bulk waste disposal sites are usually near population centers to reduce travel distances for disposal. More specialized and hazardous disposal facilities can be located in more remote areas with favorable geologic conditions for waste isolation and less potential impact from a disposal accident. In many instances, old landfill sites have become incorporated into a growing urban area and may be built on.

The development of highly reliable methods for the storage of radioactive waste is a topic of extensive research in several countries. Deep underground repositories in a suitable geologic environment coupled with waste encapsulation are currently thought to provide the lowest probabilities of any release of radioactive materials into the biosphere (National Research Council 1990). To answer some of the adequacy and design questions for such repositories, several underground laboratories have been established (for example, the Stripa mine in Sweden, the Pinawa Laboratory in Canada, the ASSE salt mine in Germany, and the Waste Isolation Pilot Plant in the United States).

These disposal uses affect underground space planning in general because disposal areas should not be disturbed by future excavation and because groundwater monitoring wells surrounding the sites should also not be disturbed.

Energy Production and Storage

The direct storage of fuels prior to use was discussed in the earlier section on storage facilities. The use of underground facilities as an adjunct to power production, and the use of underground facilities for other forms of thermal or energy storage, are addressed here.

Energy is produced principally by the following means: burning fossil or renewable fuels; using nuclear fuels; capturing solar energy; or harnessing the energy of water flowing under gravity. Most fuel-burning plants are located aboveground for reasons of cost, fuel handling, and heat dissipation. It is also necessary to use tall chimney stacks to distribute flue gases to a height that complies with local concentration limits for airborne pollutants. Hydroelectric power plants, however, involve several technical design considerations that make an underground location desirable in addition to the aesthetic advantage of a minimal impact on an often important natural setting. Norway is the world leader in the use of underground hydroelectric plants with approximately 200 out of the 300 or so underground installations throughout the world.

Geothermal energy plants are restricted to areas of the world with high ground temperatures near the ground surface (associated

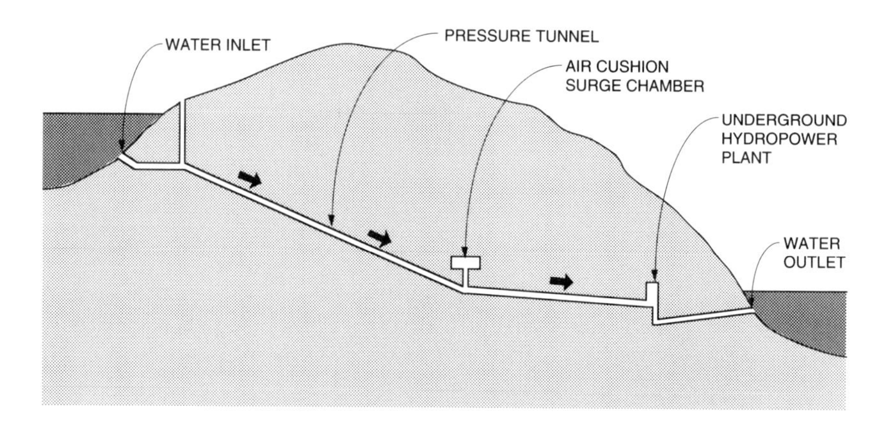

Figure 4-43: Schematic section of an underground hydroelectric power plant.

with tectonically active areas). A plant typically involves pairs of boreholes into the hot rock with cold water pumped into one borehole, through fractured rock between the boreholes, and retrieved as hot water or steam in the second borehole. Hydraulic fracturing may be used to increase the permeability of the rock between boreholes. Countries with existing geothermal energy plants include Iceland, Italy, Japan, the Philippines, and the United States.

The fear of Chernobyl-type accidents at nuclear power plants has rekindled an interest in the use of underground nuclear plants that would provide natural barriers against the release of airborne radiation in the event of a major catastrophe. A safer use of nuclear power has become a more important world issue as fears of global warming increase and the limited number of alternatives to the burning of fossil fuels are considered.

Because energy is not used at a constant rate and because it is uneconomical to provide a seldom-approached peak capacity, many energy storage techniques have evolved to level the load on power plants and to store excess energy for future use rather than wasting it to the environment. Pumped storage schemes are used in mountain regions to level electric utility loads. Water is pumped to an upper reservoir in periods of low energy demand and is allowed to flow down through hydroelectric turbines during periods of high energy demand to supplement other power plant production. The downward flow cycle is similar to a conventional hydroelectric plant and may be placed underground.

If a suitable surface topography is not available, a deep shaft and underground cavern reservoir may be connected to a small surface reservoir to provide the same function. The head difference between the reservoirs is not restricted by the available surface topography, and for larger heads reservoir size may be reduced to produce the same peak power output.

Another contender for energy storage is underground compressed air storage in which air is compressed to extremely high pressures in deep underground caverns when excess power is available. The release of the compressed air through turbines provides the energy recovery at peak demand periods. The principal advantage of underground compressed air storage is that, unlike underground pumped hydro storage schemes, the major equipment components can be located at lower cost on the surface. Air leakage from the caverns is a serious design concern, however.

Stored thermal energy systems can sometimes help reduce usage of newly produced energy. Typical schemes involve storing heat in (1) underground tanks of water, (2) beds of gravel-sized rock heated by air flowing through them, or (3) heat stores in a rock mass formed by the heat exchange with closely drilled patterns of boreholes. Other systems inject hot water into underground aquifer systems. Sweden has been a leader in investigations into underground thermal storage with investigations into all the types of storage mentioned (Sellberg 1990). The United States, France, and the Netherlands have been active in aquifer storage.

The systems may be used on a diurnal basis (day/night), a weather pattern controlled basis (a few days to a few weeks), or on an annual storage cycle. Such systems are particularly advantageous in regions with large climatic fluctuations on a diurnal or annual basis because naturally available thermal energy from half the cycle may be stored for use in the other half. Diurnal storage is often placed underground for aesthetic and thermal isolation reasons. Annual storage is almost always placed underground because of the volume of the storage medium that must be involved to store meaningful quantities of energy on an annual cycle.

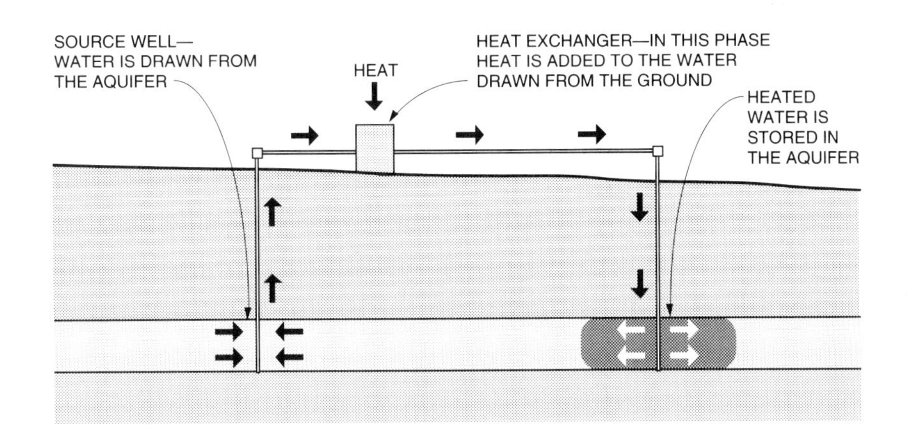

Figure 4-44: This illustrates the charging phase when heated water is injected into the groundwater – St. Paul aquifer thermal energy storage field test facility, University of Minnesota.

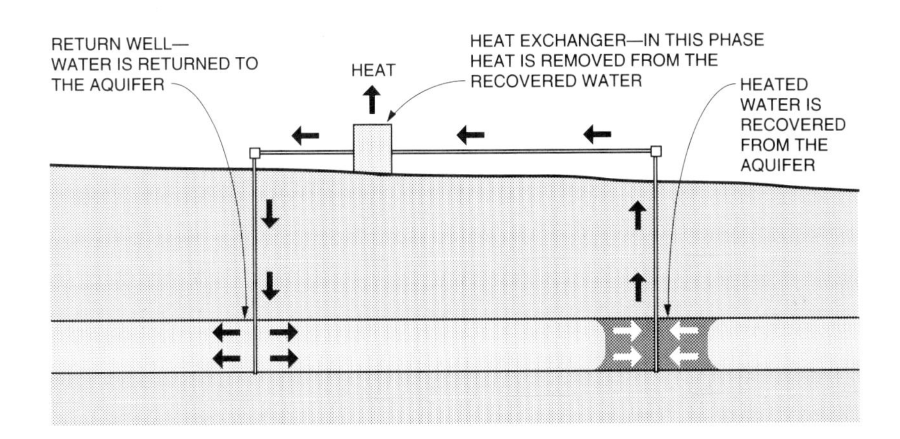

Figure 4-45: During the discharge phase, heat that was previously stored is withdrawn from the groundwater.

Systems for storing "coolth" are also used with configurations similar to those used for storing heat. Since cooling is usually produced from expensive electrical energy whereas heating can be produced from lower cost burning of fossil fuels, the economic incentive for coolth storage can be high. Design problems include the lower temperature differential between design indoor air temperature and the freezing point of water, which severely limits the amount of energy that can be stored in chilled water without using ice storage systems (which introduce some mechanical difficulties). An aquifer chill storage system has been in operation at the University of Alabama since 1984.

Mining

A detailed discussion of the historical development and current variety of mining practices is outside the scope of this handbook. This section instead provides a brief summary of mining history and other issues.

There is evidence that the first recorded civilizations already possessed the capability to mine for precious metals and other useful materials. The oldest known mine in the world is Bomvu Ridge in Swaziland in southern Africa, where Neanderthals mined hematite before 40,000 B.C. (Bieniawski 1984). Pits and tunnels were used to excavate flints by around 6000 B.C. Gold was being mined in Ur in Mesopotamia around 3500 B.C., and tin and copper were being mined by around 3000 B.C. Evidence of silver mining dates from around 2400 B.C., and by 1000 B.C. the mining of ores to make iron and steel was a fairly widespread practice. Baked bricks used for the construction of buildings were in use by the Sumerians around 3500 B.C. and would have required the excavation of clay deposits as the raw materials for the bricks (*World Book* 1988).

Figure 4-46: Rock excavation by fire setting. (Source: Agricola's De Re Metallica *in Paul 1970)*

Early mining practices included the excavation of hard rock by thermal spalling (heating the rock with fire and rapidly cooling the rock by dousing it with water) or by the use of wooden pegs in boreholes that were soaked to cause expansion and rock splitting. Some of these practices had existed and remained unchanged for many centuries. For instance, the thermal spalling technique was already in use by about 3500 B.C. (*World Book* 1988). Much of the early mining was carried out in small tunnels or pits that were self supporting or could be supported using timber sets and lagging boards.

By the 1400s, the mining of coal, iron, and other natural resources was an important activity in such countries as Germany, Sweden, and France. The foundation of a broad understanding of the practice of mining was laid by Georgius Agricola in a series of publications on geology and metallurgy between 1544 and 1556. These culminated in his most famous work, *De re metallica libri XII*, published after his death in 1555.

The introduction of explosives and specialized mine machinery together with an increasing understanding of how rock behaves around excavations permitted vast increases in the productivity of mines using a variety of mining methods. Large-scale mining today is generally an extremely efficient operation with high production rates and an extremely low unit cost of excavation compared with smaller purpose-built civil excavations.

A legacy of some mining activity is that abandoned or unstable mine excavations can pose a significant hazard to future underground or surface uses. Abandoned but partially covered or disguised mine shafts can be a hazard in areas with significant historical mining activity. The collapse of old mine workings may be a very difficult problem to counteract because of the scale of mine workings, lack of knowledge of exact layouts, and the high danger inherent in entering the mines for inspection. When mines are designed to collapse, as in longwall mining, surface subsidence can be planned for and the design and types of surface structures permitted adjusted accordingly.

Another issue that may arise for underground space use with regard to mining operations is the increasing interest in the reuse of mine excavations for other long-term uses such as industrial and warehouse facilities, thermal storage, or bulk material storage (oil storage and grain storage, for example). The Kansas City, Missouri, area in the United States is perhaps the best example of the conversion of limestone mines to a variety of other uses. In the process, current and future mining plans have been adapted to provide long-term stability and maximize the utility of the space

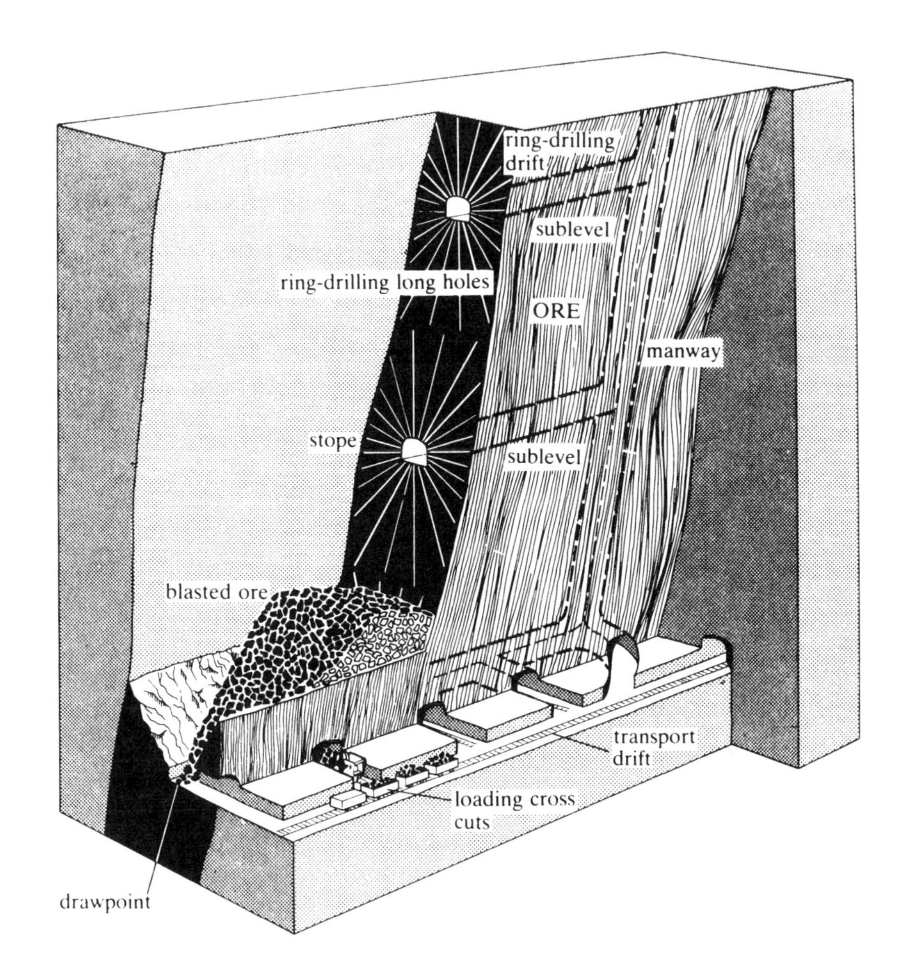

Figure 4-47: Modern mining – a schematic layout for sublevel open stoping with ring-drilled blast holes. (Source: Brady and Brown 1985)

created. Figure 4-49 illustrates the plan of one Kansas City mine. The old section of the mine near the bluff entrances has irregular pillars and poorer mining practices. The newer sections of the mine have regular pillar spacings, more careful mining, and special provision for a rail access loop through the mine. More than 20,000,000 square meters of mined space exists in the Kansas City area with 2,000,000 square meters of this in commercial/industrial use (Parizek 1975; Stauffer 1978; Woodard and Babler 1984).

Figure 4-48: Interior photo of pillar alignment, Kansas City, Missouri.

Another example is the Ohya mine in Japan, worked over many years for building stone production. This large mine is now being converted for industrial uses and food storage. An interesting feature of the mine is that over decades of use the dip of the excavations in the mine has caused a preferential cooling of the lowest levels of the mine. Cold air drops into the mine in winter whereas hot air will not do this in summer. The temperature in the mine has reached as low as 2°C at the base of the mine, and ventilation controls are now being installed to enhance this effect for cool storage of products. The dramatic nature of the space in the mine has also encouraged its use for more exotic purposes such as art exhibits, fashion shows, and other performances.

Mining can have other side benefits if proper planning is undertaken. For example, the spoil from mining has been used to create breakwaters for harbors or a new topography for a region. In central Poland, creating a 150-meter hill in a predominantly flat region is part of the Belchatow brown coal mining development. In Kentucky, USA, restoration of mining areas can involve the creation of needed flat land for development and community facilities in an area of rugged topography. Mining has also been used to lower an area of land by planned subsidence to restore use of a harbor (Legget 1976).

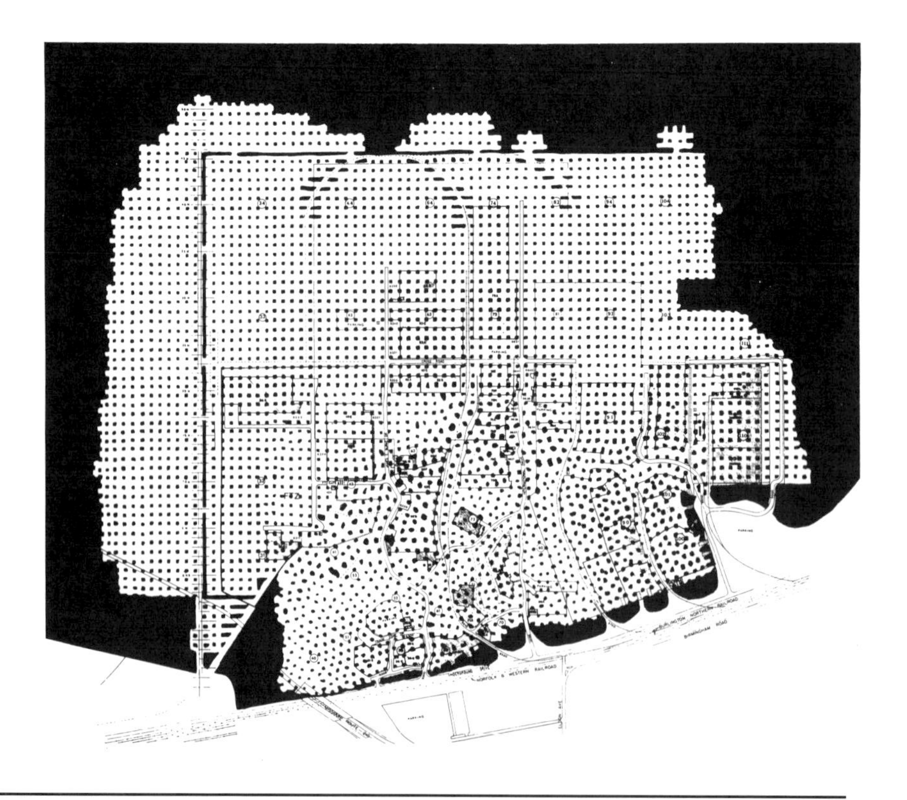

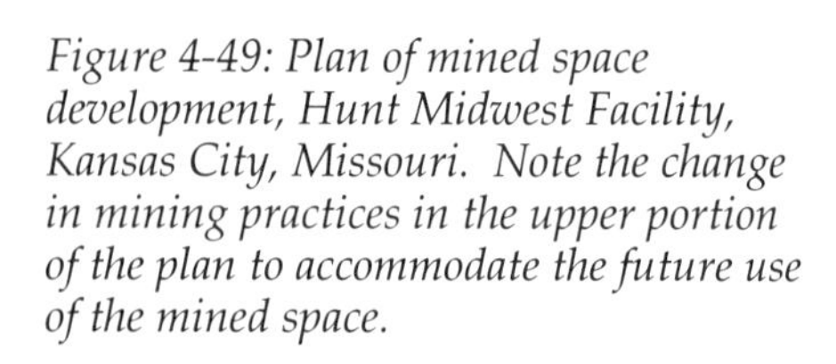

Figure 4-49: Plan of mined space development, Hunt Midwest Facility, Kansas City, Missouri. Note the change in mining practices in the upper portion of the plan to accommodate the future use of the mined space.

Agricultural Uses

There are a few specialized agricultural uses carried out in rock caverns — mostly in mines or caverns excavated for other purposes. Mushroom growing is well suited to the cool, damp conditions of underground chambers and is practiced in many different regions. Several underground mines in the western United States (at Kellogg, Idaho; Butte, Montana, and Crested Butte, Colorado) have also been used to grow seedlings under artificial light for surface restoration purposes. The seedlings are not exposed to the same dangers of disease and insect attack and can be transplanted at a later date with a much higher survival rate.

Miscellaneous Uses

While most underground uses can be placed in one of the above categories, a few uses do not readily fit such categorization but are nonetheless important in understanding the underground environment as it exists today.

A widespread miscellaneous use with significant potential impact on underground conditions is the immense number of boreholes that have been drilled for site exploration and waterwell purposes around the world. Until the last few years, boreholes that had fulfilled their purpose were often abandoned without strict procedures for grouting the boreholes closed. Open or collapsed boreholes, especially between different aquifers, can alter groundwater flow patterns and permit pollution to migrate from one aquifer to another. Ungrouted boreholes can also cause unexpected and dangerous water inflows during tunneling.

Another usurpation of near surface underground space is provided by the foundations of existing or previously demolished surface buildings. The widespread use of deep pile foundations in an urban area, for example, may restrict future tunneling either to follow street right-of-ways or to be a deep tunnel system below the pile foundations. The requirements of foundation support and tie-back style retaining walls also restrict future underground uses.

APPENDIX A

Cost Comparison for Conventional and Subsurface Facilities

INTRODUCTION

This appendix expands on the comparison of conventional and underground facilities contained in Chapter 1. In general, as land prices rise, placing facilities underground becomes more attractive economically. This appendix provides an analysis of the combined unit building area costs (land acquisition plus construction costs) for both a surface and an underground facility.

NOMENCLATURE

	Aboveground	Underground
Land area	A_l	A_l
Cost per unit land area	S	S
Average floor area per story	A	a
Total floor area of building	A_t	a_t
Number of stories	N	n
Cost ratio of underground easement cost to land cost	--	x
Construction cost per unit floor area of building	B	b
Total cost per unit floor area of building	T	t
Maximum floor area ratio permitted for aboveground building	$R = A_t/A_l$	–

ANALYSIS

It is assumed that space is allocated and costed on a unit floor area basis. A simplified diagram of the comparative building spaces is shown in Figure A-1. It is also assumed that the aboveground building is constructed to take advantage of the maximum floor area ratio permitted. For the aboveground building, the combined building and land cost is defined as the building construction cost plus a land cost spread over the total floor area of the building.

The total unit floor area cost aboveground is thus:

$$T = B + \frac{A_l S}{A_t}$$

$$= B + \frac{S}{R}$$

This is a straight line relationship as shown in Figure A-2.

For the underground building, the land cost depends on the area of the land surface requiring an easement and the ratio of the cost of this easement to the cost of the land. Figure A-1(b) shows a pair of underground caverns separated by pillars to maintain ground stability. This spacing may increase the land surface area requiring an easement, depending on whether the easement is based on a projection of only the space used or on the total projected area of the underground development. It is assumed for the purpose of this analysis that the easement cost ratio is based on the projected area of the underground openings only. This means that the land cost for an underground building is xS.

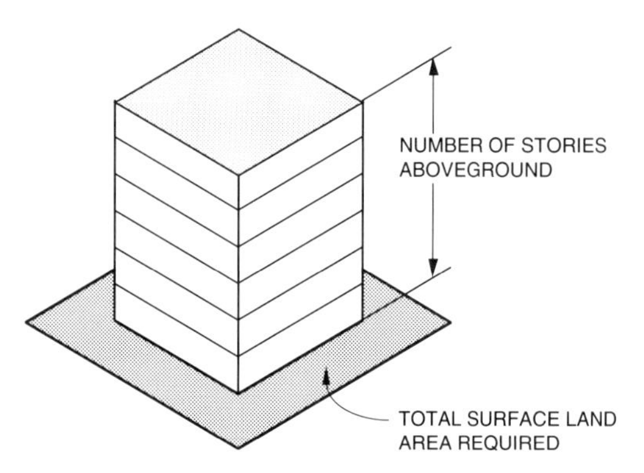

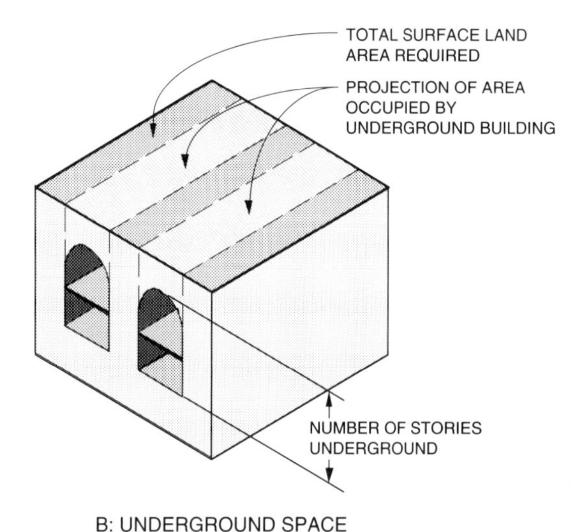

Figure A-1: Building Alternatives

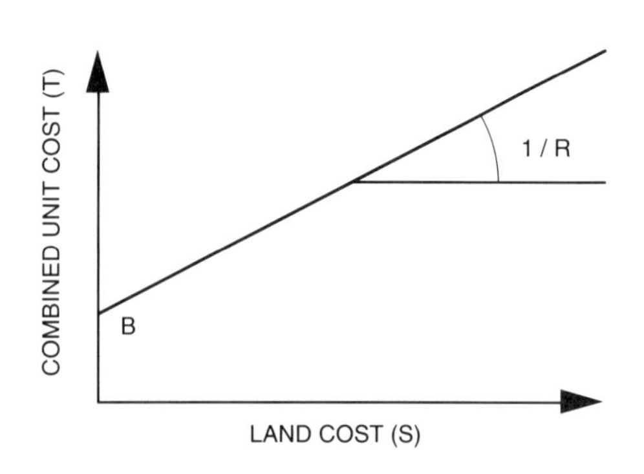

Figure A-2: Combined unit area cost for an aboveground building.

The combined unit floor area cost below ground is thus:

$$t = b + \frac{a \times S}{a_t}$$

$$= b + \frac{a \times S}{n\,a}$$

$$= b + \frac{x\,S}{n}$$

This has the same form as before, except the land cost portion of the total cost is dependent on the easement cost ratio and the number of stories constructed below ground.

To understand the effect of land cost on the viability of underground construction more clearly, it is useful to look at what the range of unit underground construction costs must be for the total cost to be competitive as the land cost varies. This can be done by equating the combined unit cost of the aboveground and underground buildings. This combined equation provides a breakeven cost ratio for the unit construction costs (b/B). If this ratio is less than 1, the underground project must be cheaper per unit floor area to construct than the aboveground building. If the ratio is greater than 1, the underground project can cost more per unit area to construct and still remain competitive in combined costs.

Setting the combined unit costs equal gives:

$$B + \frac{S}{R} = b + \frac{x\,S}{n}$$

or

$$(b - B) = \frac{S}{R} - \frac{x\,S}{n}$$

or

$$b - B = \left(\frac{1}{R} - \frac{x}{n}\right) S$$

This is a straight line relationship for (b-B) against S with slope $\left\{\left(\frac{1}{R} - \frac{x}{n}\right)\right\}$ and intercept 0 (see Figure A-3).

For a unit land cost greater than zero, the breakeven unit underground construction cost can always be somewhat higher than the aboveground construction cost provided that the slope of the line is positive, i.e., when

$$\frac{1}{R} > \frac{x}{n}.$$

This ratio merely indicates whether the land cost per unit floor area of the aboveground building is greater than that assessed to the underground building. For example, if the underground easement costs 20 percent of the land value based on the footprint area of the underground space ($x = .2$) and the underground space has two stories ($n = 2$), then:

$$\frac{1}{R} = \frac{0.2}{2} \quad \text{or} \quad R > 10$$

This means that with a floor area ratio for the aboveground building of less than 10, the underground building breakeven construction cost is greater than the aboveground construction cost. The savings (b - B) increase linearly with the cost of land.

Perhaps a more interesting comparison can be made by rearranging the equation to provide a breakeven ratio of underground to aboveground building construction costs in relation to the permitted floor area ratio aboveground. From the equation for (b - B), dividing through by B and rearranging:

$$\frac{b}{B} = 1 + \left(\frac{1}{R} - \frac{x}{n}\right)\frac{S}{B}$$

or

$$\frac{b}{B} = \left(1 - \frac{x\,S}{n\,B}\right) + \frac{S}{B}\left(\frac{1}{R}\right)$$

This equation gives a breakeven cost ratio that decays exponentially from its maximum value at N = 1 to an asymptote of

$$\left(1 - \frac{x\,S}{n\,B}\right)$$

as the number of stories becomes very large.

Since the aboveground construction cost appears on both sides of the equation, the ratio can only be evaluated from this expression by making an assumption for the aboveground construction cost for the building type considered.

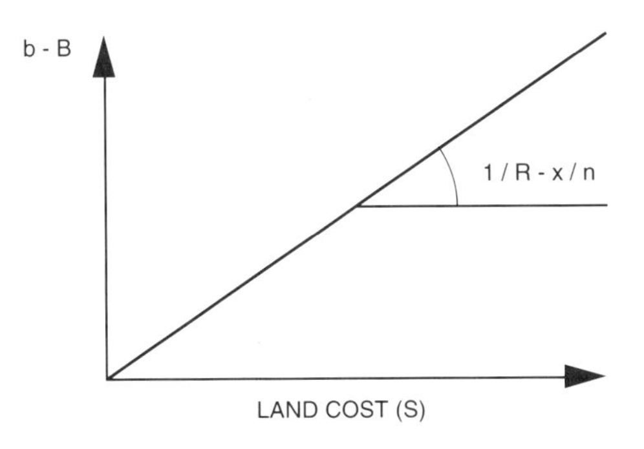

Figure A-3: Combined unit area cost for an underground building.

EXAMPLES

To provide some examples of how the breakeven cost ratio may vary under reasonable cost and land ratio assumptions, the following assumptions are made:

1. The easement cost ratio is $x = 0.2$.
2. The number of stories in the underground building (n) is 2.
3. The unit area construction cost aboveground (B) is U.S.$1500 per m^2.
4. The unit land cost (S) is given the values in U.S.$ per m^2 of 1,000, 10,000, 25,000, 100,000, and 500,000.

The previous equation for b/B then reduces to:

$$\frac{b}{B} = \left(1 - \frac{0.2\,S}{3000}\right) + \frac{S}{1500}\left(\frac{1}{R}\right)$$

$$= (1 - 6.67\text{E-}5\ S) + 6.67\text{E-}4\ S\left(\frac{1}{R}\right)$$

The asymptote value of less than 1 indicates that whenever there is some land cost assigned to the underground option, the limited number of stories underground will necessitate a breakeven cost ratio of less than 1 for large permitted floor area ratios aboveground.

Figure A-4 shows the graphs of breakeven cost ratio against the permitted floor area ratio aboveground for the selected unit land costs. The U.S.$25,000 per m^2 cost is representative of the most expensive real estate in Manhattan, New York (Downes 1989), and the U.S.$500,000 per m^2 cost is representative of the most expensive real estate in Tokyo (Kuwabara 1988). For comparison, the highest 1989 land values in Hong Kong were around U.S.$1,400 per m^2 (Vail 1989).

It can readily be seen that where floor area ratios are limited and land is very expensive (e.g., in Tokyo), a considerable construction cost penalty can be accommodated in providing an economical underground alternative to surface construction. For example, at a floor area ratio of 6, the breakeven cost ratio at central Tokyo land prices could be approximately 23. The crossover point at R=10 indicates the aboveground floor area ratio below which the underground building construction can be more expensive than surface construction for a breakeven in combined costs.

Even in cities with moderately high land costs at U.S.$10,000 m^2, underground construction can be a competitive alternative when the aboveground floor area ratio is limited. For example, an aboveground building with a floor area ratio of 5 under this scenario is comparable in combined unit area costs to a two-story underground building costing 2.4 times as much to construct.

Figure A-5 shows the trends exhibited when the underground easement cost ratio (x) is zero. The trends are the same as in Figure A-4 but all the curves asymptote to a breakeven cost ratio of 1 at high values of land area ratio (R). Under this scenario, the breakeven underground construction cost ratios when compared with an aboveground building with a floor area ratio of 10 are 1.7, 1.7, 2.7, 7.7, and 34 times the construction cost for the respective land values of 1,000, 10,000, 25,000, 100,000 and 500,000 U.S.$ per m^2.

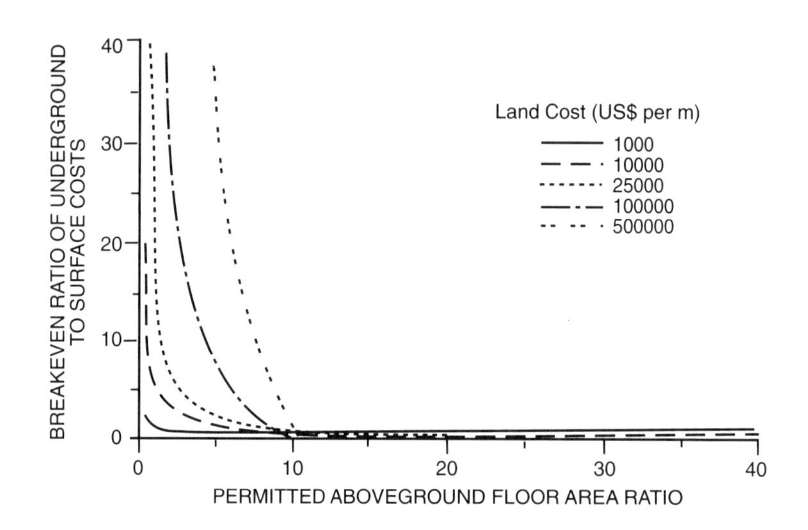

Figure A-4: Breakeven cost ratio: underground easement cost 20%.

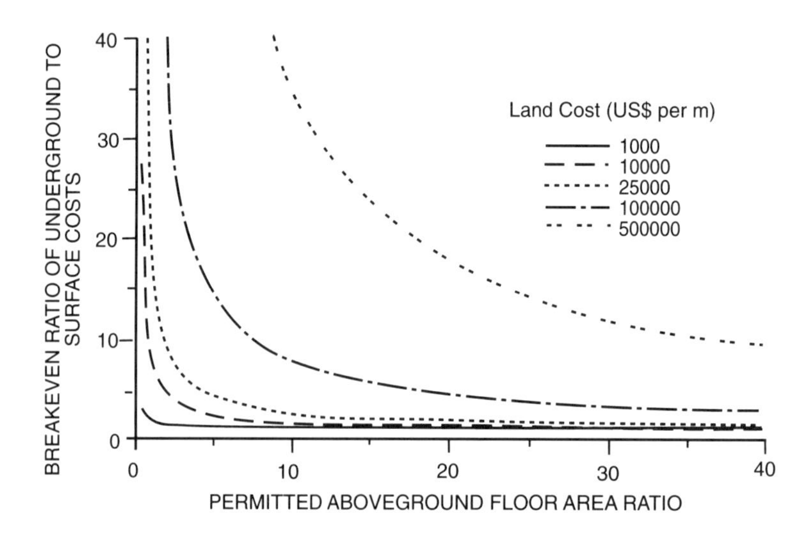

Figure A-5: Breakeven cost ratio: no underground easement cost.

APPENDIX B

A Database Format For Cataloging Underground Space Uses

INTRODUCTION

As discussed in Chapter 3, the Underground Space Center has developed a database-style classification system intended to encompass all types of underground space use and place them into a common framework. Naturally it is not possible to include all the details of any particular type of use or construction within such a generalized database without making the database overly cumbersome. Nor are all the included categories necessary for cataloging every underground use. However, the scheme can be expanded or improved for use in more specialized databases while still maintaining compatibility with the general classification. New keywords and categories can also be added without destroying the existing system. The database is currently being implemented in DBASE+ at the Underground Space Center, but transfer of data to other formats is usually relatively straightforward.

This appendix describes the database structure and keyword selection and provides several examples of the classification of uses with the database. A series of data entry screens have been designed that prompt the user for the permissible descriptions available for each database field. The major keyword categories are grouped under: **Function**, **Geometry**, **Origin/Age, Site Features**, and **Project Features**. The groupings are strongly oriented towards use of the database as a vehicle to understand the *utilization* of underground space.

KEYWORD CATEGORIES

Function

Currently identified keyword options are shown on the first two data entry screens (Figures B-1 and B-2) under the categories **Use Type Keywords** and **Importance of Human Acceptance**. In defining the use or function of the underground space, users should choose one or more major use groupings with the appropriate specific identifier(s). Keywords representing both types of uses and major modifiers are given, e.g., *storage food frozen*. Keywords linked by an underline, e.g., *bank_vault*, should normally be used together. Most terms should be self-explanatory, and the hierarchy indicated is provided only for ease in choice of terms. The level of detail of the keywords is only intended to distinguish between uses with significant differences in layout, design, or operational details and for uses with a number of available examples. This group of keywords is used to categorize existing projects or types of end uses.

The degree of importance of human acceptance describes the level of need for psychological and physiological issues to be considered in the design of a facility.

Geometry

These keywords will permit users to define the major geometrical types of space present, their relationship to the surface, and important dimensions (Figure B-2). An indication of the scale of the use is also given. Keywords may be combined for complex projects, but only the major or interesting features of the space need be represented.

Figure B-1: *Data Entry Screen 1 of the underground facilities database.*

UNDERGROUND FACILITIES DATABASE

PROJECT NAME/IDENTIFIER

USE TYPE KEYWORDS

RESIDENTIAL - MULTIFAMILY SINGLE-FAMILY SHELTER
RELIGIOUS - CHURCH CATACOMB TEMPLE VAULT CRYPT
RECREATIONAL - SPORTS PARK CONCERT THEATER CINEMA TOURISM SWIM HEALTH
INSTITUTIONAL - INTERPRETATIVE CORRECTIONAL RESEARCH SERVICE MUSEUM ASSEMBLY
COMMERCIAL - SHOPPING OFFICE MIXED_USE SERVICE RESTAURANT AUTO_REPAIR RESEARCH
INDUSTRIAL - PARKING RESEARCH MANUFACTURING LIGHT HEAVY PRECISION HAZARDOUS
MILITARY - FALLOUT SUBMARINE SILO COMMAND AMMUNITION FORTIFICATION ATTACK
AGRICULTURE - NURSERY MUSHROOM
STORAGE - FOOD DRY COLD FROZEN CONTROLLED ATMOSPHERE HAZARDOUS RADIOACTIVE OIL GAS AMMUNITION BANK_VAULT WINE RECORDS
DISPOSAL - SOLID HAZARDOUS RADIOACTIVE WASTE
ENERGY - PRODUCTION STORAGE HYDROELECTRIC
UTILITY - SEWER STORM SANITARY SEPARATION STORAGE WATER TREATMENT GAS ELECTRIC PHONE DATA PNEUMATIC CABLE UTILIDOR DISTRICT HEATING FACILITY TUNNEL
TRANSPORTATION - TRAFFIC SUBWAY RAIL LIGHT HEAVY BUS PEDESTRIAN GOODS CANAL
MINE - COAL METAL OIL GAS SALT AGGREGATE MINERAL PRECIOUS

Under **Space Type Keywords**, *boreholes* used for normal site investigation would not be listed as a type of space for a building project, but boreholes used in their own right as a thermal storage system would. *Microtunnel* is separated from *tunnel* as being below the size of person entry. This is an increasingly important class of space use in urban areas and is not differentiated under the scale of project, which relates to the extent of a tunnel system. *Cave* or *cavern* is used to refer to any chamber-like opening existing or created below ground, with size the principal distinguishing factor. Excavations from surface (other than shafts or boreholes) are classed as *open_pit* or *trench*, depending on relative surface dimensions. Modifiers to describe the orientation of tunnel or borehole/shaft elements are available if necessary. The term *guided* indicates a remotely steered or deviated microtunnel or borehole, which may follow an irregular path.

Surface Relationship Keywords, which principally relate to near-surface underground buildings and follow terminology from previous classifications, describe the nature of the relationship of underground space to the ground surface level and the nature of openings made for access and provision of natural lighting. Table 3-4 in Chapter 3 illustrates the use of the keywords.

The overall dimensions of the space should be listed in terms of volume or floor area according to the function or type of space created. The individual dimensions should be for the principal elements of the space, e.g., largest cavern, main tunnel, open-pit excavation dimensions, etc. The depth listed should be the deepest representative depth for the space or use described (Figure B-2).

It was not felt that a keyword system would be appropriate for identifying **Scale** of use. As in the discussion on depth in Chapter 3, what is considered a large project depends heavily on the type of project. To provide some consistency across all uses, a five-point numerical scheme has been used to describe the scale of a project or of a type of use (Figure B-3). This allows for some types of settlements or widespread regional uses affecting a whole region, e.g., cave dwellings in central China, to be identified as a major use rather than as a series of individual (and small) projects. The indication of scale provides a measure of the size, complexity, and investment required to achieve the use described. For example, the extent and area serviced by the utility are defined in this grouping rather than the cross-sectional size of a utility.

UNDERGROUND FACILITIES DATABASE

IMPORTANCE OF HUMAN ACCEPTANCE

HIGH MEDIUM LOW UNIMPORTANT

GEOMETRY

SPACE TYPE KEYWORDS

PORE_SPACE FISSURE BOREHOLE SHAFT TUNNEL MICROTUNNEL CAVE CAVERN TRENCH OPEN_PIT VERTICAL HORIZONTAL INCLINED SPIRAL GUIDED

SURFACE RELATIONSHIP KEYWORDS

CHAMBER ATRIUM ELEVATIONAL PENETRATIONAL TUNNEL BASEMENT BERMED EARTH_COVERED OPEN CLOSED HILLSIDE MIXED

SIZE TYPE sqm floor area cum volume **SIZE VALUE**

LENGTH m **WIDTH** m **HEIGHT** **m**

CROSS SECTIONAL AREA sqm

DEPTH TO BASE OF STRUCTURE m

Figure B-2: Data Entry Screen 2 of the underground facilities database.

UNDERGROUND FACILITIES DATABASE

SCALE

RESIDENTIAL
1. *SINGLE FAMILY (0 - 500 sqm)*
2. *SMALL MULTIFAMILY (0 - 2000 sqm)*
3. *LARGE MULTIFAMILY (> 2000 sqm)*
4. *SETTLEMENT*
5. *WIDESPREAD REGIONAL BUILDING TYPE*

NONRESIDENTIAL
1. *SMALL STORAGE OR WORKING CHAMBER (< 25 sqm OR < 1000 cum)*
2. *MEDIUM-SIZED (BUILDING SCALE)*
3. *LARGE (BUILDING SCALE)*
4. *BLOCK SCALE (E.G., LES HALLES)*
5. *DISTRICT SCALE (> 1-2 BLOCKS) (E.G., MONTREAL)*

INFRASTRUCTURE
1. *UTILITIES/TUNNELS/MINES - BLOCK SCALE (<1000 M)*
2. *UTILITIES/TUNNELS/MINES - DISTRICT SCALE*
3. *UTILITIES/TUNNELS/MINES - CITY SCALE*
4. *UTILITIES/TUNNELS - REGIONAL SCALE*
5. *UTILITIES/TUNNELS - NATIONAL SCALE*

Figure B-3: Data Entry Screen 3 of the underground facilities database.

UNDERGROUND FACILITIES DATABASE

ORIGIN & AGE KEYWORDS

ORIGIN - EXCAVATED CIVIL MILITARY MINING - STABLE CAVING SOLUTION BACKFILL - NATURAL ADAPTED MIXED REUSE
AGE - MODERN TRADITIONAL (in use) HISTORICAL ARCHAEOLOGICAL

SITE FEATURES

PROJECT LOCATION

COUNTRY
STATE
CITY

PROJECT LOCATION TYPE

LDC (lesser developed country) MDC (more developed)
URBAN SUBURBAN RURAL REMOTE

Figure B-4: Data Entry Screen 4 of the underground facilities database.

UNDERGROUND FACILITIES DATABASE

CLIMATE TYPE

HOT TEMPERATE CONTINENTAL COLD ARCTIC HUMID ARID

TEMPERATURE Deg C

YEARLY AVG *MAX MONTHLY* *MIN MONTHLY*

RAINFALL mm/month

YEARLY AVG *MAX MONTHLY* *MIN MONTHLY*

HUMIDITY avg. daily R.H.%

YEARLY AVG *MAX MONTHLY* *MIN MONTHLY*

LAND COST $ per sq m in area

POPULATION DENSITY population per sq km in city or region

SURFACE USE BEFORE DEVELOPMENT
SURFACE USE AFTER DEVELOPMENT

OPEN_LAND AGRICULTURE URBAN_OPEN_SPACE RECREATIONAL BUILDING RELATED UNRELATED
TRANSPORTATION WATERWAY MULTIPLE

Figure B-5: Data Entry Screen 5 of the underground facilities database.

Origin and Age

The keywords in this category differentiate between natural spaces such as caves and excavated spaces resulting from mining, military, or civil (other non-military excavation) operations (Figure B-4). The ability to identify adapted natural spaces, reuse of prior developments, and mixed developments involving, for example, excavated and natural spaces, is provided.

Classification of the use or space by age is intended to differentiate modern uses, which apply to purpose-designed uses using modern equipment and methods, from traditional (or vernacular) uses, which are still utilized; historical uses, which are no longer used but have a written description of their use; and archaeological uses for which we depend solely on the information gleaned from archaeological investigations.

Site Features

These keywords are intended to allow the identification of particular site characteristics that favor certain types of underground uses. Most of the categories are self-explanatory.

Project Location and **Project Location Type** together allow geographical, economic, or regional distinctions to be made among locations of underground space use (Figure B-4). Utilization issues are quite different in urban versus rural areas and among the more and lesser developed nations.

Climate Type keywords describe the gross climate type in which a use is located (Figure B-5). The energy efficiency design issues, moisture control, and relative advantage of underground facilities can relate strongly to climate type. The terminology is standard.

Climate, Land Cost, and Population Density data can be entered to the accuracy available. It is hoped to collect information on the extent to which these factors encourage or inhibit underground development.

Since land use is often a critical issue in the development of underground facilities, it is useful to document the *surface use before development* and the *surface use after development*. Combinations of keywords can describe complex sites, or unaffected may be used, for instance, to describe a utility tunnel that does not impact surface land use. Usually, open space is merely maintained by underground structures, but in some cases an underground project may be designed to reclaim open space from an existing transportation or building use.

Building Relationship Keywords describe the underground space use in relation to any *existing* neighboring buildings (Figure B-6). Underground spaces are often developed because of the need for a new facility related to existing buildings that does not usurp surface

UNDERGROUND FACILITIES DATABASE

BUILDING RELATIONSHIP KEYWORDS

BASEMENT ADDITION FREESTANDING INFILL CONNECTED INDEPENDENT (e.g., bldg. utility) NONE

GROUND KEYWORDS

ground conditions GROUNDWATER ABOVE BELOW base of structure ROCK SOIL GOOD POOR MIXED principal geologic description

PROJECT FEATURES

DEVELOPER

PRIVATE PUBLIC COMBINATION NATIONAL LOCAL REGULATED DEFENSE UNIVERSITY

REASON KEYWORDS

ENERGY_CONSERVATION ENERGY_PRODUCTION ENERGY_STORAGE SURFACE_CONGESTION AESTHETICS ENVIRONMENTAL_PROTECTION LOCATION PROTECTION SECURITY TERRAIN CROSS_BARRIER TEST_FACILITY

Figure B-6: Data Entry Screen 6 of the underground facilities database.

open space. These keywords allow groupings of similar projects for design comparison.

Basement describes an underground space developed beneath a surface structure during construction and in the traditional basement form.

Addition describes a new underground space added to an existing facility and essentially contiguous with the existing facility.

Freestanding implies the new underground space is a building in its own right.

Infill is used to describe an addition or freestanding building developed on an essentially enclosed surface site (such as a courtyard).

Connected indicates that the underground facility has direct physical connections permitting personnel access to/from surrounding buildings.

Independent describes a facility (such as a utility system) that is in proximity to building uses and may connect to buildings, but which has an independent function.

None describes a facility with no marked relationship to any existing buildings. Examples would include major tunnels and mined space facilities.

Under **Ground Keywords**, only groundwater levels relative to the facility and the broadest nature of ground conditions are assigned keywords. A geologic description using standard terms provides additional classification potential.

Project Features

The category **Developer** identifies the organizational structure behind the decision to develop and use an underground facility (Figure B-6). This identification may allow a better understanding of the organizational circumstances that favor underground development.

Reason Keywords, **Design Keywords**, and **Construction Keywords** allow special features of a particular use, design, or construction to be noted (Figures B-6 and B-7). These can be used to group similar types of projects or projects utilizing the same design or construction features. Note that the reason keywords are not necessarily the same as a use, i.e., security or energy conservation may be contributing reasons for building underground even though the principal use of the facility may be for education. Design keywords relate to the

UNDERGROUND FACILITIES DATABASE

DESIGN KEYWORDS

special or noteworthy design features
BEAMED_DAYLIGHT ATRIUM OPEN ENCLOSED ENTRANCE LAYOUT WAYFINDING INTERIOR_DESIGN INTERIOR_GLAZING SURROGATE_WINDOWS INTERIOR_VIEWS LIGHTING FULL_SPECTRUM FIRE_PROTECTION EGRESS

CONSTRUCTION KEYWORDS

TBM DRILL&BLAST NATM COMPRESSED_AIR GROUTING PILOT_TUNNEL GROUND_FREEZING SLURRY_WALL TIEBACKS SOIL_NAILING RAISE_BORE CAVING ROCKBOLTS SHOTCRETE
SPILING SETS ROAD_HEADER CABLES IMPACT IMMERSED_TUBE SHIELD EARTH_PRESSURE_BALANCE
SLURRY_SHIELD CONCRETE SEGMENT ONE_PASS-LINING MULTIPLE_DRIFT PIPE JACKING

YEAR STARTED if B.C. list as a negative number

YEAR COMPLETED

COST BASIS currency, unit for cost i.e., total or per sq ft etc.

PROJECT DESCRIPTION
Give description, references and contacts

Figure B-7: Data Entry Screen 7 of the underground facilities database.

architectural design of spaces. Construction keywords relate to the excavation and support of the underground openings.

The final grouping of data for classifying and documenting underground projects is additional specific reference information; documentation of project cost and construction period; and a description of the project with key features and references to project descriptions or contacts for further information.

CONCLUSION

It is hoped that the establishment of a general structure for recording data on underground projects will allow the accumulation of a large database of underground uses that can be searched and/or sorted to analyze the similarities and differences among projects with shared characteristics. A second important use is the identification of reference projects for a planned use. Decision-makers are more likely to seriously consider an underground option if well-documented, successful examples are available with similar site and geographical conditions.

The Underground Space Center would welcome cooperation with other institutions and organizations to expand and/or improve this database.

APPENDIX C

Legal and Administrative Issues in Underground Space Use

A Preliminary Survey of Member Nations of the International Tunnelling Association

INTRODUCTION

Legal and administrative restrictions on the development and use of underground space may act as significant barriers to the use of this resource. The protection of the rights of existing surface or underground users, the administrative control of mineral reserves of national importance, and the provision of personal safety and environmental protection are issues that must be resolved in all countries involved in underground construction or mining regardless of their political structure.

In 1987, at the request of the Executive Committee of the International Tunnelling Assocation (ITA), the Working Group on Subsurface Planning of the ITA began collecting data on this issue from the member countries of the ITA. A questionnaire was developed and mailed during the early part of 1987 and the first round of responses were received during mid to late 1987. Fourteen responses were received during 1987 from a mailing to the 35 ITA member nations existing at that time. A preliminary tabulation of responses was completed during 1988 for review by the working group. In September 1989 the questionnaire was remailed to those ITA member countries that had not previously responded.

The questionnaire was also mailed to two additional member countries admitted to the ITA since the previous questionnaire had been circulated, and three additional responses were obtained by the end of 1989. A final report was prepared based on the total of 19 responses received. The countries responding were: Australia, Belgium, China, Czechoslovakia, Denmark, Finland, France, Hungary, Italy, Japan, Mexico, Norway, South Africa, Sweden, Switzerland, UK, USA, Venezuela, and West Germany.

The questionnaire was not intended to be definitive in its detail or comprehensive in its coverage because of the complexity of legal issues and administrative law in most countries. Rather, it was intended to document the major similarities and differences among the countries responding and to share information on how such issues restrict underground development. The final report is a compilation of the responses from this first survey and is intended as a basis for future study by the working group. This appendix is a condensed version of the report.

The summary of the responses is arranged according to the topic of each question. A brief review of the legal or administrative issue is given followed by an outline of the question posed and a synopsis of the responses. Responses concerning specific permits or restrictions are not conducive to summarization in a short paper. The full report providing complete responses of each country to the questionnaire is available from the International Tunnelling Association.

LIMITS OF SURFACE PROPERTY OWNERSHIP

Background

Since national territories, local jurisdictions, and private ownership are normally defined in terms of boundaries of surface land area, it is necessary for both underground space use and the use of airspaces to define how surface ownership extends downwards to the underground and upwards to the sky.

The most common maxim applied to this definition has been: *Cujus est solum ejus est usque ad coelum et ad infernos,* meaning "The owner of the surface also owns to the sky and to the depths." This extension of surface ownership was common in British, French, Germanic, Jewish, and Roman law and was cited as early as 1250 AD (Thomas 1979).

In communist countries where private land ownership is either nonexistent or else very restricted, the underground and airspace belongs to the State. This does not eliminate, however, all the problems of determining the right to develop an underground facility. The rights of existing surface uses must be protected or compensated for, and competing claims for use by different State organizations must be resolved.

A model often proposed to ease restrictions on underground development (especially in urban areas) is that surface ownership would only extend below ground to a distance that the owner could occupy and use in conjunction with the land. Such a restriction in surface ownership rights in the upward direction has typically been made as aviation developed in countries with private land ownership. In the United States, the Congress in 1926 and 1938 and the Supreme Court in 1946 limited the upward ownership of land to that which is needed for the enjoyment of the land. It was decided that trespass by an airplane would only be considered to have occurred if it entered into the immediate airspace above the land and interfered substantially with the owner's use and enjoyment of the land (Thomas 1979).

It is possible to legally separate the ownership of the subsurface from that of the surface at particular depths or well-defined changes in geological formation. It is also common to separate the ownership of minerals from surface ownership (see next section). When the ownership of underground openings is being defined, it must also be considered that an underground opening depends on a certain volume of soil or rock surrounding the opening for its stability or the overall stability of the ground structure. Thus, it is not likely that two major underground openings can be excavated immediately adjacent but on opposite sides of the same property line.

Question 1

Is ownership to the core of the earth? Are there depth restrictions? Other restrictions? Comments.

Synopsis of Responses

Four main conditions appear to exist in the countries responding to the survey:

- The surface owner owns to the center of earth.
- The surface owner owns as far as a reasonable interest exists.
- The surface owner owns only to a limited depth beneath the land surface (as little as 6 m).
- Private land ownership is almost nonexistent and hence the underground is also publicly owned.

The question did not distinguish between cases in which the basic presumption of ownership is to the center of the earth but the practical extent is that to which the owner can demonstrate a significant interest. Out of the 17 responses, there were 13 "yes" responses and 4 "no" responses. A "yes" was given if the basic presumption is ownership to the center of the earth since, in many cases, it will then be necessary to demonstrate in court that an uncooperative owner, in fact, has no significant ownership right even at great depth. A "no" was given if the surface rights are explicitly limited or if there appears to be a presumption of public right below the immediate subsurface, i.e., the surface owner would have to prove otherwise. Countries with all State-owned lands have a "yes" answer because of the way the question was worded.

EXPLOITATION OF NATURAL AND MINERAL RESOURCES

Background

The occurrence of valuable natural and mineral resources below the surface has given rise to a variety of means of controlling the exploitation of these resources and severing the ownership of these resources from the ownership of the surface land.

The intent of the legal and administrative systems is generally to provide an orderly means for determining claims to the exploitation of mineral resources and preventing the deterioration of natural resources. Regulations differ in their aggressiveness in reserving mineral rights to the State or in the encouragement of private development of minerals of national importance. The questionnaire responses showed a substantial variation in the governing structures for resource exploitation among the countries responding.

Some of the problems that have occurred in implementing laws governing resource extraction have included:

- Fluid resources in permeable ground strata are not fixed in space and hence are not fully amenable to control by geometric definitions based on surface land ownership. It is possible for one owner to withdraw fluid resources from beneath an adjacent owner's land by pumping from his own land and causing those resources to flow towards his well.
- When mineral rights are severed from the surface ownership rights, it may also need to be specified who owns any underground space left by the mining operation—the surface owner or the owner of the mineral rights.
- Extraction of high proportions of a mineral resource may not be possible without causing surface settlement and damage to surface facilities. The extent to which mineral rights may

be exploited with respect to interference with existing and planned surface uses must be specified.

Question 2

Are there natural resource restrictions? Water, oil/gas, coal, metals, minerals, other.

Synopsis of Responses

Depending on the type of resource—oil, gas, coal, mineral, aggregate, etc.—several conditions appear to exist:

- Resources belong to the State—they are managed by the State or others may obtain a concession to develop.
- Resources belong to the surface landowner.
- Resources may be developed by anyone who discovers them notwithstanding surface ownership (limitations apply depending on existing surface or subsurface uses).
- Mineral rights are severed from surface ownership and may be sold separately.
- The State reserves a share of the resource value.

A distinction is often made as to whether the mineral has economic value.

Groundwater extraction restrictions vary significantly. In South Africa, groundwater may be withdrawn even if it causes damage to a neighbor's property as long as malice is not intended. In Norway, groundwater may only be extracted as long as no inconvenience is caused to others. In some other countries, groundwater is considered public property and can only be used in amounts and for uses that will not harm the environment.

OWNERSHIP AND THE RIGHT TO DEVELOP SUBSURFACE SPACE

Background

In countries where mineral rights are held by the State, permission must be given to a private company or to a State agency to develop the resource. Likewise, for the development of public underground facilities beneath one or more private surface landowners, the public entity must have the powers to negotiate an easement for the use of the subsurface with the surface landowner(s) or if negotiation fails, to condemn the easement in the public interest. It is also possible that these powers may be invoked on behalf of a private company that will build or operate a needed public facility.

In many countries, legislation defines the power of local, regional, or national government entities to promote commercial development, urban renewal, and infrastructure provision. This legislation may assist local units of government by granting condemnation rights for commercial development as part of urban renewal and providing favorable tax structures for encouraging such development. Since the implementation of such legislation is often politically sensitive, it is important to identify specifically whether underground development is intended to be included within the scope of those powers (Nelson 1985).

Question 3

How is ownership and development of subsurface space defined? Is there development by any responsible party? Who owns the space?

Synopsis of Responses

The right to develop subsurface space can usually be assigned to any responsible party. Who arranges this development depends on the ownership and resource rights described above. In Denmark, a time-limited concession is given for subsurface development.

REQUIREMENTS FOR PERMITS

Mining and underground excavation projects often require a wide range of permits for their construction and use.

Underground excavation and resource removal are regulated to control undesirable environmental impacts and excessive depletion of important natural resources. They are also regulated to assure safety for existing surface uses, life safety during construction, and to provide a healthy and safe environment in an eventual use of the space. The nature of the regulatory process varies from country to country and sometimes from region to region within a country.

Because historically most underground excavations were for mining, defense, or utility purposes and not for occupation and use by the public or a regular work force, underground excavations for non-mining purposes often have not had a well-defined regulatory basis. Building and life safety codes for surface structures usually have poor application to deep underground structures and mining and construction regulations do not address the eventual use of space created by the excavation process.

Question 4

Are major permits required? National, state or provincial, municipal, other.

Synopsis of Responses

Many similarities exist among the countries responding in the permit granting agencies for subsurface development. Sometimes there is a lack of clarity as to which set of regulations should apply, e.g., mining or building code. Most countries require several permits, involving each of the governmental levels. State ministries or agencies usually control permits related to the use of the space, e.g., oil storage, rail tunnel, etc. Local planning permission must usually be obtained.

APPLICATION OF SURFACE LAND USE REGULATIONS

Background

Most countries and regions exert some form of planning control over the use of the land surface. This may involve protecting areas of natural beauty, maintaining agricultural land, or setting zoning regulations that control the type and density of development in built-up areas.

Since underground space may allow functions to occur within the space independent of the surface land above, questions often arise as to what extent surface land use regulations should apply to the development of underground space.

Land use regulations may have several aims, e.g., to preserve the aesthetic character of an area, to separate incompatible land uses, to avoid overloading community services with new development, or to encourage high density development in certain areas. It is clear that some of the problems cited are not an issue if a structure is completely underground (the aesthetic issue, for example) whereas others are not solved simply because the structure is underground (overloading the community infrastructure, for example).

Even though it is not conceptually difficult to separate whether various land use regulations have merit when applied to underground space use, it is usually not so easy to obtain a political consensus that allows the land use or zoning regulations to be modified. Most new developments have some detractors who will oppose the modification of regulations or the granting of variances.

To forestall the need to apply for changes in land use regulations on a case-by-case basis, some areas with the potential for underground development have developed and gained approval for a statement of the applicability of existing land use regulations to any future underground developments (Kansas City and Minneapolis are examples in the United States).

Question 5

Does land use zoning extend to the subsurface? If yes, to what depth or degree?

If no, is there no use control?

Synopsis of Responses

In the majority of countries responding (10 out of 17), land use zoning does extend to the subsurface. In a few, it definitely does not. For the remainder, zoning does not extend to the subsurface mostly as a result of a lack of clarity in the application of surface-based laws. Land use zoning is usually not as clearly developed for the subsurface as it is for the surface.

ENVIRONMENTAL CONTROLS

Background

The environmental impacts of underground developments may include some of the following problems:

- Lowering of regional or local groundwater tables due to pumping or drainage into underground structures. This may in turn lead to the settlement of surface structures and the deterioration of existing building foundations.
- The potential for pollution of groundwater systems from the underground facility.
- The provision of unwanted connections between different aquifers in a regional hydrologic system.
- Disposal of the excavated material.
- Introduction of ground vibrations, e.g., subway systems.
- The usual environmental impacts of the type of facility constructed.

Question 6

Are there environmental controls? National, state/ provincial, municipal.

Synopsis of Responses

Environmental controls usually exist or environmental concerns can usually be invoked to restrict subsurface development if necessary. Some mining laws or other laws regulating underground development specifically address environmental protection, but this is not always the case. Permits may be required at any administrative level according to the aspect of environmental protection being considered.

RESTRICTIONS DUE TO SURFACE AND SUBSURFACE STRUCTURES

Background

When mining, tunneling, or creating deep open-pit surface excavations, there is always a potential danger of creating undesirable ground movements that may damage existing surface or underground structures.

There are two parts to this issue:

- Is construction of the underground or surface structure permitted if a significant risk exists or if conditions are especially critical (such as damage to a national monument or if a large loss of life could be involved)?
- If it is permitted, who bears the liability for damage to existing structures? This question is not always clear cut—for example, when development occurs above a mining area with anticipated ground settlement or if the foundations of existing buildings were inadequate and causing damage prior to the effect of any underground structure.

How the issues are resolved for various projects (in laws regulating land use or in legal definitions of liability in different countries) seems to depend in large measure on the importance of the underground development to the country or region in which it is located. Where a mining development or a subway is considered a critical national or local need, regulations will tend to ensure that the project can proceed and that surface uses do not have an automatic priority.

Question 7

Are there restrictions and/or liability due to existing structures?

Synopsis of Responses

In most countries, subsurface development is restricted so as to cause the minimum amount of damage to existing structures. The responsibility for the damage usually rests with the underground developer (if cause and effect can be proven). In South Africa, the mining laws reverse this condition for undeveloped land and restrict surface development above identified mineral resources.

CONCLUSIONS AND FUTURE ACTIVITIES

The survey of legal and administrative issues in ITA member countries was intended as a first step in a continued effort to study the institutional impediments to an increased use and a wise use of underground space.

The responses have indicated a similarity of issues to be addressed in the various countries—as might be expected—but, also, a significant divergence in the way some of these issues are handled in legislation and administrative structure.

The working group plans to continue to study these issues and in particular to concentrate on the following areas:

- Follow up on the impact of radically different subsurface ownership policies (such as in Denmark) on the ease of development of underground facilities.
- Compare the value assigned to easements for underground facilities at different depths. It is believed that a compilation of the practices of various countries in this regard will be useful to all in establishing precedents for the valuation of contested easements.
- Document the administrative structure and data-keeping practices of selected urban areas with respect to subsurface space use. Urban areas that have made a significant attempt to coordinate such record-keeping will be targeted.

Contributions and participation in the study of these and other issues related to the planning of subsurface use are welcomed.

ACKNOWLEDGMENTS

This appendix is taken from a report prepared by Ray Sterling, Michael Barker (The Burley Partnership, Waitsfield, VT), and Syver Froise (Ingenior A.B. Berdal A/S, N-1300 Sandvika, Norway).

The authors of this paper would like to gratefully acknowledge the efforts of the many people who contributed to this paper and the working group report. Foremost are the representatives of each of the member nations of ITA who responded to the survey (see list below). Syver Froise compiled preliminary results of the first questionnaire responses. Michael Barker coordinated the research with the working group members and correspondents and the Executive Council of the ITA. The Underground Space Center, acting as a consultant to the Working Group on Surface Planning, prepared the final report. Raymond Sterling was the principal author.

Questionnaire responders:

Australia, A.D. Henderson and R. Bushnell; Belgium, L. Van Hove, A. Wittemans and P. Hostyn; China, Q. Gao and X. Hou; Czechoslovakia, J. Gran; Denmark, F. Schaarup; Finland, S. Johansson; France, P. Duffaut and J. Bregeon; Hungary, M. Müller; Italy, L. Orusa and S. Pelizza; Japan, K. Matsushita; Mexico, L.V. Utesa; Norway, S. Froise; South Africa, N. Schmidt; Sweden, T. Franzen, B. Jansson and A. Grönvall; Switzerland, F. Ruckituhl; UK, R.N. Craig; USA, R. Sterling; Venezuela, A.D. Aidos; West Germany, W. Dietz.

References: Part 1

Chapters 1-4 and Appendices A-C

AWPA. See American Public Works Association.

Ahrens, D., T. Ellison, and R. Sterling. 1981. *Earth Sheltered Homes: Plans and Designs*. New York: Van Nostrand Reinhold. ISBN 0-442-28676-7.

Ahrens, D., and C. Fairhurst. 1976. Going underground to stay on top. *Underground Space* 1 (2): 71-86. Pergamon Press.

Allen, E. 1971. *Stone Shelters*. Cambridge, Mass.: MIT Press.

American Public Works Association (AWPA). 1971. *Feasibility of Utility Tunnels in Urban Areas*. Special Report No. 39, Feb. Chicago: American Public Works Association.

American Society of Civil Engineers (ASCE). 1983. The outstanding civil engineering achievement of 1983. *Civil Engineering*, June: 33-37. New York: American Society of Civil Engineers. ISSN 03660-0556.

Andreadaki-Chronaki, E. 1983. Vernacular architecture of Greece: Earth sheltered buildings of Santorini. *Energy Efficient Buildings with Earth Shelter Protection*. Proc. 1st Int. Earth Sheltered Buildings Conf., Sydney, Australia, Aug. 1-6, 1983, pp. 25-30. Stillwater, Okla.: Arch. Extension, Oklahoma State Univ.

Aoki, S., et al. 1985. Research on underground dwellings in the loess land of China. *Proc. Int. Symp. Earth Architecture*, Beijing, Nov. 1-4, 1985, pp. 209-15. Beijing: Arch. Society of China.

Associated Engineers. 1976. *Subway Environmental Design Handbook, Volume 1: Principles and Applications, Second Edition*. Washington, D.C.: Urban Mass Transportation Administration. UMTA-DC-06-0010-76-1, NTIS.

Aughenbaugh, N. (ed.). 1978. *Journal of the People-to-People Underground Space Geotechnical Delegation to Europe and the U.S.S.R.*, May 22-June 13.

Auhl, I., and P. Finch. 1979. *Burra in Colour*. Hawthorndene, S. Australia: Investigator Press. ISBN 0 85864 032 5.

Baggs, S.A. 1980. A taxonomy of underground space. *Collected Papers*, presented at the Earth Sheltered Housing Conf. and Exhib. 1, Minneapolis, Minn., April 9-11, 1980. Underground Space Center, Univ. of Minnesota.

Barker, M.B. 1986. Toronto's underground pedestrian system. *Tunnelling and Underground Space Technology* 1 (2): 145-52. Pergamon Press.

Bartali, E.H. 1987. Underground storage pits in Morocco. *Tunnelling and Underground Space Technology* 2 (4): 381-83. Pergamon Press.

Bergman, M. 1979. *A Report on the Potential for Underground Industrial, Commercial and Storage Facilities in Minnesota*. Underground Space Center, Univ. of Minnesota, for the Minnesota Energy Agency.

Besner, J. 1990. The underground city: The Montreal model. Presentation at Geotech '90, Tokyo, April 9-12, 1990. World Import Mart, Japan.

Bieniawski, Z.T. 1984. *Rock Mechanics Design in Mining and Tunneling*. Rotterdam: A. A. Balkema. ISBN 90 6191 5530 9.

Birkerts, G. 1974. *Subterranean Urban Systems*. Univ. of Michigan, Ann Arbor, Mich.

Bobrick, B. 1981. *Labyrinths of Iron*. New York: William Morrow and Company, Inc.

Buchanon, C. 1963. *Traffic in Towns.* Specially shortened editon of the Buchanon Report. Penguin Books.

Carmody, J., and R. Sterling.
—1983. *Underground Building Design: Commercial and Institutional Structures.* New York: Van Nostrand Reinhold. ISBN 0-442-28686-4.
—1985. *Earth Sheltered Housing Design. Second Edition.* New York: Van Nostrand Reinhold. ISBN 0-442-28746-1.

Charneau, N., and J.C. Trebbi. 1981. *Maisons Creusées, Maisons Enterrées.* Paris: Editions Alternatives.

Chester, C.V. 1981. Preparing underground structures for civil defense. *Underground Space* 6 (3): 160-65. Pergamon Press.

Chester, C.V., H.B. Shapira, and G.A. Cristy. 1983. *Hazard Mitigation Potential of Earth-Sheltered Residences. Final Report, 1982-83.* Oak Ridge, Tenn.: Oak Ridge National Laboratory, 218 pp.

Chester, C.V., and G.P. Zimmerman. 1987. Civil defense shelters: A state-of-the-art assessment. *Tunnelling and Underground Space Technology* 2 (4): 401-28. Pergamon Press.

Coogan, A.H. 1979. Classification and valuation of subsurface space. *Underground Space* 3 (1): 1-7. Pergamon Press.

Daga, A.W., M.A. Daga, and W.R. Wendel. 1990. A preliminary assessment of the potential of lava tube-situated lunar base architecture. *Engineering, Construction and Operations in Space II: vol. 1.* Proc. Space 90, Albuquerque, N. Mex., April 22-26, 1990, pp. 568-77.

DiCristofalo, S., S. Orioli, G. Silvestini, and S. Alessandro. 1989. Thermal behavior of "Scirrocco Rooms" in ancient Sicilian villas. *Tunnelling and Underground Space Technology* 4 (4): 471-74. Pergamon Press.

Downes, S.R. 1989. Personal communication. New York: Cushman & Wakefield, Inc.

Duffaut, P. 1979. Site reservation policies for large underground openings. *Underground Space* 3 (4): 187-93. Pergamon Press.

Dunkel, F.V. 1985. Underground and earth sheltered food storage: Historical, geographic, and economic considerations. *Underground Space* 9 (5-6): 310-15. Pergamon Press.

Dunkel, F.V., R.L. Sterling, and G.D. Meixel Jr. 1987. Underground bulk storage of shelled corn in Minnesota. *Tunnelling and Underground Space Technology* 2 (4): 367-71. Pergamon Press.

Engineering News Record (ENR).
—1986. TARP covering Chicago well. *Engineering News Record*, Mar. 13, p. 15.
—1986. Egypt sewerage fix begins to take hold. *Engineering News Record*, Mar. 27, p. 22.

Fairhurst, C. 1976. Going under to stay on top. *Underground Space* 1 (2): 71-86. Pergamon Press.

Fairweather, V. 1990. U.S. tackles leaking tanks. *Civil Engineering*, Dec. New York: American Society of Civil Engineers.

Flores, C., and F. Bravo. 1984. *Los Silos de Villacanas.* Madrid: Ministerio de Obras Públicas y Urbanismo. ISBN 84-7433-335-0.

Fluor Technology, Inc. 1987. *Waste Hoist Technology.* DOE/CH/46656-06. Hereford, Tex.: U.S. Dept. of Energy, Salt Repository Project Office.

Gilbert, D.A. 1981. Earth-sheltered housing in Appalachia. *Underground Space* 6 (2): 89-92. Pergamon Press.

Golany, G.S.
—1988. *Earth-Sheltered Dwellings in Tunisia: Ancient Lessons for Modern Design.* Newark, Del.: Univ. of Delaware Press. ISBN 0-87413-297-5.
—1989. *Urban Underground Space Design in China.* Associated University Presses.

Goldfinger, M. 1969. *Villages in the Sun.* London: Lund Humphries.

Hamrin, H.O. 1982. Choosing an underground mining method. *Underground Mining Methods Handbook,* ed. W.A. Hustrulid, pp. 88-112. New York: Soc. of Min. Engineers, American Inst. of Mining Metallurgy Petroleum Engineers.

Hannon, B.M., R.G. Stein, B.Z. Segal, D. Serber, and C. Stein. 1976. *Energy Use for Building Construction.* Center for Advanced Computation, Univ. of Illinois at Urbana-Champaign, Dec.

Hannon, B.M., R.G. Stein, B.Z. Segal, P.F. Deibert, M. Buckley, and D. Nathan. 1977. *Energy Use for Building Construction: Supplement.* Center for Advanced Computation, Univ. of Illinois at Urbana-Champaign, Oct.

Hazer, F. 1975. Cultural-ecological interpretation of the historic underground cities of Coreme, Turkey. *Alternatives in Energy Conservation: The Use of Earth Covered Buildings.* Conf. Proc., Ft. Worth, Tex., July 9-12, 1975, pp. 21-36, ed. F. Moreland. NSF-RA-760006.

Heim de Balsac, R. 1980. No soul for the heart of Paris. The operation and architectural quality of Les Halles. *Underground Space* 5 (3): 166-70. Pergamon Press.

Hillman, E. 1983. Cities beneath. *The Environmentalist* 3:187-98. The Netherlands: Elsevier Sequoia. ISSN 0251-1088.

Hoffman, M.S. (ed.). 1989. *The World Almanac.* New York: Pharos Books.

Hou, X., and Y. Shu. 1988. The model of underground space of the city. *Proc. 3rd Int. Conf. on Underground Space Use,* Shanghai, Sept. 1-6, 1988, ed. X.Y. Hou. Shanghai: Tongji Univ. Press.

Howell, P. 1989. New Gardiner promised for $1 billion land swap. *Toronto Star,* Sept. 13.

Huet, O. 1982. Troglodyte habitations in France. *Underground Space* 6 (6): 343-54. Pergamon Press.

ITA. See International Tunnelling Association.

International Energy Agency (IEA). 1988. *Energy Balances of OECD Countries 1985/86*. Paris: Int. Energy Agency, Org. for Economic Cooperation and Development.

International Tunnelling Association (ITA) Working Group on Contractual Sharing of Risks. 1988. ITA recommendations on contractual sharing of risks. *International Tunnelling Association* 3 (2): 103-40. Pergamon Press.

International Tunnelling Association (ITA) Working Group on Costs-Benefits of Underground Urban Public Transportation. 1987. Examples of benefits of underground urban public transportation systems. *Tunnelling and Underground Space Technology* 2 (1): 5-54, Pergamon Press. *Urban Transportation,* ISSN 0886-7798.

International Tunnelling Association (ITA) Working Group on Subsurface Planning. 1990. *Legal and Administrative Issues in Underground Space Use: A Preliminary Survey of ITA Member Nations*. Int. Tunnelling Association.

Jackson, D.D. 1982. *Underground Worlds*. Chicago: Time-Life Books, 176 pp. ISBN 0-8094-4320-1.

Jansson, B., and T. Winqvist. 1977. *Planning of Subsurface Use.* Swedish Council for Building Research, D7-1977, 165 pp.

Japan Tunnelling Association. 1988. *Tunnelling Activities in Japan*. Tokyo: Japan Tunnelling Association.

Jason Consultants S.A. 1987. Research Proposal for a Technical and Economic Multi-client Study into Trenchless Pipelaying. Jason Consultants, Geneva and the Water Research Center, U.K.

Kirkland, C.J. 1986. The proposed design of the English Channel tunnel. *Tunnelling and Underground Space Technology* 1 (3-4): 271-82. Pergamon Press.

Kjelshus, B. 1984. Encouraging underground space development: Modifications to Kansas City's building code and zoning ordinance. *Underground Space* 8 (5-6): 320-30. Pergamon Press.

Kommendant, A.E. 1978. Earth covered structures. *Earth Covered Buildings: Technical Notes,* Conf. Proc., Ft. Worth, Tex., May 17-19, 1978, eds. F.L. Moreland, F. Higgs, and J. Shih. NTIS CONF-7805138-P1.

Komroff, M. (ed.). 1982. *The Travels of Marco Polo (The Venetian)*. New York: Liverright Publ. Corp.

Kuwabara, K. 1988. Land costs luring builders underground. *Japan Economic Journal,* June 25, p. 32.

Labs, K. 1976. The architectural underground. *Underground Space* 1 (1): 1-8, and 1 (2): 135-56. Pergamon Press.

Labs, K., J. Carmody, R. Sterling, L. Shen, Y. Huang, and D. Parker. 1988. *Building Foundation Design Handbook*. Oak Ridge, Tenn.: Oak Ridge National Laboratory, 350 pp. Prepared by the Underground Space Center, Univ. of Minnesota.

LaNier, R. 1971. *Geotecture*. Thesis, Univ. of Notre Dame.

Lecomte, D. 1990. La Defense, the modern district that could not do without the underground. Presentation at Int. Symp. on Underground Space Use, Milan, Nov. 15-16, 1990. Milan: COCIS/SIG.

Legget, R.F. 1976. Underground mining with controlled subsidence in lower Duisburg Harbou. *Underground Space* 1 (1): 51-58. Pergamon Press.

Lemperiere, F., A. Broto, P. Gravost, and I. de Maublanc. 1989. LASER - A miracle solution to Paris traffic, or just a gadget. *Tunnelling and Underground Space Technology* 4 (3): 261-78. Pergamon Press. ISSN 0886-7798.

Li, K.C. 1989. Fire protection in caverns. *Rock Cavern - Hong Kong*. Proc. Seminar, Hong Kong, Dec. 8-9, 1989, eds. W.A. Malone and P.G.D. Whiteside. Inst. of Mining and Metallurgy, pp. 343-50. ISBN 1870706 14 5.

Li, X. 1985. The origin and development of cave dwellings in China. *Proc. Int. Symp. Earth Architecture,* Beijing, Nov. 1-4, 1985, pp. 209-15. Beijing: Arch. Society of China.

Lien, R., and F. Løset. 1982. A review of Norwegian rock caverns storing oil products or gas under high pressure or low temperature. *Norwegian Hard Rock Tunnelling.* Publication No. 1, Norwegian Soil and Rock Engineering Association, pp. 43-45. Trondheim, Norway: Tapir Publishers.

Lundström, B. 1983. Demand and technical requirements for food storage in developing countries. *Underground Space* 7 (4-5): 251-56. Pergamon Press.

Malone, W.A., and P.G.D. Whiteside (eds.). 1989. *Rock Cavern - Hong Kong*. Proc. Seminar, Hong Kong, Dec. 8-9, 1989. Inst. of Mining and Metallurgy. ISBN 1 870706 14 5.

Medway, K.E. n.d. *Coober Pedy: Opal Wonderland of Australia*. Sydney: Bushwacher Publishing Co. ISBN 0-9594221-4-5.

Mooney, B. 1985. Modern cavemen of Spain "wouldn't trade for house."*Toronto Globe and Mail,* Sept. 18.

Moreland, F. (ed.). 1975. *Alternatives in Energy Conservation: The Use of Earth Covered Buildings*. National Science Foundation, NSF-RA-760006. Washington, D.C.: U.S. Government Printing Office.

Moreland, F., et al. 1981. *Earth-Covered Buildings: An Exploratory Analysis for Hazard and Energy Performance.* Final Report, contract no. 81-600091, FEMA 4411E.

Muller, C.A., and R.A. Taylor. 1980. No cause for apprehension about costs of insuring earth-sheltered homes. *Underground Space* 5 (1): 28-30. Pergamon Press.

National Geographic Society. 1988. The peopling of the earth. *National Geographic* 174 (4).

National Research Council, Comm. on Geosciences, Environment & Resources. 1990. *Rethinking High-Level Radioactive Waste Disposal*. Washington, D.C.: National Academy Press.

Nelson, S., and W.H. Rockenstein, II. 1985. Legislating underground space use: Minnesota's mined underground space development act. *Underground Space* 9 (5-6): 289-92. Pergamon Press.

Newman, P.W.G., and J.R. Kenworthy. 1989. Gasoline consumption and cities: A comparison of U.S. cities with a global survey. *APA Journal* (winter). American Planning Association.

Nicoletti, M. 1980. L'architettura delle caverne. *Editori Laterza*, Italy, CL-20-1745-8.

Norwegian Soil and Rock Engineering Association (NSREA). 1982. *Norwegian Hard Rock Tunnelling*. Publication No. 1, Norwegian Soil and Rock Engineering Association. Trondheim, Norway: Tapir Publishers. ISBN 82-519-0473-0.

O'Reilly, M.P. 1978. Some examples of underground development in Europe. *Underground Space* 2 (3): 163-78. Pergamon Press.

O'Rourke, T.D., E.W. Flaxman, and I. Cooper. 1985. Pipe laying comes out of the trenches. *Civil Engineering* 55 (12): 48-51. New York: American Society of Civil Engineers.

Parizek, E.J., T. Stauffer, and J. Vineyard 1975. *Proc. Symp. on the Development and Utilization of Underground Space*, Kansas City, Mo., March 5-7, 1975. Kansas City, Mo.: Univ. of Missouri.

Pasqual, J., and P. Riera. 1990. *Considering Urban Underground Land Value in Project Evaluation Studies. A Practical Way of Estimating It.* Working Paper 90.01, Dept. of Appl. Econ., Univ. Autonoma de Barcelona.

Paul, W. 1970. *Mining Lore*. Portland, Ore.: Morris Publishing Co.

Pilon, B. 1980. In Paris, a "city center" goes underground. *Underground Space* 5 (2): 102-20. Pergamon Press.

Pinzon-Isaza, H. 1983. The underground salt cathedral of Zipaquira - Columbia. *Energy Efficient Buildings with Earth Shelter Protection,* Proc. 1st Int. Earth Sheltered Buildings Conf., Sydney, Australia, Aug. 1-6, 1983. Stillwater, Okla.: Arch. Extension, Oklahoma State Univ.

Riera, P., and J. Pasqual. 1992. The importance of urban underground land value in project evaluation: A case study of Barcelona's utility tunnel. *Tunnelling and Underground Space Technology* 7 (3): 243-50. Pergamon Press.

Rigaud, J.P. 1988. Art treasures from the ice age Lascaux Cave. *National Geographic* 174 (4): 485-99.

Rowlinson, K.M. 1984. *Bulletin #3*. British Earth Sheltering Association, Oct.

Rowlinson, K.M., J. Fitzpatrick, and P. Southgate. 1983. *Bulletin #1*. British Earth Sheltering Association, Oct.

Rygh, J.A. 1990. Sports halls, swimming pools and similar installations in rock in Norway. *Proc. Int. Symp. on Unique Underground Structures*, Denver, Colo., June 12-15, 1990, 81:1-18, ed. R.S. Sinha. Golden, Colo.: CSM Press, Colorado School of Mines. 0-918062-83-7.

Saari, K. (ed.). 1988. *The Rock Engineering Alternative*. Finnish Tunnelling Association. ISBN 951-754-374-3.

Saetersmoen, G. 1982. Underground water treatment plant and reservoirs in Oslo. *Norwegian Hard Rock Tunnelling*. Publication No. 1, Norwegian Soil and Rock Engineering Association, pp. 81-82. Trondheim, Norway: Tapir Publishers.

Sartori, M.R. 1987. Underground storage of corn and dry beans in Brazil. *Tunnelling and Underground Space Technology* 2 (4): 373-80. Pergamon Press.

Savage, J.S. 1979. Mutual of Omaha Building. *Going Under to Stay on Top - Non-Residential Applications*, Conf. Proc., Nov. 18-20, 1979, Minneapolis, Minn., pp. 145-53. Underground Space Center, Univ. of Minnesota.

de Saventhem, E.M. 1977. Insuring risks underground - some general considerations. *Underground Space* 2 (1): 19-26. Pergamon Press.

Sellberg, B. 1990. Sweden's research and development program for thermal energy storage. *Tunnelling and Underground Space Technology* 5 (1-2): 85-89. Pergamon Press.

Setter, Leach and Lindstrom, Inc., and the Underground Space Center.

—1980. *Energy and Cost Analysis of Single Story, Non-Residential Buildings*. Report to the U.S. Naval Facilities Engineering Co., Aug.

—1981. *Energy, Cost and Design Evaluation of Non-Residential Buildings*. Report to the U.S. Naval Facilities Engineering Co., May.

—1983. *Earth Sheltered Construction Navy Design Manual DM 1.4*. Report to the U.S. Naval Facilities Engineering Command.

Shimizu. 1988. *Into the Earth*. Shimizu Bulletin Vol. 56. Tokyo: Shimizu Corporation.

Silver, M.L., and J.F. Peters. 1977. Planning and its importance in reducing the cost of urban tunnels. *Underground Space* 2 (2): 65-79. Pergamon Press.

Sinha, R.S. (ed.). 1990. *Proc. Int. Symp. on Unique Underground Structures*. Denver, Colo., June 12-15, 1990. Golden, Colo.: CSM Press, Colorado School of Mines. 0-918062-83-7.

Society of Mining Engineers. 1973. *SME Mining Engineering Handbook*.

Stanford, G. 1983. Thermal environment of the lithotectural dugouts of White Cliffs, Australia. *Energy Efficient Buildings with Earth Shelter Protection*. Proc. 1st Int. Earth Sheltered Buildings Conf., Sydney, Australia, Aug. 1-6, 1983, pp. 265-69. Stillwater, Okla.: Arch. Extension, Oklahoma State Univ.

Stauffer, T., Sr. 1978. *Underground Utilization: A Reference Manual of Selected Works.* Dept. of Geosciences. (In 8 volumes). Kansas City, Mo.: Univ. of Missouri.

Sterling, E.E., et al. 1984. Legal principles and practical problems in the two-tier development of underground space. *Underground Space* 8 (5-6): 304-19. Pergamon Press.

Sterling, R.L. (ed.). 1981. *Journal of the People-to-People Underground Space Delegation to the People's Republic of China,* Aug. 12-Sept. 5, 1981.

Sterling, R.L., and J. Carmody. 1990. The experience with innovative underground structures at the University of Minnesota. *Proc. Int. Symp. on Unique Underground Structures,* Denver, Colo., June 12-15, 1990, 1 (77): 1-19, ed. R.S. Sinha. Golden, Colo.: CSM Press, Colorado School of Mines. 0-918062-83-7.

Sterling, R.L., J. Carmody, and G. Elnicky. 1981. *Earth Sheltered Community Design.* Underground Space Center, Univ. of Minnesota, Minneapolis. New York: Van Nostrand Reinhold.

Sterling, R.L., G.D. Meixel, F. Dunkel, and C. Fairhurst. 1983. Underground storage of food. *Underground Space* 7 (4-5): 257-62. Pergamon Press. 0-08-030155-X.

Sterling, R.L., and S. Nelson. 1982. Planning the development of underground space. *Underground Space* 7 (2): 86-103. Pergamon Press.

Strakosch, G.R. 1983. *Vertical Transportation: Elevators and Escalators.* 2nd ed. New York: Wiley.

Swayze, J. 1980. *Underground Gardens & Homes.* Hereford, Tex.: Geobuilding Systems, Inc., 136 pp.

Thomas, W.A. 1979. Ownership of subterranean space. *Underground Space* 3 (4): 155-63. Pergamon Press.

Tokyo Metropolitan Government, Underground River Plan Study Comm. 1989. *Underground River: Aiming at a Flood-free World City.* Tokyo Metropolitan Government, Japan.

U.S. Army. 1961. *Design of Underground Installations in Rock: General Planning Considerations.* Dept. of the Army Technical Manual TM 5-8671, Jan.

Vail, A.J. 1989. Underground works in rock in Hong Kong. *Rock Cavern - Hong Kong.* Proc. Seminar, Hong Kong, Dec. 8-9, 1989, eds. W.A. Malone and P.G.D. Whiteside. Inst. of Mining and Metallurgy. ISBN 1870706 14 5.

Walton, M. 1978. Environmental trade-offs of tunnels vs. cut-and-cover subways. *Underground Space* 3 (2): 61-67. Pergamon Press.

Warnock, J.G. 1978. New frontiers of inner space-underground. *Underground Space* 3 (1): 1-7. Pergamon Press.

Wells, M. 1977. *Underground Designs.* Brewster, Mass., 87 pp.

Willett, D.C., and J.C. Warnock. 1983. The evolution of a technological opportunity: Underground pumped hydro storage. *Underground Space* 7 (6): 347-52. Pergamon Press.

Winqvist, T., and K.E. Mellgren. 1988. *Going Underground.* Stockholm: Royal Swedish Academy of Eng. Sci. ISBN 91 7082 432 0.

Woodard, D.R., and L. Babler. 1984. The Kansas City underground: A future rooted in the past. *Underground Space* 8 (5-6): 331-40. Pergamon Press.

World Almanac. 1989. New York: Pharos Books.

World Book Encyclopedia. 1988. Chicago: World Book, Inc.

Yip, C.H. 1983. *The "Home" of Peking Man: Fossil Man in China.* Hong Kong: Museum of History.

Zhang, M., and S. Jing. 1989. Recent developments in railway tunnelling in China. *Tunnelling and Underground Space Technology* 4 (4): 455-59. Pergamon Press.

Zhu, W., D.X. Feng, and S.W. Bai. 1982. Some considerations of research on stability of underground storage caverns. *Proc. Int. Symp. Rock Mech.: Caverns and Pressure Shafts* 2:1021-30. Rotterdam: A.A. Balkema.

Part 2: Design for People in Underground Facilities

by John Carmody

CHAPTER 5
by John Carmody

Psychological and Physiological Effects in Underground Space

There are numerous practical benefits to utilizing the underground for a variety of purposes. For uses such as storage, utility infrastructure, or transportation tunnels, the involvement of people in the space is relatively low and few concerns are raised. However, when underground space is to be utilized for functions that involve human occupancy, initial reactions are often negative and a wide range of concerns and questions are raised. The broad fundamental question is: "What are the psychological and physiological effects on people utilizing underground space?" A related question is: "If there are negative effects in some cases, what design strategies can be employed to alleviate these concerns and create a positive, healthy environment?"

Figure 5-1: Images of dark, cold, and damp caves contribute to negative associations with underground space.

The purpose of this chapter is to identify the potential psychological and physiological problems related to placing people in underground environments. Information is drawn from two sources: (1) the images of the underground that seem to be rooted in history, culture, language, and possibly the subconscious, and (2) the actual experience of people in underground or other analogous enclosed environments. These sources combine to produce a list of potential problems to overcome. Also noted at the end of the chapter are the mitigating factors that influence the impact of these problems as well as an identification of offsetting positive associations with the underground.

THE IMAGE OF THE UNDERGROUND

In spite of the usually well-lighted and well-ventilated examples of modern subsurface environments, the idea of the underground seems to provoke some powerful images and associations from the past. Natural caves that served as shelter to primitive humans are dark, somewhat cold places with humid, stale air. The darkness itself creates a feeling of mystery and fear of the unknown. In the book *Labyrinths of Iron*, Benson Bobrick (1981) documents the history of tunnel construction, noting the extremely dangerous activities done under the most dire conditions of foul air, wetness, and darkness. In tunnels and mines in particular, fear of entrapment is a common association. Other manmade underground structures such as catacombs, tombs, vaults, basements, and dungeons were places of enslavement, incarceration, or burial.

Paradoxically, the underground in its role as shelter also evokes the more positive associations with safety, security, and protection. The image of Mother Earth as a source of fertility and life is powerful, and yet the space within the earth is usually envisioned as a lifeless and static environment. The mystery of a dark cave inspires fear but also a sense of adventure.

These basic associations are both reflected in and enhanced by the use of underground imagery in literature, religion, language, and psychology. In *The Life Below the Ground*, Wendy Lesser (1987) explores the underground as a metaphor in literature. She points out that the underground has always been only partially visible and partially accessible to people, in spite of the access provided by continuing technological advances. She continues:

> *What this indeterminacy means is that the underground has always been situated oddly between the visible and the invisible – between that which one can see and touch in one's normal life, and that which one must accept on faith.*
>
> *This may explain, in part, why the real underground . . . has given rise to so many fictional or imaginary undergrounds. There was, to begin with, Hades – that is, the imaginary underground is first of all the locus of death and rebirth, the place where dead souls go to be washed of their memories and returned to life on earth. In this sense, the underground is both place of origin and place of final rest. From this land of the shades developed the idea of the Christian hell – no longer the abode of*

the undifferentiated dead, but a place of eternal punishment for the damned alone. The notion of the underworld has always held something of mystery and terror for the living, but with Christianity the subterranean began to be equated with evil — a connotation which carries through to the present. The word "underground" is associated with poverty, with criminal activity, with the socially unacceptable. Even when a group purposely describes itself in this way (as do certain political or artistic movements), the choice signifies a rejection of the conventional notion of good, an adherence to the opposite of the accepted political code or aesthetic standard (Lesser 1987).

This predominantly negative imagery associated with the underground is based on the true conditions in caves and more primitive manmade spaces below grade, combined with the power of the underground metaphor for the mysterious and unknown. In the relatively recent past, it has become technologically possible to provide artificial illumination and mechanical ventilation that contradict the cave-like images of dark humid spaces with stale air. In many respects, underground environments have become quite similar to modern above-grade environments that are essentially artificial. In spite of solving these technical problems of providing light and air, however, other aspects of negative underground imagery persist — in particular, the lack of connection to the natural world.

In the recent book, *Notes on the Underground*, Rosalind Williams (1990) explores the broad issue of people making the century-long transition from a fundamentally natural environment to a technologically dominated environment present in cities today and likely to be developed to a greater extent in the future. She sees the underground (both in reality and in literature) as an ideal model of a completely technological environment.

. . . since the nineteenth century, narratives about underground worlds have provided a prophetic view into our environmental future. Subterranean surroundings, whether real or imaginary, furnish a model of an artificial environment from which nature has been effectively banished. Human beings who live underground must use mechanical devices to provide the necessities of life: food, light, even air. Nature provides only space. The underworld setting therefore takes to an extreme the displacement of the natural environment by a technological one. It hypothesizes human life in a manufactured world.

The exclusion of nature is the key element of this model:

. . . the defining characteristic of the subterranean environment is the exclusion of nature — of biological diversity, of seasons, of plants, of the sun and the stars. The subterranean laboratory takes to an extreme the ecological simplification of modern cities . . .

While Williams acknowledges that there are other completely artificial environments such as spacecraft, and that modern cities are becoming largely enclosed artificial environments as well, she still sees the underground as the ultimate model of a technological environment with its particularly powerful psychological associations.

> *Unlike the mine, the spaceship fails to convey a sense of permanent enclosure in a finite world. Furthermore, because of the indeterminacy of the interstellar void, space travel lacks the verticality that gives the underworld its unique power in the human imagination.*
>
> *Stories of descent into the underworld are so ancient and universal that their fundamental structure, the opposition of surface and depth, may well be rooted in the structure of the human brain. The congruence may be explained by the Freudian hypothesis of an Oedipal experience that splits human beings into conscious and unconscious selves, or by Jungian hypothesis of a collective subconscious. In any case, the metaphor of depth is a primary category of human thought.*
>
> *It is the combination of enclosure and verticality – a combination not found either in cities or spaceships – that gives the image of an underworld its unique power as a model of a technological environment. If we imagine going underground, we not only imagine an environment where organic nature is largely absent; we also retrace a journey that is one of the most enduring and powerful cultural traditions of humankind, a metaphorical journey of discovery through descent below the surface (Williams 1990).*

It is clear from the work of Lesser and Williams that underground images and associations are rooted in the past and infuse our culture in many ways, but they also reflect some important issues about the present and future development of the built environment. These images help to form the backdrop against which problems and solutions for underground design can be formulated.

A Japanese research team has attempted to explore the basic negative imagery associated with underground space (Hane et al. 1991; Sawada and Hane 1991; Muro et al. 1990). They state:

> *Underground space is often considered unappealing, even when there are no fundamental problems. Underground places do not provide as much stimulation; thus, imagery, which would not be an issue in other environments is a consideration in underground spaces. To utilize underground space, it is necessary not only to provide such stimulation . . . but to eliminate anxiety and dissatisfaction from the negative imagery . . . that exists within deep consciousness.*

In order to determine the imagery associated with the underground, these researchers conducted a survey with both Japanese and American subjects. Respondents selected adjectives from a list that conveyed the images of comfort, discomfort, and the underground. The words selected for underground imagery by people in both countries were mostly words that conveyed images of discomfort, although not all words reflecting discomfort were chosen for underground as well. Commonly selected words in

Figure 5-2: Rock caverns are commonly used for a variety of purposes in Norway, Sweden, and Finland. Negative attitudes persisted in early underground factories; little research has been done on most other types of facilities.

both groups were *fear*, *uneasiness*, and *timidity*. Americans used *anxiety* and *dejection* more often than the Japanese to describe the underground, but they also associated the positive word *comfort* more often as well. Both Japanese and American subjects used the words *expectancy* and *anticipation* to reflect underground imagery, and these words also are associated with comfort. The authors suggest that designs intended to enhance these more positive associations may be a means of reducing the negative imagery of underground space. They also note that the similarity between Japanese and American responses suggests that design approaches and guidelines developed in one country can be applied in another.

ACTUAL EXPERIENCE IN UNDERGROUND BUILDINGS

While underground space is utilized all over the world and for almost every human activity, relatively little research exists on the responses of people to these environments. Some researchers have attempted to summarize the limited existing literature (Wise and Wise 1984; Carmody and Sterling 1983, 1987; Fritzell and Ranhagen 1980). These and other researchers have then drawn from many related sources of information to hypothesize the pertinent psychological issues in underground buildings (Paulus 1976). Of the few actual studies of people in underground settings, the responses are predominantly, although not entirely, negative.

Experience in Europe

Underground factories opened in Sweden in 1946 resulted in negative occupant attitudes as well as frequent reports of headaches and fatigue. A comparison of underground and conventional facilities revealed that underground workers complained much more of headaches, fatigue, eye ache, nervousness, and insomnia; however, the incidence of absenteeism was only slightly higher. After becoming accustomed to the underground conditions, absenteeism decreased to the same level as found in the above-grade facility. A blood examination revealed no significant difference between the two groups. While it was concluded that there was no proof of negative physiological effects underground, negative attitudes persisted. In 1958 a follow-up investigation revealed that the negative attitudes associated with working underground had practically disappeared. Moreover, blood tests on 100 workers who had been in the underground facility for eight years proved normal. According to researchers, however, "the psychological atmosphere remained sensitive" (Holister 1968).

In another study of Swedish workers in underground factories, there were initial complaints of fatigue, headache, impaired vision, and general depression. When inadequate lighting, ventilation, and inappropriate color schemes were improved, however, the complaints stopped (Holister 1968). Holister also describes a study of London subway workers showing that they had no higher incidence of absenteeism or any physical or mental problems caused by working underground.

In the Scandinavian countries, extensive rock caverns have been constructed in the past 20 years to relieve land use pressures and to provide civil defense facilities. In many cases these caverns are then utilized for community recreational functions such as swimming pools and gymnasiums, as well as art museums and theaters. Office and meeting spaces accompany these other functions, and as noted above, there is a history of placing some factories underground. In a review of Finnish underground facilities, Jaakko Ylinen (1989) writes of several factors that appear to affect occupant satisfaction:

> *Dissatisfaction is more common in offices or control rooms than factories or department stores, where contacts with other people, the changing surroundings, and spaciousness compensate for the lack of windows. Isolated and remote work stations should be avoided in underground spaces . . . strict control or restriction of movement in underground spaces is extremely harmful . . . It has been observed that the lack of windows in underground spaces makes the psychological atmosphere susceptible to disturbances. People using such a space often feel that something is missing; consequently, they tend to imagine that what the space lacks is perhaps more significant than it really is. This phenomenon manifests itself in various expressions of dissatisfaction directed at the environmental conditions . . . For example, an accusing finger is often pointed at the air-conditioning system, even when it is functioning properly.*

It should be noted that Scandinavian underground spaces are generally quite brightly lighted and well ventilated, compared with similar facilities elsewhere in the world.

Experience in the United States

Robert Sommer (1974) conducted a series of interviews with employees in underground offices and noted that major complaints included stuffiness and stale air, lack of change and stimulation, and the unnaturalness of being underground all day. The interviews revealed some strong opinions and images.

> *"I come out like a mole at lunchtime. It is more dull here. Time loses meaning. I have that basement feeling, burrowed in for the day. There is a lack of any buoyancy and change."*
>
> *"I get claustrophobia, I need to get out to see sunshine. I am depressed and go out whenever possible. The basement has the connotation of storage."*
>
> *"I am depressed when I get home. I have a much lower efficiency here . . . There is a stifling atmosphere, the stagnant air, the noise, the telephone ringing. It is especially bad in winter – it's dark when I come in and dark when I leave."*
>
> *"The lack of windows creates more tension. It is relaxing to look out a window for a few seconds. Artificial light, no matter how good, is less good than natural light."*

Sommer indicates that there were other employees who were less negative about working underground and appeared to have accepted their surroundings, but no one was enthusiastic. It should be noted that the subjects interviewed by Sommer did relatively boring, repetitive work and the underground spaces apparently lacked any significant amenities such as high quality furnishings, finishes, or lighting.

A systematic survey of workers in several types of office environments at the University of Minnesota revealed remarkably negative reactions in underground space (Hollon et al. 1980). Workers in the completely underground building had lower levels of satisfaction and higher ratings of anxiety, depression, and hostility than in three other settings – the basement of an above-

Figure 5-3: A survey of office workers at the University of Minnesota revealed negative attitudes toward working in underground environments, even when compared to windowless above-grade spaces.

Figure 5-4: A study of hundreds of workers in the Kansas City underground revealed relatively favorable attitudes toward their environment.

grade building, an above-grade windowless setting, and an above-grade setting with windows. Adjectives most associated with the underground spaces were "unpleasant, dangerous, musty, dark, smothering, unfriendly, gloomy, and isolating." By contrast, the adjectives least associated with the underground were "relaxing, attractive, open, interesting, cheerful, warm, inviting, stimulating, secure, and silent."

While the Hollon et al. study appears to reveal a significant negative bias toward underground environments, even in contrast to other windowless spaces, there are a number of mitigating factors which raise questions over the ability to generalize such a study. The underground office setting was overcrowded, and the areas selected for study had virtually no amenities such as daylight and view, which were present in much of the rest of the building. The authors noted that the most frequent complaints about the underground were poor air quality and ventilation, high humidity, and poor temperature control. While these problems evoke associations with a more primitive underground cavern, they are not really intrinsic to modern underground buildings. Similar problems exist in enclosed above-grade buildings and can be resolved through proper design. In fact, air quality problems have been identified and resolved in the underground building in subsequent years (Sterling and Carmody 1990).

In contrast to these relatively negative responses to underground space, a study of workers in deep underground caverns in Kansas City, Missouri revealed a generally favorable attitude toward their environment (Hughey and Tye 1983). Unlike more typical basement space near the surface, the underground developments in Kansas City are in limestone mines at depths up to 50 meters that are entered through tunnels. Over 2 million square meters of this space is used for offices, manufacturing, and storage. In five different mined developments, 312 people were surveyed. They rated the underground environment as safe and efficient, viewed it as comparable to above-grade settings, and positively evaluated the temperature and humidity conditions. Workers were neutral with respect to overall ratings of their work areas, lighting, and ventilation. While some workers cited the conventional complaints about underground settings (i.e., no view and sunlight, poor ventilation), others found offsetting positive attributes such as a constant, pleasant temperature and being in a novel work environment with features such as exposed rock walls. It should be noted that the vast majority of the space in the Kansas City underground lacks any special amenities such as high quality finishes, furnishings, or lighting, and the air quality is not always particularly good due to the extensive truck traffic within the mines.

Experience in China

In the People's Republic of China, networks of tunnels and caverns have been constructed particularly under major cities for civil defense purposes. In recent years these spaces have been utilized for various manufacturing, storage, and community recreational purposes (Hou and Su 1988). Compared to environmental standards found in North America, Europe, and Japan, these underground spaces in China are poorly ventilated and lighted. There are few amenities and in many cases the tunnels are low and cramped. Recently a survey was conducted of workers in several underground settings in Shanghai (Su and Peng 1990). The researchers placed a number of concerns that emerged from the survey into three categories: the entrance, the underground working environment, and concerns for health and safety. Long dark tunnel entrances reinforced negative feelings, and artificial windows to improve the tunnel were disliked. Generally, most people disliked working underground and were unsatisfied with their jobs. They wished for sunlight and greenery and noticed the unusual smells underground. Most workers feared illness from the conditions and expressed concerns over their safety in fire, flood, earthquake, or structural collapse. In potential emergencies, they feared losing their way and being unable to escape. Many of these concerns seem to reflect the relatively unsafe and substandard conditions often found in Chinese underground spaces.

Experience in Japan

Severe land use pressures in Japan have led to an intense interest in extensive underground development in recent years. Researchers have begun to conduct surveys to attempt to identify the underlying psychological problems in underground work environments (Nishi et al. 1990; Wada and Sukugawa 1990). Nishi et al. compared the attitudes of above- and below-grade workers toward various aspects of underground environments. There was no significant difference between the two groups with regard to disaster prevention and safety in the underground — both were neutral. With regard to other issues, however, there was a notable difference in the attitudes of above- and below-grade workers toward underground space. More aboveground workers felt that an underground work place would present a hindrance to achieving a good interior environment, and more felt they would be extremely burdened psychologically by working underground. A remarkable 60 to 85 percent of underground workers approved of working below grade while only 25 percent of the aboveground workers approved. This study reflects the inherently negative attitudes about underground space that are based on images and associations rather than direct experience.

Another Japanese study seems to be consistent with most of the research in actual underground settings, which indicates predominantly negative feelings about the environment (Wada and Sakugawa 1990). Workers surveyed in an underground office, subway station, shopping center, and security center reported high levels of anxiety over isolation from the outside (67 percent of those interviewed) and their physical health (50 percent). Some anxiety was expressed over mental stress (36 percent) and earthquake or fire (18 percent). The most dominant complaints were (in rank order): bad air quality, lack of knowledge about the weather, an oppressive feeling, and low ceilings (even though they were the same as comparable above-grade settings). A few of those interviewed recognized the positive benefits of a quiet environment for work; however, the majority saw no advantages. More than 70 percent of those interviewed wished to work above grade, although the authors note that the physical conditions in fact were not very good in these facilities. It is interesting to note that while these workers were negative about the underground setting, they would continue to work there if conditions in the physical environment were improved—in particular, if sunlight, plants, surrogate windows, spaciousness, and more ventilation were provided. They also included a greater willingness to work there if they were compensated financially.

Figure 5-5: An increasing number of underground facilities are being constructed in Japan. The Diet Library in Tokyo extends seven stories below grade.

Wada and Sakugawa (1990) also conducted a series of experiments in laboratory settings. The performance of workers doing a variety of tasks was compared in three settings—above grade with a window, below grade with no amenities, and below grade with various amenities such as a sunlight tracking system, plants, and video monitor. While the performance was similar in all cases at the beginning, the performance of above-grade workers improved after a rest period, indicating the relaxing, restorative effect of the window view. The amenities in underground space (beamed sunlight, plants, and video monitor) seemed to reduce fatigue, but the data were insufficient to draw definite conclusions. In the underground setting, workers performed better when they descended four stories by elevator rather than by stairs. This implies that the entrance sequence may help people understand the location of the space and may have an effect on establishing the impression of and reaction to an underground environment.

ACTUAL EXPERIENCE IN WINDOWLESS AND OTHER ANALOGOUS ENVIRONMENTS

Underground spaces share some basic characteristics with certain analogous environments (Carmody and Sterling 1990). These include completely artificial environments like space capsules, submarines, and arctic or antarctic bases. Similarities include the almost complete dependence on technology for light and air as well as a sense of enclosure and isolation from the natural environment of the surface. However, these extreme environments present significant differences in that people are confined to them 24 hours a day for periods of a few days to up to several months and in the future, possibly, years. In underground environments, people have periodic access to the surface and at most spend eight hours a day in the facility. Another key difference is that the occupants of these extreme environments are there by choice and are motivated to accomplish a particular mission or scientific endeavor. Because of these differences, overall reactions to these environments do not seem to provide directly analogous information for underground settings. A review of literature related to these extreme environments does reveal, however, some specific design problems that are similar (i.e., enhancing spaciousness, using interior design to create stimulation, developing surrogate views, and designing artificial light to replicate characteristics of natural light). Research findings on these specific design issues appear in the appropriate design guidelines in Chapters 7 through 11.

There is one category of analogous environments—windowless buildings—that is so similar to underground space that they are sometimes treated as interchangeable. The lack of windows in buildings above and below grade seems to contribute to the majority of negative attitudes and associations (i.e., claustrophobia, lack of view, natural light, stimulation, and connection to nature). Underground buildings, however, seem to elicit an additional set of negative associations not entirely attributable to lack of windows (i.e., disorientation, coldness, high humidity, poor ventilation, lack of safety, and various cultural and status associations discussed in the previous section). Nevertheless, experience in windowless

Figure 5-6: The interior environment of a windowless building such as this high school has many characteristics that are similar to underground spaces.

environments can enhance the overall understanding of people in underground space, but it too is relatively limited.

Several researchers have surveyed the existing literature on windowless buildings (Holister 1968; Collins 1975; Wotton 1981; Wise and Wise 1984; Heerwagon 1990). Each of these surveys is, of course, constrained by the time of the study, and in some cases the survey is selective in order to focus on particular aspects of windows in buildings. In most cases the researchers infer from the literature the multiple functions and values associated with windows in buildings. Drawing from these surveys as well as specific studies on windowless buildings, there appears to be information on people's reactions to windowless schools, offices, hospitals, and factories.

Windowless Schools

Windowless schools in the United States were constructed to provide emergency shelter as well as to reduce vandalism, glare, overheating, outside distraction, and wasted wall space (Collins 1975). In one set of studies in California, there were no significant differences between students in windowed versus windowless classrooms as measured by achievement tests, personality tests, school health records, and grades (Demos et al. 1967). A Michigan study revealed similar findings—there were no conclusive detrimental effects on students in windowless classrooms (Larson 1965). In the Larson study, teachers surprisingly were highly in favor of the windowless classrooms. In these and other studies conflicting attitudes about windows were found. In her survey of these and several other studies of windowless schools, Collins (1975) notes: "If any single conclusion is to be reached from the studies of windowless schools, it is that the absence of windows neither improves nor impairs performance. Although some students like the situation, others, possibly a majority would prefer to have windows. The most striking conclusion seems to be the absence of significant findings, either for or against."

Windowless Offices

Predominantly negative reactions to underground windowless offices were discussed in the previous section (Sommer 1974). Another notable study of windowless above-grade offices was conducted by Ruys (1970). Ninety percent of the female office workers expressed dissatisfaction with the lack of windows, and almost 50 percent thought the lack of windows negatively affected them or their work. Complaints included no daylight, poor ventilation, inability to know about the weather, inability to see out and have a view, feelings of being "cooped up," isolation and claustrophobia, and feelings of depression and tension. It should be noted that these workers were in small, often single-occupant offices with little freedom of movement. Cuttle (1983) conducted a more recent survey of 471 office workers in New Zealand and England indicating a strong preference for windows. On the other hand, in other studies the presence of windows and views was rated as a relatively unimportant factor in contributing to a good office environment (Heerwagon 1990).

Windowless Hospital Rooms

Hospital settings have yielded some useful information on the impact of windows since patients are in small spaces continuously and their physiological reactions are being monitored. Wilson (1972) compared patients in intensive care units with and without windows. Those in the windowless setting developed post-operative delirium twice as often (40 percent versus 18 percent) as those in the unit with windows. Wilson also noted an increased incidence of post-surgical depression in patients in the windowless setting. In another study of patients in post-operative recovery rooms, Ulrich (1984) found that the content of the view through the window also affected the patients' recovery time and medication needs. Patients viewing trees had more beneficial results than those viewing a brick wall.

Windowless Factories

A previous section discussed underground windowless factories in Sweden. Although negative attitudes predominated and there were frequent complaints of physical symptoms, no major physiological problems were discovered. Elsewhere, studies of workers in windowless textile factories in the United States, Austria, and the former West Germany revealed no indication of illness attributed to the windowless condition (Holister 1968).

The Functions of Windows

Wyon and Nilsson (1980) conducted a study that included occupants of windowless factories, offices, shops, and colleges in Sweden. Their attitudes toward windows were compared with those of workers in settings with windows. The underlying hypothesis of the researchers was that it is difficult for those in conventional environments with windows to analyze what it is they appreciate about the windows since they take them for granted. This hypothesis was confirmed by the attitudes toward windows expressed by these two groups. Interesting findings included the fact that people in windowless rooms were less, not more, positive toward windows compared with those in settings with windows. In windowless settings the trend is for those with the least interesting jobs to miss windows the most. In fact, the authors suggest that windows may be important in reverse proportion to job status. Remarkably, the survey found that blind people missed windows more than sighted people. The sounds of wind, rain, and activity as well as smells from outside were an important source of stimulation for them.

The research of Wyon and Nilsson (1980) led them to conclude that windows have multiple functions and effects on the indoor environment. They influence the lighting and thermal environments in several ways; they provide visual and acoustical information from the outside; they affect air quality and ventilation; and they may serve as emergency exits. Collins (1975) would classify the major window functions as providing view, stimulation, sunlight, and a sense of spaciousness. Heerwagon (1990) describes these functions as providing access to environmental information, access to sensory change, a feeling of connection to the outside world, and restoration and recovery. She further suggests that existing research on windows only probes people's conscious awareness of their obvious benefits, and that "there are good reasons to believe . . . that our response to windows may be largely unconscious and the benefits are much more profound than previously believed" (Heerwagon 1990). In any case, to design underground space effectively the broadest possible range of window attributes should be identified so that they can be provided or compensated for by design.

Potential Psychological Problems Associated with Underground Space

1. Because it is largely not visible, an underground building is likely to lack a distinct image.
2. Because there is no building mass, finding the entrance can be difficult and confusing.
3. The movement at the entrance is usually downward, which potentially elicits negative associations and fears.
4. Because the overall mass and configuration of the building is not visible and the lack of windows reduces reference points to the exterior, there can be a lack of spatial orientation within underground facilities.
5. Because there are no windows, there is a loss of stimulation from and connection to the natural and manmade environments on the surface.
6. Without windows to the exterior, there can be a sense of confinement or claustrophobia.
7. In underground space, there are associations with darkness, coldness, and dampness.
8. Underground space sometimes connotes less desirable or lower status space.
9. The underground is generally associated with fear of collapse or entrapment in a fire, flood, or earthquake.

Potential Physiological Problems Associated with Underground Space

1. Most artificial lighting lacks the characteristics of sunlight, which raises physiological concerns in environments without any natural light.
2. Underground spaces sometimes may have poor ventilation and air quality.
3. High levels of humidity, which have potentially negative health effects, are found in underground spaces that are improperly controlled.

SUMMARY OF PROBLEMS

While the research on people in underground and windowless spaces is not conclusive, the major issues appear fairly clear and the same set of problems emerge to varying degrees in most cases. Drawing from the existing research as well as from the generally shared images and associations of the underground discussed earlier, it is possible to identify a set of potentially negative psychological and physiological effects. These are listed in the adjacent box.

While the psychological and physiological problems are listed separately, the physiological concerns (sunlight, ventilation, and humidity) all have a psychological component. Even though a building may have adequate artificial lighting, mechanical ventilation, and humidity control, these factors can still be perceived as inadequate regardless of the actual conditions.

It is interesting to note that these potentially negative effects are all related to one of three basic physical characteristics of underground buildings: (1) lack of visibility from the exterior, (2) lack of windows, and (3) being underground. Lack of visibility from the exterior causes the lack of a distinct image and the inability to find the entrance, while it contributes to a lack of spatial orientation inside the building since the overall configuration cannot be easily understood. The absence of windows causes a sense of confinement, lack of stimulation and connection to the outdoors, and lack of sunlight. The windowless nature of underground buildings also contributes to lack of spatial orientation since reference points to the exterior are missing, which is related to a fear of not being able to escape in an emergency. Although windows are often sealed in modern buildings, the lack of windows nevertheless seems to contribute to a perception of poor ventilation. Finally, simply being underground elicits associations with darkness, coldness, dampness, poor air quality, lower status, and fear of collapse or entrapment.

Although the research on people in subsurface buildings and the generally perceived characteristics of the underground result in a predominantly negative picture, there are, nevertheless, some positive associations and characteristics as well. These are a sense of security and protection, a quiet environment without distractions, and sometimes a setting that is stimulating due to its novelty and even sense of mystery and adventure.

Mitigating Factors

While the general list of problems related to people in underground space is a valid set of hypotheses on which to proceed with design solutions, it is important to recognize that a number of mitigating factors affect the importance or even the relevance of these design issues. In several of the research studies cited throughout this chapter, authors have identified key factors that affect the acceptability of underground space (Collins 1975; Wyon and Nilsson 1980; Wada and Sukugawa 1990). These are:

1. **The building function.** Obviously, all psychological and physiological issues are irrelevant for functions such as

utilities and storage underground, whereas they are extremely important for functions that are highly people-oriented such as offices or hospital rooms. Even among the various people-oriented functions, however, there are facility types that are relatively well suited to an enclosed, windowless environment and are often intentionally built that way (i.e., theaters, museums, libraries, gymnasiums, laboratories, and manufacturing plants).

2. **Occupancy patterns and freedom of movement.** The effects of an underground environment are mitigated by the amount of time spent there. Greater concern is raised for office workers or hospital patients who have little or no freedom of movement, compared with a museum visitor or an executive who spends the day moving around.

3. **Type of activity.** The acceptability of windowless, underground space appears to be related to the type of activity. Basically, people doing boring, monotonous work seem to complain more about lack of windows than those with more stimulating activities.

4. **Social contact and stimulation by internal activity.** The inherent lack of stimulation underground is offset to some degree by social contact and dynamic activity within a space. For example, the windowless nature of a department store does not seem to bother people as much as with other functions due to the continual contact with people as well as the constant activity.

5. **Size of space.** Smaller spaces such as private offices and hospital or hotel rooms exacerbate the feelings of confinement underground. Larger, more open spaces not only are less claustrophobic but also are likely to contain more activity and stimulation.

6. **The degree to which a building is underground.** Generally, underground buildings can be classified as near surface or deep. In deeper facilities, entered through long shafts or tunnels, the negative associations with being underground are likely to be greater while the opportunities to provide amenities such as light and view through courtyards are diminished. In some cases near-surface facilities may be completely windowless and raise the full set of people-related concerns with underground space. However, near-surface buildings may also be connected to the surface in various ways (i.e., hillside exposure or sunken courtyards) that largely overcome any negative perceptions.

7. **The quality of the interior spaces.** Many of the studies about people in windowless and underground facilities have been conducted in settings with marginal conditions of lighting and ventilation with little or no attention to providing any amenities of interior design. Obviously, the level of furnishings, finishes, lighting, and other amenities will influence perceptions.

8. **Individual variation.** Most studies of people in windowless underground environments indicate a range of responses.

CHAPTER 6
by John Carmody

Summary of Design Guidelines for Underground Space

The previous chapter demonstrates that placing people in underground environments can result in a number of potential psychological and physiological problems. These problems either are documented from actual experience in underground or analogous environments, or they are reflected in general attitudes based on associations with the general image of the underground.

In this chapter, an approach to identifying and communicating appropriate design solutions to alleviate these problems is presented. While the general problems with underground space are not difficult to identify, there has been little systematic research to identify and test solutions. Nevertheless, there is an immediate need to establish at least a set of hypothetical solutions, and to present them in the form of guidelines that are useful to designers.

Figure 6-1: Many examples exist of well-designed underground facilities such as the Smithsonian Museums of African and Eastern Art. The remainder of this book attempts to organize various design approaches into a set of guidelines or patterns that can be applied to improve underground environments for people. (Architect: Shepley Bulfinch Richardson and Abbott; photographer: Robert C. Lautman)

The first part of this chapter, in effect, describes the methodology and organization employed in all the remaining chapters that form Part 2 of this book. Chapters 7 through 11 each focus on a particular aspect of underground building design (i.e., entrance and exterior design, layout and spatial configuration, interior design elements and systems, lighting, and life safety). Within each chapter the specific problems, related research, design objectives, and possible design responses (patterns) are presented. A summary of design objectives and patterns drawn from Chapters 7 through 11 forms the second part of this chapter. This is followed by a discussion of how these patterns fit into the larger context of urban design.

An important issue throughout Part 2 is an understanding of the scope of this work. This is not intended to provide guidelines related to all aspects of design to meet human needs. Each activity within a facility has its particular functional, social, psychological, health, and safety requirements to be met regardless of whether a building is above or below grade. The focus of this work is on the problems and solutions that appear to be intrinsic to and sometimes unique to people in underground space.

Development of Design Guidelines

While there is no comprehensive research on underground environments that systematically defines each problem and tests alternative solutions, relevant research to address these concerns does exist. It is spread across several fields including planning, architecture, mechanical engineering, environmental psychology, human factors engineering, and medical science. While this information is often fragmentary and scattered, it represents a potentially useful body of knowledge if it is collected, synthesized, and applied appropriately. The majority of the concerns expressed in Chapter 5 are not typical engineering problems, but are most closely related to environmental psychology and architectural design.

Regardless of the amount of available research, the nature of research findings in the field of environment and behavior is "suggestive" rather than "conclusive." Findings often document problems and behavior patterns in certain existing settings, but do not clearly tell designers what to do to resolve the problem in a form to which the designer is receptive. In *Design Guidelines: A Bridge Between Research and Decision Making*, Clare Cooper-Marcus (1985) notes that a vast majority of designers believe environment influences behavior and are aware of research in the field, but very few ever apply the findings to their work. She suggests developing design guidelines in response to two problems: (1) the proliferation of potentially applicable research, and (2) the inability of designers to use and apply this work.

The intent of a design guideline is "to offer a succinct, pragmatic statement regarding people's behavior in, or attitudes toward the physical environment, such that it might become the basis for a more informed design decision" (Cooper-Marcus 1985). Design guidelines can take several forms that include broad statements of objectives, performance standards, or prescriptive guidelines. Prescriptive guidelines, the most specific form, are best suited to precise topics (i.e., health and safety standards) where there is good research to back up the recommendations. For areas where there is only limited research support or the nature of the topic is inherently less specific (i.e., aesthetic preferences), broad objectives or performance standards are more appropriate. While these forms give designers less specific direction, they state the general issues in a way that is clear and leaves open many possible design solutions. It is often useful to accompany statements of design objectives and performance standards with descriptions, photographs, and drawings of possible design responses, but these are not to be confused with prescriptive solutions (Cooper-Marcus 1985).

Organization of the Design Guidelines

For most issues, the nature of the design problems and relevant research related to people in underground space does not lead to the development of conclusive, prescriptive guidelines. Instead, it is more appropriate to state broad design objectives and then identify possible design responses. The remainder of Part 2 is divided into five chapters that reflect major sets of design issues relevant to people in underground space. These are: exterior and entrance design, layout and spatial orientation, interior design elements and systems, lighting, and life safety. To some degree this order reflects the sequence of design, proceeding from larger to smaller scale decisions. Within each chapter is a discussion of problems pertinent to the chapter topic, a statement of design objectives, and a set of possible design responses referred to as "Patterns" (based on *A Pattern Language* by Alexander et al. 1977). Relevant research is cited both in the discussion of problems as well as within the pattern descriptions.

The source material for developing the design guideline chapters includes:

1. Studies on behavior, health, and attitudes of people in underground space and other analogous environments.
2. Suggestions and hypotheses of appropriate design solutions from other researchers.
3. Design guidelines (and the source material behind them) developed for other building types that address similar problems found in underground spaces.
4. Visits to a wide range of underground facilities to record and evaluate problems and design approaches specifically intended to improve the environment for people.

The Purposes and Evolving Nature of Design Guidelines

It has been stated that the design guidelines presented in Chapters 7 through 11 are suggestive rather than conclusive. Moreover, they must always be examined in the context of the mitigating factors described in the previous section (i.e., building function and connection to the surface environment). Design guidelines, as presented here, are intended to be a means of organizing information in a useful way for a variety of possible purposes. They can be used as:

1. A list of design concerns and objectives for underground structures.
2. A set of possible design responses to these problems.
3. A survey of selected existing research related to people in underground environments.
4. A set of hypotheses to be tested by further research.

This last function of design guidelines as a set of hypotheses to be tested is particularly important and reflects their continually evolving nature—especially in an area like underground space which is novel and inadequately researched. Clare Cooper-Marcus (1985) concludes in her analysis of design guidelines:

> *It should be emphasized here – and in any guideline document – that guidelines are not immutable recommendations. Every guideline should be thought of as a hypothesis about environment and behavior, to a greater or lesser degree backed up by research. As more research appears, or society changes, guidelines may need to be modified and revised. Some may see this as reason enough not to attempt to articulate guidelines. Indeed, I have heard some researchers argue that we cannot make any definitive statements of use to decision-makers until 'all the evidence is in.' But that will probably never be, in a world as complex and rapidly-changing as the one we live in. Meanwhile, houses, hospitals, schools, prisons, parks, and playgrounds are being built; the least we can do is to take the plunge and be willing to present research findings in a form that can be readily used by the user and designer of environmental settings.*

Summary of Design Objectives and Patterns

The following pages contain a summary of the design objectives and patterns that are presented separately in Chapters 7 through 11. Within each of these chapters is a more complete discussion of relevant problems that lead to the design objectives. In addition, each of the patterns is described in greater detail and illustrated with drawings and photographs in the chapters that follow.

SUMMARY OF CHAPTER 7: EXTERIOR AND ENTRANCE DESIGN

Design Objectives

1. When appropriate to the building function, create a distinct overall building image. Articulate building boundaries and exposed architectural elements to clarify the building's location and extent.
2. Avoid permitting the building services (ventilation shafts, loading docks, fire escape doors) to create the dominant building image. Separate the pedestrian entrance, vehicular drop-off, and service entrances as much as possible.
3. Provide a clear, legible entrance (or entrances) that can be recognized from a distance along major paths of approach.
4. Give the entrance a sense of place by creating variety and complexity in the entry approach that stimulates curiosity and heightens experience.
5. When the underground facility is entered through adjacent above- or below-grade buildings, create a distinct entrance or demarcation where people cross into the facility.
6. Provide a graceful transition to lower levels.
7. Make the entrance area and vertical circulation spacious and well lighted.
8. Use the entrance to establish a visual connection between the exterior surface environment and the building interior.
9. Provide barrier-free entrances for mobility-impaired individuals. Make these entrances part of the main entry sequence, not a separate secondary path.

Design Patterns

Pattern 7-1: Terraced Building with a Hillside Entrance.

On sites with sloping terrain, build underground facilities into hillsides so they can be entered horizontally without any downward vertical circulation.

Pattern 7-2: Hillside Entrance to an Isolated Facility.

For caverns built beneath hilly terrain, enter through horizontal tunnels in addition to or instead of vertical shafts.

Pattern 7-3: Entrance through a Sunken Courtyard.

On a flat site where there is no above-grade building mass, enter through a sunken courtyard.

Pattern 7-4: Open Air Structures over Stairways and Escalators.

Place open air structures over entrance stairways and escalators to create an identifiable image and ease the transition into the facility.

Pattern 7-5: Above-Grade Entrance Pavilion.

Particularly on a flat site, use an enclosed above-grade structure to serve as the entrance to an underground facility.

Pattern 7-6: Entrance through Large Above-Grade Building Mass.

Enter an underground facility through an above-grade building mass—either an adjacent building or built as part of the underground structure.

Pattern 7-7: Open Stairways, Ramps, and Escalators.

Place stairways, ramps, and escalators in open multistory spaces to enhance orientation and improve the transition from above to below grade.

Pattern 7-8: Glass-Enclosed Vertical and Inclined Elevators.

Place glass-enclosed elevators in multistory open spaces to enhance orientation and relieve feelings of confinement. Use glass-enclosed inclined elevators alongside escalators to improve accessibility, orientation, and security.

SUMMARY OF CHAPTER 8: LAYOUT AND SPATIAL CONFIGURATION

Design Objectives

1. Create an interior layout that is easy to understand, thereby enhancing orientation as well as emergency egress.
2. Arrange space to create a distinct image within the building to compensate for the lack of image outside.
3. Develop a layout and spatial configuration that contributes to creating a stimulating, varied indoor environment to compensate for a lack of windows. Create a stimulating environment from the point of view of people occupying the facility as well as people passing through.
4. Provide visual connections between the interior and exterior environments whenever possible.
5. Arrange spaces and building circulation to enhance a feeling of spaciousness through the facility by providing extended interior views as much as possible.
6. Design each space to enhance a feeling of spaciousness by manipulating room size and shape.
7. Arrange spaces to protect privacy as much as possible.

Design Patterns

Pattern 8-1: A System of Paths, Activity Nodes, and Landmarks.

In order to improve orientation and provide a stimulating environment, arrange the layout of an underground building (or an interconnected group of underground facilities) into a system of paths, zones, activity nodes, and landmarks similar to the elements that form the public spaces in a city.

Pattern 8-2: Building with Hillside Exposure.

On sloping sites, build underground facilities into hillsides so that interior spaces have a maximum exposure to sunlight and exterior views.

Pattern 8-3: Sunken Exterior Courtyard.

On a flat site, utilize sunken exterior courtyards in underground facilities to provide sunlight, view, a connection to the outdoors, and to improve orientation within the facility. Design the courtyard to maximize sunlight penetration, utilize plants and other natural elements, and make the courtyard accessible to people.

Pattern 8-4: Interior Atrium Space.

Create multistory interior atrium spaces within underground facilities to provide extended views, visual stimulation, a sense of orientation, sunlight (in some cases), and a focus of activity within the building.

Pattern 8-5: Building Thoroughfare.

Rather than using conventional corridors alone, create a major thoroughfare through an underground facility. Make it wider and higher than a normal corridor (multistory if possible), and provide places for sitting and social interaction similar to a lively exterior street.

Pattern 8-6: Short, Lively Passageways.

Eliminate long, windowless corridors as much as possible and replace them with short, lively passageways.

Pattern 8-7: Zones of Distinct Character.

Within large underground facilities (or interconnected groups of facilities), create zones of distinct character to enhance orientation and provide a more stimulating interior environment.

Pattern 8-8: Interior Windows Overlooking Activity.

Use interior windows within underground buildings to overlook areas of activity and create long interior views.

Pattern 8-9: Hierarchy of Privacy.

When interior windows are used in underground facilities, preserve a sense of privacy by arranging spaces so that the most private areas cannot be viewed from public realms.

Pattern 8-10: Complex Room Shapes and Interconnected Spaces.

Make individual spaces (or groups of interconnected spaces) more geometrically complex in order to increase the perception of spaciousness in underground buildings. Subdivide large simple volumes into interconnected, smaller spaces using lofts, alcoves, and half-height walls, for example. Arrange spaces so they are only partially enclosed and permit long views into adjacent spaces without being able to see the entire volume at a glance.

Pattern 8-11: High and Varied Ceilings.

In underground facilities, make ceilings higher than in conventional buildings to enhance a feeling of spaciousness. Vary ceiling heights to reflect the different function and character of each space within a building and to create a stimulating interior environment.

SUMMARY OF CHAPTER 9: INTERIOR ELEMENTS AND SYSTEMS

Design Objectives

1. Create a stimulating indoor environment to compensate for a lack of windows. Environmental stimuli should be varied, integrated, and balanced to avoid overstimulation as well as understimulation.
2. Provide connections with the natural world.
3. Create a feeling of spaciousness.
4. Create a feeling of warmth to offset associations with cold, damp underground environments.
5. Provide fresh air and thermal comfort.
6. Use interior elements that are perceived as high quality to compensate for the negative status associated with below-grade space.
7. Provide a clear, attractive system of signs and maps (if necessary) to facilitate orientation.

Design Patterns

Pattern 9-1: Colorful, Warm, and Spacious Environment.

Use color to provide visual stimulation, warmth, and to enhance spaciousness in underground environments.

Pattern 9-2: Pattern, Line, and Texture.

Use applied lines, patterns, and textures on enclosing surfaces in underground facilities to enhance spaciousness and create visual interest. Vertical lines on walls increase the perception of ceiling height, while diagonal lines on floors make spaces seem larger. Surfaces with patterns and textures composed of finer elements seem farther away than those with bolder elements.

Pattern 9-3: Natural Elements and Materials.

Use natural elements and materials in underground spaces to create visual stimulation, warmth, and a feeling of quality, as well as to evoke associations with the natural world. Green plants, pools and fountains of water, and materials such as wood or stone are effective. Where possible, expose rock walls in underground caverns to highlight their rough-textured, natural characteristics.

Pattern 9-4: Sculpture and Manmade Artifacts.

Incorporate sculpture and other manmade artifacts into the design of underground spaces. Sculpture can provide a focal point and may introduce color, texture, movement, sound, natural materials, or symbolic manmade elements.

Pattern 9-5: Uncluttered Furnishings.

Select furnishings that are not massive in design with materials and colors that provide warmth, texture, a sense of quality, and associations with nature.

Pattern 9-6: Mirrors.

In confined underground spaces, use mirrors to reflect light and to create a feeling of spaciousness.

Pattern 9-7: Alcoves and Window-like Recesses.

Use alcoves and window-like recesses in the walls of underground spaces to create visual interest and enhance spaciousness. Place plants, sculpture, or other objects of interest in the alcoves and light them indirectly from above.

Pattern 9-8: Paintings and Photographs.

Use paintings and photographs to provide color and visual interest in underground spaces. Select paintings or photos with natural elements—notably water, trees, and mountains—and scenes that create the illusion of extended views to enhance a feeling of spaciousness.

Pattern 9-9: Transmitted and Reflected Exterior Views.

Provide exterior views to isolated underground spaces by reflection with optical devices or by transmission with video systems. High quality video systems may also enhance the interior by providing visual images, information, and entertainment that is not related to the immediate building exterior environment.

Pattern 9-10: Clear System of Signs and Maps.

In all underground facilities, provide a clear, complete system of signs and maps to assist in wayfinding and maintaining spatial orientation.

Pattern 9-11: Well-ventilated, Comfortable Environment.

Design the mechanical system in underground buildings to provide a high level of thermal comfort, an acceptable humidity level, and adequate ventilation to overcome air quality problems. To compensate for images of stuffiness, coldness, and dampness underground, make ventilation air movement perceptible and create slightly warmer, dryer, and better-ventilated conditions than are typically provided.

SUMMARY OF CHAPTER 10: LIGHTING

Design Objectives

1. Provide appropriate levels of illumination to enhance visual clarity and facilitate all activities. Spaces should be well lighted to offset associations with darkness underground.
2. Provide natural light whenever possible.
3. Design artificial lighting systems to simulate the characteristics of natural light.
4. Use lighting to enhance feelings of spaciousness.
5. Use lighting to create a stimulating, varied environment. Lighting patterns should help define and reinforce social spaces.

Design Patterns

Pattern 10-1: Natural Light through Windows and Skylights.

Whenever possible, provide natural light through windows and skylights in underground facilities.

Pattern 10-2: Transmitted and Reflected Natural Light.

When natural light enters an underground building through windows and skylights, reflect it off surfaces and other devices to maximize its penetration and distribution in the space. In deeper, more isolated spaces, use systems that transmit or reflect natural light into the building through shafts, conduits, or cables.

Pattern 10-3: Artificial Light with Natural Characteristics.

Design artificial lighting systems to simulate characteristics of natural light such as its color, lack of flicker, and variation in direction and intensity.

Pattern 10-4: Skylights and Wall Panels with Artificial Backlighting.

Place artificial lighting above translucent skylights and wall panels to create the illusion of natural light entering the space.

Pattern 10-5: Indirect Lighting of Ceilings and Walls.

To enhance spaciousness in underground facilities, use uniform indirect lighting on perimeter walls and ceilings.

Pattern 10-6: Dark, Ambiguous Boundaries.

To enhance a feeling of spaciousness in underground settings, leave the peripheral surfaces in darkness to give the impression of infinite space.

Pattern 10-7: Patterns of Light and Shadow.

Create varied patterns of light and shadow in underground buildings to provide visual stimulation, to define social spaces, and to highlight pathways and landmarks that will aid in orientation.

SUMMARY OF CHAPTER 11: LIFE SAFETY

Design Objectives

1. Minimize hazardous, combustible materials or separate them from occupied areas.
2. Construct a fire-resistant building.
3. Construct an earthquake-resistant building where appropriate.
4. Provide systems for early detection of emergencies and alarm systems with directive information for occupants.
5. Remove smoke from the area of the fire and suppress or extinguish it as quickly as possible.
6. Provide for the efficient evacuation of people from areas of danger to places of safety (either within or outside the facility).

Design Patterns

Pattern 11-1: Clear Internal Organization and Egress System.

Provide a clear emergency egress system by using a simple, understandable layout. When possible, egress paths should correspond with familiar circulation patterns used to enter and leave the facility. When unconventional or unfamiliar egress routes are required, they should be clearly highlighted and explained.

Pattern 11-2: Safe Vertical Egress—Stairwells, Elevators, and Escalators.

Design stairwells, elevators, and escalators to maximize safe vertical egress. Make egress stairwells enclosed, smoke-proof, ventilated, and open in the center to provide visual access. Elevators used for egress in deeper facilities require enclosed, smoke-proof, ventilated lobbies with voice communication to the surface.

Pattern 11-3: Compartmentalization and Places of Safe Refuge.

Create compartments within underground facilities that serve as places of safe refuge during emergencies. Separate compartments with fire-resistant walls and ventilate each compartment as a separate zone.

Pattern 11-4: Clear Signs and Emergency Lighting.

Provide clear emergency signs and lighting along paths of egress.

Pattern 11-5: Effective Detection, Alarm, and Communication Systems.

In underground facilities, provide effective detection, alarm, and two-way voice communication systems.

Pattern 11-6: Effective Smoke Removal and Air Handling.

Provide an effective smoke removal system so that smoke is mechanically exhausted from the zone where the fire occurs, and outside air is supplied to adjacent zones.

Pattern 11-7: Effective Fire Suppression.

Use automatic sprinklers or other fire suppression systems in underground facilities.

Pattern 11-8: Fire-Resistant Construction and Restriction of Hazardous Materials.

Construct underground buildings with fire-resistant materials and methods. As much as possible, avoid the placement of hazardous or flammable materials in habitable underground facilities.

Placing Design Patterns into the Larger Context of Urban Planning

The design objectives and patterns summarized in the previous section predominantly address elements within a building at a relatively small scale—mostly within a room or group of spaces. This focus on smaller scale design responses is generally appropriate for the nature of many problems encountered by placing people in underground or windowless environments. For example, problems such as lack of light and view, lack of stimulation, claustrophobia, and associations with coldness or dampness are addressed mainly in the design of individual spaces by using appropriate materials, lighting, furnishings, ventilation systems, and the geometry of the space itself to alleviate these concerns. Of course, there are larger scale implications such as the arrangement of the building to provide sunlight if possible, or the use of a multistory atrium to provide interior views and a sense of spaciousness.

This predominance of smaller scale design responses, however, is not intended to suggest that designing for people in underground facilities is mainly limited to single buildings or rooms within buildings. On the contrary, larger scale design issues are extremely important if underground space is to be utilized effectively in an urban setting. One key problem is making isolated underground facilities into larger interconnected systems of spaces. Another related issue is integrating the underground with the aboveground urban environment. In attempting to design underground space in urban settings that is acceptable to people, it is important for designers to work at several scales—the city, the district, the building complex, the individual facility, and the individual space—even though the larger scales are not always under the control of the designer.

Unfortunately, it is difficult to provide guidelines for larger scale underground development in urban settings. Unlike individual buildings or spaces within buildings where the designer has considerable control, the opportunity for larger scale development is shaped by factors such as the geology and topography of the area as well as the existing patterns of urban development. Generally, surface development precedes extensive underground use and it tends to influence the shape, extent, depth, and function of the subsurface facilities.

Given the complexities of the urban planning process and the secondary role usually assigned to underground space utilization, it is not appropriate to suggest an overall urban environment shaped by a concern for maximizing the underground resource. Instead, it is more reasonable to assume that underground development will arise as a design solution at various scales and in various contexts. For this reason, the design guidelines presented here for people in underground space do not attempt to address whether a facility should be deep or shallow, or whether the space should be utilized for particular functions that minimize the number of people below grade. Instead, the design patterns in this book should be viewed as building blocks or elements of design that have application in underground projects of virtually any scale. Many of the patterns shaping a single building—i.e., a clear entrance, a central interior space, and interior windows overlooking activity—work at many scales. In fact, Pattern 8-1 suggests a system of paths, activity nodes, and landmarks underground that can be applied to an entire underground city network as well as to a small individual facility.

In order to help visualize the larger context in which many of the smaller scale patterns may be placed, some urban design concepts utilizing underground space are shown in Figures 6-2 through 6-6. Figure 6-2 illustrates shallow cut-and-cover space in an urban setting. Connections between underground spaces can create a below-grade pedestrian circulation system. Problems such as lack of orientation and stimulation must be addressed in extended networks of below-grade space. Compared with deep isolated spaces, shallow buildings provide a greater range of opportunities to enhance the environment for people.

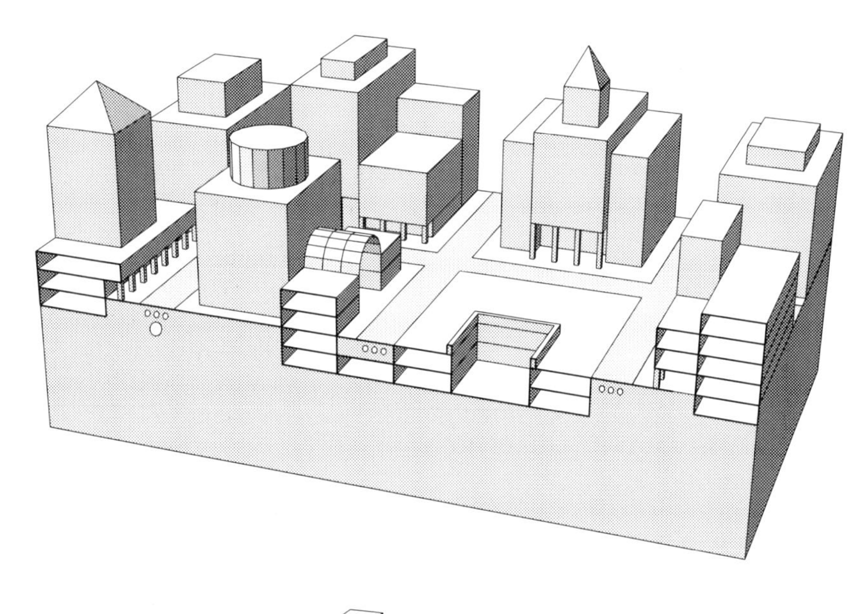

Figure 6-2: Cut-and-cover underground space near the surface is commonly used to create open space in urban settings. Shallow buildings provide a greater range of opportunities to enhance the environment for people.

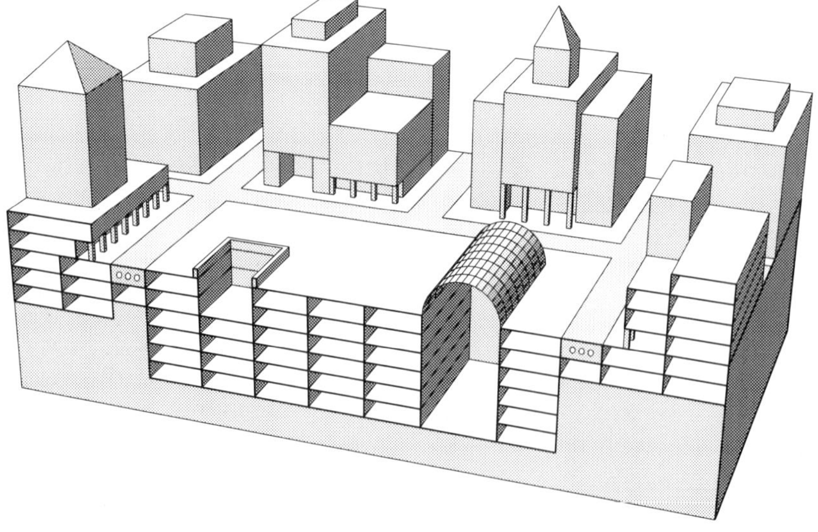

Figure 6-3: Deep-cut underground structures increase concerns over creating an acceptable environment for people. While opportunities still exist for connection to the surface with atriums and courtyards, designs must address problems of lack of orientation and stimulation in such large complexes.

In some settings, more extensive use of underground space can be made in urban areas by extending cut-and-cover structures to greater depths. Figure 6-3 illustrates the use of deep-cut structures that permit intensive land use while creating open space on the surface. Lack of orientation can become a very significant problem in such large, multistory developments. Opportunities exist for major connections to the surface by the use of atriums and courtyards, but the greater depth and scale of development will tend to increase concerns over creating an acceptable environment for people.

Deep mined space can be created beneath some urban areas depending on the geology. As shown in Figures 6-4 and 6-5, this type of space can be entered through shafts from the surface. Depending on the situation, the underground space may be related or completely unrelated to surface uses. Figure 6-5 also illustrates steeply sloping topography which permits access to deep mined

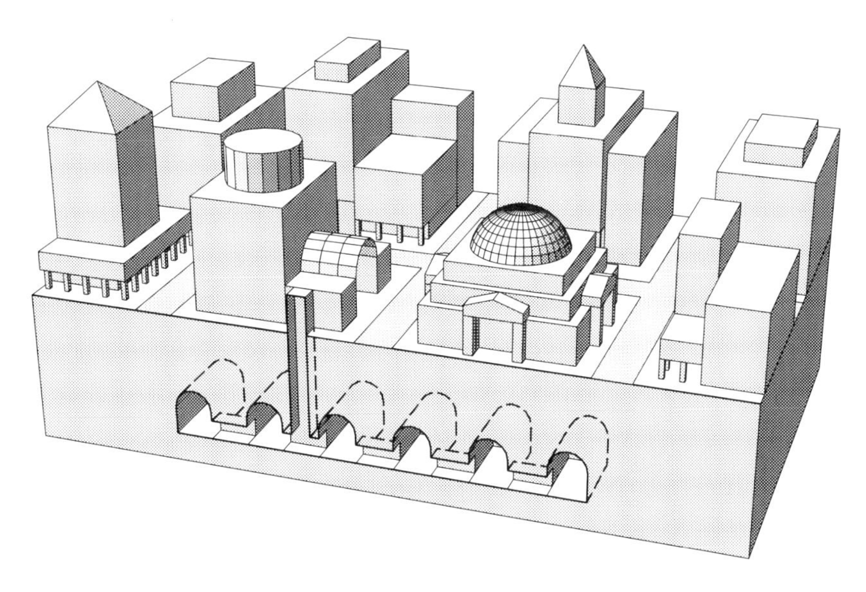

Figure 6-4: Deep mined spaces can be created beneath urban areas and can be entered vertically through shafts. Deep isolated spaces present the most limitations and greatest challenges in designing acceptable environments for people.

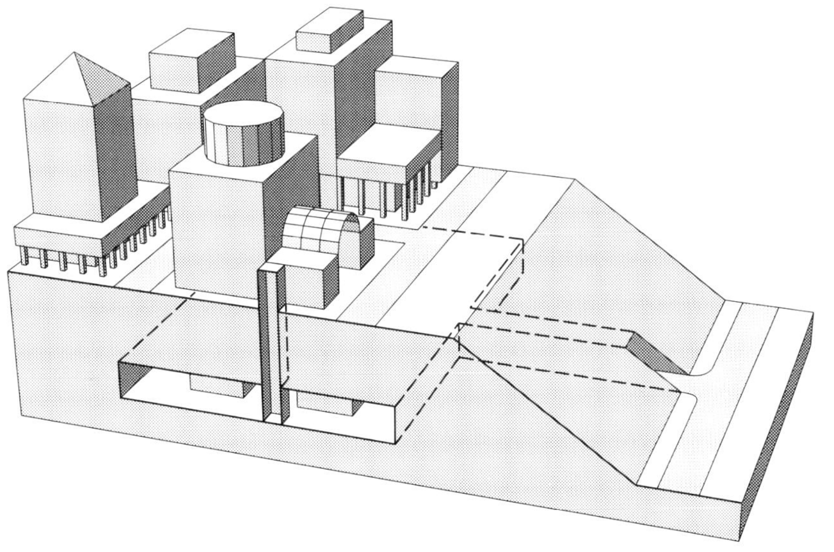

Figure 6-5: Some sloping sites may permit horizontal access through tunnels to deep mined space. If there is no vertical shaft access, there may be no direct connection between the underground and aboveground environments.

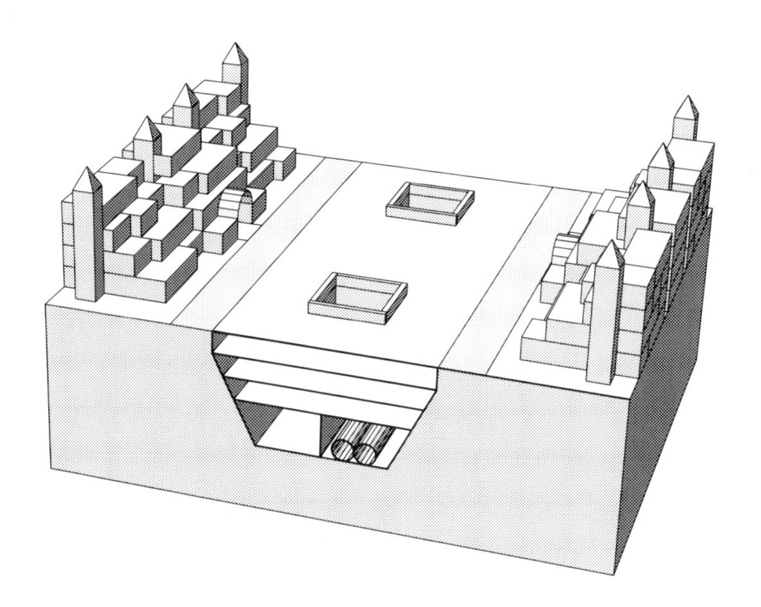

Figure 6-6: As shown in this underground corridor concept, subsurface space utilization may be used to shape urban development. Patterns for creating an acceptable environment for people can be applied to these larger scale concepts as well as to smaller facilities.

space through a horizontal tunnel. If access occurs exclusively through tunnels rather than shafts, the deep underground space and the surface environment above may not be directly connected at all. While these deep mined spaces may offer some excellent opportunities for efficient land use as well as isolation of undesirable functions below grade, they present the greatest challenges in designing an acceptable environment for people. Even though opportunities for light, exterior views, and other connections to the outside world are limited in deep space, many other design techniques discussed in Chapters 7 through 11 can be applied.

Finally, while underground space for people-oriented uses is typically created in a piecemeal fashion on individual sites, in the future it may grow to be seen as a tool for shaping urban development. Figure 6-6 illustrates a concept of creating an underground corridor that contains commercial and industrial space, as well as traditional transportation and utility systems (Birkerts 1974). This approach permits the surface to be used for housing, recreation, and open space. Even at this citywide scale, the same basic problems regarding people in underground space exist, and the smaller scale design patterns in this book can be used as an evolving set of potential solutions. As more extensive underground development occurs in urban areas, new patterns will emerge that address the larger scale design and planning issues more completely.

CHAPTER 7
by John Carmody

Exterior and Entrance Design

Exterior Design Issues and Problems

Compared with a conventional building, the exterior design of an underground facility presents a difficult set of challenges to the designer. By its very nature, most or all of an underground building is not visible. While buildings are often placed underground to benefit people by providing open space or improving the environment in other ways, their lack of visibility can confuse people and make the use of these facilities a more negative experience. Moreover, since only a small portion of the

Figure 7-1: The Pusey Library at Harvard University maintains an unobtrusive character while providing information about the building's location and entrance to people approaching the facility. (Architect: Hugh Stubbins and Associates; photographer: Edward Jacoby)

exterior design is visible, it carries added importance and must be handled sensitively to perform the necessary functions of the building while creating an attractive design integrated with its surroundings.

The exterior design of an above-grade facility can be appreciated purely as an aesthetic experience. Likewise, an unobtrusive, underground building with a well-landscaped and detailed design of its surface elements can be a rich aesthetic experience as well. The contradiction in designing an underground facility is to couple this unobtrusive character with the need to communicate many things about the facility to enhance its use by people. There are three key exterior design problems related to most underground facilities:

1. Because it is largely not visible, the building is more likely to lack a distinct image.
2. Because there is no object in space that can be perceived as a whole, there is no sense of the overall configuration and size of the facility.
3. With few building elements exposed to view, necessary utilitarian building functions such as loading docks, ventilation shafts, and fire escapes may dominate the surface environment of an underground facility.

Building Image

The first problem listed above, the lack of a distinct building image, has important implications for people. Kevin Lynch, in *Image of the City*, suggests that "a good environmental image gives its possessor an important sense of emotional security. He can establish a harmonious relationship between himself and the outside world." Furthermore, "This image is the product both of immediate sensation and of the memory of past experience, and it is used to interpret information and guide action" (Lynch 1960). The unconventional nature of underground facilities may limit the past associations people can draw on to form a meaningful image. Or possibly, deeply rooted past associations with death and burial, or simply dark, humid basements, may arise. Thus, special attention must be paid to facilities with these inherent drawbacks to create an environmental image that enhances security and well-being, and even contributes to a richness of experience.

A facility with a good environmental image must effectively communicate several things to potential users. These include informing people (1) what the facility is, (2) what benefit it offers, (3) how one gets in, (4) what is inside, and (5) how one will be received (Deasy 1985). Particular problems of entrance design are discussed later in this chapter, but the general problem of establishing an exterior image with a largely invisible building remains. In most cases this problem of establishing a clear image cannot be solved in the traditional way without defeating the purpose of the underground placement. However, special emphasis of the available visible elements may be sufficient compensation.

Figure 7-2: Necessary building services may dominate the exterior appearance of an underground facility, giving it an unattractive image when approached from some directions.

Inability to See Overall Configuration

The second general problem identified in exterior design is the inability to perceive an overall configuration and size of the facility. In his book *Wayfinding in Architecture,* Romedi Passini suggests that there are three important factors in enabling people to create a mental image of places so they can orient themselves and find their way in buildings. These are: (1) understanding an internal organization principle for the building, (2) perceiving the external organization principle given by the spatial enclosure or building volume, and (3) understanding relationships among spaces (Passini 1984). The first and last factors are related to the interior building layout, and are addressed in Chapter 8, although the last factor (perceiving relationships among spaces) is applicable to entrance design also. It is the second factor that is of major concern with respect to exterior building design. Passini cites several examples of underground commercial complexes in Montreal with significant wayfinding and image formation problems. In some of the worst cases, it is this inability to comprehend the overall form that is a major cause of confusion. While some design solutions such as building into a hillside or creating a large visible sunken courtyard can begin to create an understanding of building form, many underground buildings will simply have to be designed with a well-organized interior to compensate for the inability to perceive the exterior configuration.

Exposed Building Services

The final exterior design problem listed above is the potential for unattractive utilitarian elements to dominate the exterior image of the building. This potential problem results from the lack of surface building mass to hide or at least diminish the visual impact of these less attractive elements. Some solutions can avoid this problem by providing services through adjacent attached buildings, but in many cases extremely sensitive site arrangement and landscaping around utilitarian elements may be required to overcome the potential for a negative exterior image.

Entrance Design Issues and Problems

In virtually any building or complex of buildings above or below grade, the entrance has an important role. It gives people a sense of arrival; it can set the mood of a building; it strengthens the orientation on the exterior and interior of the building; and it represents a place of physical and psychological transition between the exterior and interior world (Bain 1990). In *A Pattern Language,* Christopher Alexander et al. state that "placing the main entrance (or main entrances) is perhaps the single most important step you take during the evolution of a building plan." They explain that the entry controls the building layout by controlling movement to and from the building. They further state that "the entrance must be placed in such a way that people who approach the building see

Figure 7-3: This cave entrance illustrates the negative associations with entering the underground – the movement is downward, from light to darkness, and from openness to confinement.

the entrance or some hint of where the entrance is, as soon as they see the building itself. This makes it possible for them to orient their movements toward the entrance as soon as they start moving toward the building without having to change direction or change their plan of how they will approach the building" (Alexander et al. 1977).

In the case of an underground building, designing a successful entrance is compounded by two additional factors. First, since the building form is mostly or entirely below grade, the entrance usually cannot be designed in the familiar pattern of a distinct form or opening placed within a larger building mass. In some cases it may be virtually the only visible element of the underground building. Second, in addition to representing the transition from exterior to interior, it is the transition from above to below grade. This transition potentially can elicit some of the more negative associations with underground space. For example, the movement is usually downward, from light to darkness, from openness to confinement, and from a surface environment with familiar patterns and images to an unknown environment. The key entrance design problems for most underground facilities can be summarized as follows:

1. Because there is no visible building mass, finding the entrance(s) can be difficult and confusing.
2. Because underground facilities inherently have limited exposure to the surface environment, people in the underground may feel disconnected from what is above grade, leading to problems of disorientation. The entrances may present the only opportunities to establish this connection.
3. The movement at the entrance is usually downward, which potentially elicits negative associations and fears.
4. Because surface forms and space are limited in many cases, clear separation of pedestrian, vehicular drop-off, and service entrances may be difficult to achieve.
5. The necessary use of escalators and stairways to enter some underground facilities forces mobility-impaired people to use secondary means of entry often located away from the main entry sequence.

Entrance Visibility and Image

The problem of designing a successful entrance to an underground facility is not simply a matter of making the entrance easy to find. Bain (1990), in attempting to identify the elements of a successful entry sequence, has defined the following five issues: legibility, sense of place, sequential art, mystery, and sense of dignity. Legibility refers to the use of visual cues to help maintain orientation, distinguish boundaries, and determine the function of a building. In particular, a legible entry sequence should clarify the direction of travel and communicate the building function. While creating legibility is essential in designing the entry sequence, according to Bain and others, it is not sufficient by itself to create a

Figure 7-4: Typical entrances to underground transit are often difficult to find and seldom provide a feeling of openness or connection to the surface.

"successful" entry. Also important is the creation of a "sense of place." This rather subjective term refers to places with a distinct, recognizable identity—presumably a place with architectural qualities that elicit a rich, satisfying experience—a feeling of well-being.

One of the contributing factors to creating a "sense of place" is the development of a sequence of spatial experiences leading to the climax of entering the building. As one approaches the entrance, a changing series of viewpoints can be arranged to provide an aesthetic experience that is a function of movement and time. In *A Pattern Language*, Alexander et al. suggest that the underlying purpose in creating an entry sequence is to make a transition between the more public exterior and the more private, enclosed building interior. In fact, they state that buildings with "a graceful transition between the street and the inside, are more tranquil than those which open directly off the street." This transition can be regarded as a space between the exterior and interior world marked by "a change of light, a change of sound, a change of direction, a change of surface, a change of level, perhaps by gateways which make a change of enclosure, and above all with a change of view" (Alexander et al. 1977). It is important to note that this concept of creating an entry transition does not apply equally to all building functions. Making a definite transition may not be desirable or appropriate for certain public functions that are intended to be an extension of the exterior environment.

A particularly intriguing aspect of successful entrance design discussed by Bain is the creation of "mystery." This quality implies that the entrance is not completely obvious. Information unfolds slowly as one moves through the entry sequence. The observer is lured along by curiosity and feelings of anticipation and is rewarded by pleasant surprises (Bain 1990). Passini also discusses the fascination with labyrinths and the stimulating and rewarding aspects of solving a complex wayfinding problem (Passini 1984). Mystery can enrich the experience of approaching and finding the entrance, but it must be accompanied by legibility.

Lack of Connection to Surface Environment

The second problem related to underground entrance design is the lack of connection between the surface and below-grade environment. Passini suggests that one of the three major factors facilitating effective orientation and wayfinding is understanding spatial correspondence (Passini 1984). By this he means a recognition of how parts of the environment fit together. For example, how do the interior and exterior of a building relate, and how does the underground correspond to the surface environment above? In underground buildings with limited opportunities for exposure, the entrances become the primary and sometimes only places where this connection can be made. To some extent, then, the entrance to an underground facility may represent a scarce opportunity to bring light and openness into the building. To the degree that the entrance can provide some visibility of outside landmarks, orientation within the facility will be enhanced.

Fear of the Underground

The negative associations and fears related to downward movement of the entrance represent a key design problem for underground buildings. A number of fundamental psychological issues may arise including claustrophobia, fear of entrapment, or negative cultural or status associations. These associations may be further exacerbated by an entrance design that is dark, spatially confining, and confusing. This aspect of entrance design requires an understanding that the entrance is not an isolated architectural element like a door or a simple foyer-type space. Rather, the entrance is part of a continuum that includes the building exterior and entry approach as well as the interior layout and vertical circulation system. For example, creating an entrance that is recognizable and appealing is one aspect of the overall site and exterior design. Likewise, creating a spacious, well-lighted entrance area within the building is only the beginning of an overall interior layout that enhances orientation through a variety of techniques (see Chapter 8). As one proceeds downward into an underground space, the escalators, ramps, stairs, and elevators are integral parts of the entrance transition into the building as well as components of the interior circulation system.

Separation of Entrance Functions

The problem of clearly separating pedestrian, vehicular drop-off, and service entrances for an underground building is obviously related to the limited surface exposure. Not only is there less land than for a comparable above-grade building, there are fewer building masses that naturally divide and separate exterior surface spaces. Use of an adjacent above-grade structure when possible, along with sensitive site planning and landscaping, is important.

Access for Mobility-Impaired People

Finally, access for mobility-impaired people at entrances to underground facilities may require special attention. Although this must be addressed for all facilities, most underground facilities by nature require vertical circulation at the entrance. Stairways and escalators characteristically make graceful and spacious transitions to lower levels but are not easily accessible. Creating secondary elevator entrances away from the main sequence may not be a desirable solution, because the front entrance is symbolic and denotes a certain status. Mobility-impaired individuals prefer to use main entrances and tend to feel dependent, disoriented, and degraded when access is not available (Bain 1989). It is this sense of dignity that Bain has identified as one of the characteristics of a successful entry that creates a "sense of place."

Design Objectives for Exterior and Entrance Design

1. When appropriate to the building function, create a distinct overall building image. Articulate building boundaries and exposed architectural elements to clarify the building's location and extent.
2. Avoid permitting the building services (ventilation shafts, loading docks, fire escape doors) to create the dominant building image. Separate the pedestrian entrance, vehicular drop-off, and service entrances as much as possible.
3. Provide a clear, legible entrance (or entrances) that can be recognized from a distance along major paths of approach.
4. Give the entrance a sense of place by creating variety and complexity in the entry approach that stimulates curiosity and heightens experience.
5. When the underground facility is entered through adjacent above- or below-grade buildings, create a distinct entrance or demarcation where people cross into the facility.
6. Provide a graceful transition to lower levels.
7. Make the entrance area and vertical circulation spacious and well-lighted.
8. Use the entrance to establish a visual connection between the exterior surface environment and the building interior.
9. Provide barrier-free entrances for mobility-impaired individuals. Make these entrances part of the main entry sequence, not a separate secondary path.

Design Patterns: Exterior and Entrance Design

This section presents several exterior and entrance design approaches for underground facilities that meet the design objectives stated previously. The intention is to present the basic pattern or concept, discuss its characteristics, and illustrate it with a representative drawing and/or photograph. This does not imply that the pattern should be replicated in this exact manner. Many diverse design responses can be developed based on the objectives and approaches presented here. (See the last section of Chapter 6 for a discussion of how to place these patterns into a larger context.)

The patterns discussed here are intended to complement those related to interior layout and spatial configuration (Chapter 8). There is no precise line within the building where the entry sequence ends and the internal circulation begins. Internal vertical circulation systems (stairs, elevators, escalators) that occur near the entrance can be correctly regarded as part of the entry sequence as well as part of the building interior circulation. Since these two categories of design issues occur in separate chapters in this book, the choice has been made to discuss major vertical circulation elements as part of the entrance sequence since these elements relate so strongly to the need for a graceful downward transition into the facility.

In addition to complementing the interior layout and spatial configuration patterns in Chapter 8, exterior and entrance design approaches discussed here must be integrated with patterns related to interior design elements (Chapter 9) and lighting (Chapter 10) in order to enhance their effectiveness.

Exterior and Entrance Design Patterns

7-1: Terraced Building with a Hillside Entrance

7-2: Hillside Entrance to an Isolated Facility

7-3: Entrance through a Sunken Courtyard

7-4: Open Air Structures over Stairways and Escalators

7-5: Above-Grade Entrance Pavilion

7-6: Entrance through Large Above-Grade Building Mass

7-7: Open Stairways, Ramps, and Escalators

7-8: Glass-Enclosed Vertical and Inclined Elevators

PATTERN 7-1: TERRACED BUILDING WITH A HILLSIDE ENTRANCE

Figure 7-5: This one-level office building is set into a hillside, giving it an exterior image and a visible entrance much like a conventional structure. (National Arts Education Center; architect: The Benham Group, Oklahoma City)

On sites with sloping terrain, build underground facilities into hillsides so they can be entered horizontally without any downward vertical circulation.

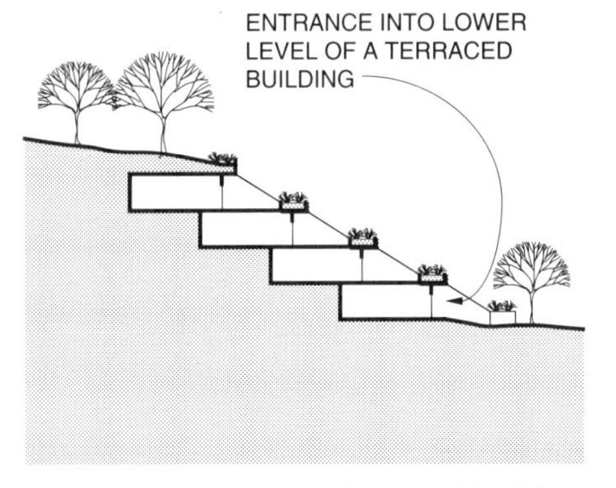

Figure 7-6: A multilevel terraced building with a hillside entrance.

A typical hillside terraced building of one or more levels is partially below grade, but the building facades remain exposed. When viewed from downhill, this type of structure can appear very much like a conventional above-grade building. In fact, it may not be clear that the facility is partially set into the hillside. Basic problems of creating a distinct exterior image and perceiving an overall building mass that are present for most underground facilities are minimized with a hillside structure. Terraced buildings can have a complex, organic form that is very distinctive yet blends into the surrounding land forms to a great degree. Designing a distinct entrance that is easy to recognize is important but can be done in a more conventional context against the background of a visible building mass. Since there is a "front" but no "back" to most terraced structures, separation of public and service entrances requires special attention. Plant materials, walls, and grade changes can be used to partially hide service entrances.

PATTERN 7-2: HILLSIDE ENTRANCE TO AN ISOLATED FACILITY

For caverns built beneath hilly terrain, enter through horizontal tunnels in addition to or instead of vertical shafts.

While the building facade and mass are not visible, the entrance to an isolated cavern is set against the mass of a bluff or hill, which gives a better sense of the location and possible size of the facility compared with an entrance opening on a flat site. The contrast of a manmade entrance against a natural backdrop is likely to make the entrance stand out, but its scale may need to be exaggerated so that it is recognized as an entrance when approaching. Since this main entrance opening is limited in size, it is desirable to have multiple openings for other building services. Otherwise, loading docks and ventilation outlets will dominate the exterior image.

An advantage of the horizontal nature of this type of entrance is that no downward movement in the entry sequence is required. However, once inside the doorway, a long and possibly narrow tunnel leading to the facility is a potentially negative experience. Besides enlarging the passageway as much as possible, use of lighting, color, artwork, sound, and other techniques can increase the feeling of spaciousness and create a more stimulating trip through the passageway. At the end of a long narrow passageway, a spacious area with a sense of arrival is an important climax to this type of entry sequence.

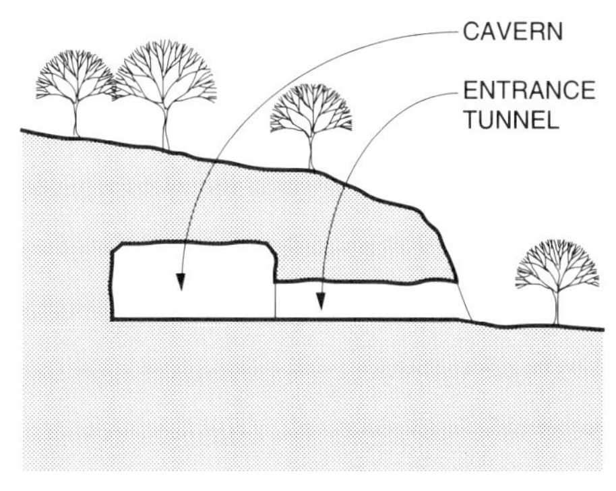

Figure 7-7: A deep isolated cavern entered through a horizontal tunnel.

Figure 7-8: This underground recreation center in Norway is entered through a portal in the bluff that leads to a long corridor terminating at the facility within a deep rock cavern.

PATTERN 7-3: ENTRANCE THROUGH A SUNKEN COURTYARD

On a flat site where there is no above-grade building mass, enter through a sunken courtyard.

The courtyard itself becomes an important part of the building's exterior image and a large courtyard may, in some cases, help to define the shape and extent of the building below. Even courtyards of limited size reveal facades of the building, making it more understandable while at the same time connecting the interior spaces to the exterior environment. For near surface buildings, courtyards not only help resolve problems of exterior image and entrance transition, they also bring light into the building and provide views out.

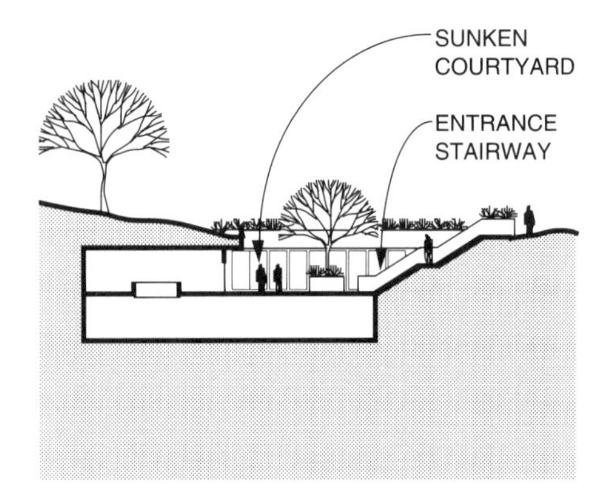

Figure 7-9: The entrance to an underground facility through a sunken exterior courtyard.

While a courtyard viewed from above can be attractive and create a distinctive image, it can be somewhat invisible while approaching from a distance on a flat site. The creation of a legible entrance through a courtyard may require distinctive forms extending above the ground plane (see Pattern 7-4: Open Air Structures).

Making the actual transition from the ground level to the entrance level at the courtyard floor is most gracefully done with open stairways, ramps, or possibly escalators. A drawback to this approach is that elevators for mobility-impaired people will often be located away from this main entry sequence since there may be no above-grade mass and the transition occurs outdoors. Moreover, in colder climates exterior stairways and ramps in courtyards exposed to snow and ice can be difficult to keep clear.

Aside from these practical problems, it has been suggested that an entrance through a courtyard has characteristics that effectively offset the negative associations of going downward into an

Figure 7-10: The main entrance to the Civil and Mineral Engineering Building at the University of Minnesota is through a large semicircular courtyard. This approach creates a gradual descent into the building in an unconfined open space. (Architect: BRW Architects)

Figure 7-11: This secondary entrance to Williamson Hall at the University of Minnesota is through a small exterior sunken courtyard. (Architect: BRW Architects)

underground building (Bennett 1978). The downward transition occurs in an open exterior space with no associations of darkness or confinement. Then, the actual entrance into the facility is horizontal and can evoke conventional images of entering the facade of a building. Traveling downward into the courtyard space itself becomes an interesting part of the entry sequence and is an effective transition space between the exterior and interior worlds.

PATTERN 7-4: OPEN AIR STRUCTURES OVER STAIRWAYS AND ESCALATORS

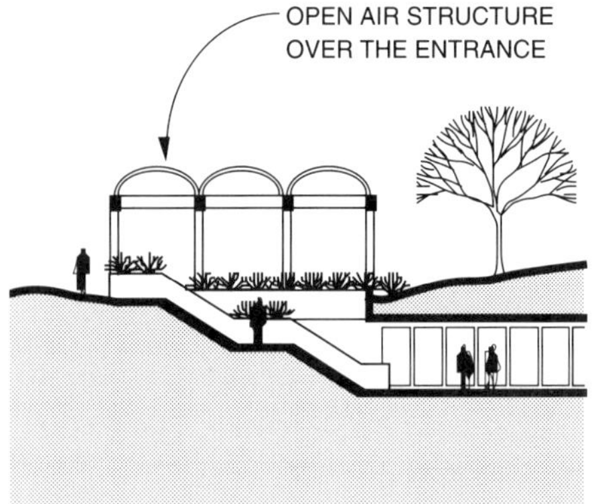

Figure 7-12: An open air structure over the entrance stairway to an underground facility.

Place open air structures over entrance stairways and escalators to create an identifiable image and ease the transition into the facility.

Two common entrances to underground facilities, particularly for subways and commercial spaces in urban settings, are the sunken courtyard described above and a simple opening for a staircase or escalator. While functional and unobtrusive, these entrances can be difficult to recognize, especially from a distance, and thus tend to lack a distinctive image when they are approached. To some degree, signs and logos help direct people to these entrances, but an open air structure over these openings is more recognizable and has a distinct image. An excellent example are the arch-shaped trellis structures over the open air entrances to the Les Halles underground complex in Paris. Any distinctive roof form supported on columns, a space frame, or a tent structure can perform a similar function.

While a primary purpose of these open air structures is to create a recognizable form, they also tend to enhance the transition experience from the exterior surface to the interior subsurface. Rather than an abrupt entry through a door into an entrance building or simply disappearing into a stairwell, an open air structure like a trellis is partially enclosed and serves as the zone that provides a necessary psychological transition between two somewhat disconnected worlds. Another advantage of open air structures over open stairways and escalators is that they may provide shelter from rain, although trellises and space frame structures do not necessarily do so.

Figures 7-13 and 7-14: Arch-shaped trellis structures over the entrances to the underground Les Halles complex in Paris create a transition between the exterior and interior environments. They are recognizable from a distance and establish a distinct image for the entire complex.

PATTERN 7-5: ABOVE-GRADE ENTRANCE PAVILION

Figure 7-15: Entrance pavilions at the underground Smithsonian museum complex are recognizable and create a distinct exterior image. (Architect: Shepley Bulfinch Richardson and Abbott; photographer: Nick Wheeler / Wheeler Photographics)

Particularly on a flat site, use an enclosed above-grade structure to serve as the entrance to an underground facility.

At a minimum, an above-grade entrance pavilion will contain the means of vertical circulation downward into the facility. The presence of an above-grade mass also provides a convenient opportunity to provide outlets for some building services such as ventilation shafts that are hidden or integrated into the pavilion design. While an above-grade mass can be enlarged to include some other building functions and spaces, this pattern refers to structures with the primary function of providing an entrance (see Pattern 7-6 for a discussion of larger, multipurpose above-grade structures connected to underground facilities).

An above-grade entrance pavilion has some characteristics of a conventional entrance—it can be seen from a distance, and if designed appropriately, it can have a distinct image that communicates something about the facility below. It has the practical advantages of providing enclosure from the weather and can usually be designed to accommodate mobility-impaired people through the main entry sequence.

By its nature, an entrance pavilion is relatively small and gives little indication of the size or extent of the facility below. This is not desirable in helping people form a mental image of how a facility is organized, and the limited size of the structure may make it more difficult to recognize as one approaches from a distance. The familiar image of an entry form or opening against the background of a larger, visible building mass is missing.

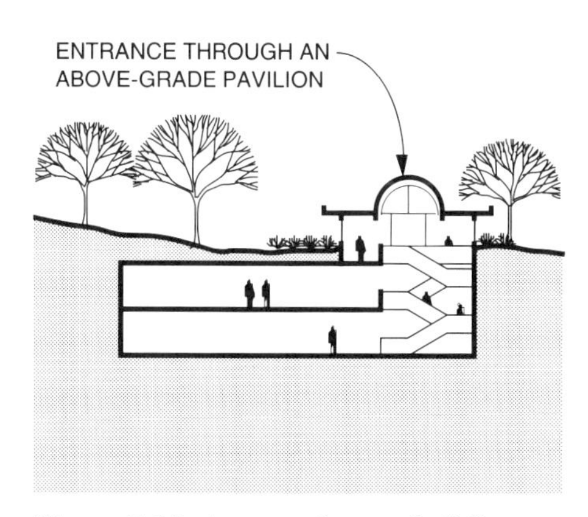

Figure 7-16: A cut-and-cover building with an above-grade entrance pavilion.

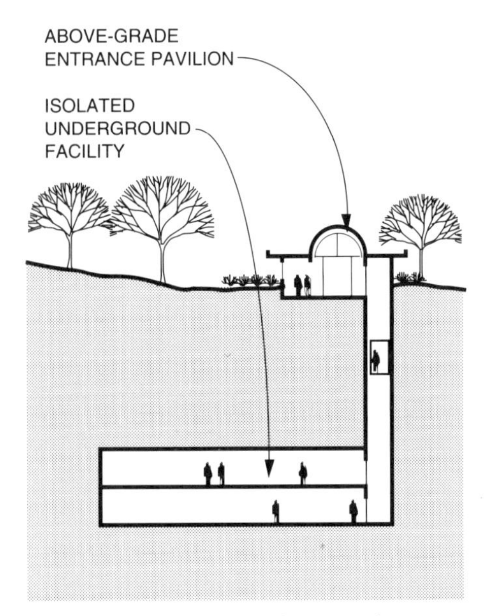

Figure 7-17: A deep underground space entered through an above-grade pavilion. Such pavilions may enclose escalator or elevator entrances, and may be used for any size and depth of facility.

Nevertheless, careful attention to detail with a special emphasis on creating a distinctive image can have a successful result as evidenced by the entrance pavilions for the underground Smithsonian Museums of African and Eastern Art (Figures 7-15 and 7-18).

Since the predominant function of an above-grade entrance pavilion is to get people in and down into the main structure below, making this downward transition in a positive manner is an important aspect of its design. Frequently, the minimal size of the entry pavilion does not permit this transition to occur gradually or within a larger open space such as an interior atrium or exterior sunken courtyard. Any efforts to create open multilevel space extending from the surface entry level to building floors below are desirable, along with the use of natural light and exterior views during the downward movement on stairs or escalators. Other interior design strategies such as the use of artwork and the sound of falling water enhance this transition (see the Smithsonian entrance pavilion).

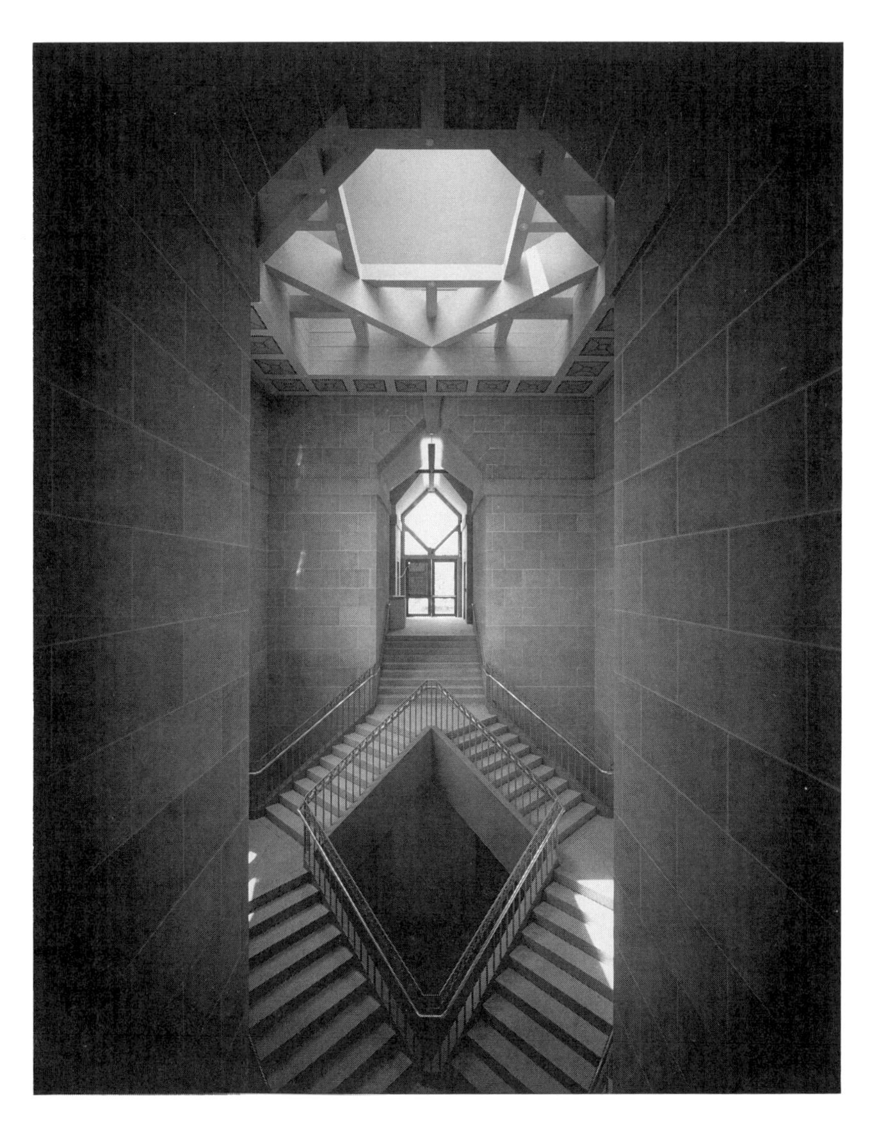

Figure 7-18: The underground Smithsonian museum complex is entered through three small pavilions. Although the space inside the pavilions is confined, the entrance experience is enhanced by natural light and the sound of water in pools and fountains below. (Architect: Shepley Bulfinch Richardson and Abbott; photographer: Nick Wheeler / Wheeler Photographics)

PATTERN 7-6: ENTRANCE THROUGH LARGE ABOVE-GRADE BUILDING MASS

Figure 7-19: The entrance to the library addition at the University of Michigan is through the existing above-grade building. (Architect: Gunnar Birkerts; photographer: Timothy Hursley)

Enter an underground facility through an above-grade building mass—either an adjacent building or a facility built as part of the underground structure.

Shallow underground facilities are frequently built as additions to existing above-grade buildings or at least as complementary facilities in built-up urban areas. They are also built as independent facilities that include some portion of the building volume above grade. In both cases, the result is that a relatively conventional-looking building mass is visible either above or immediately adjacent to the underground facility. With this design approach the entrance can occur in the above-grade building mass. It is more recognizable from a distance and a distinct image can be more easily created because there is a visible mass to work with. Also, building services can be embodied in the above-grade building mass, while service and public entrances can be more easily separated.

Where an underground facility is placed adjacent to historic buildings of distinct character, this design approach can be extremely unobtrusive as evidenced by the Law Library addition at the University of Michigan. There are no visible entry pavilions or building service outcroppings to clutter the open space. Depending on the situation, of course, entering one building to get to another can be confusing, especially if the extent or location of the underground facility cannot be perceived from the surface. One approach to improve orientation in these cases is to make a clear demarcation as one crosses from the basement of the above-grade

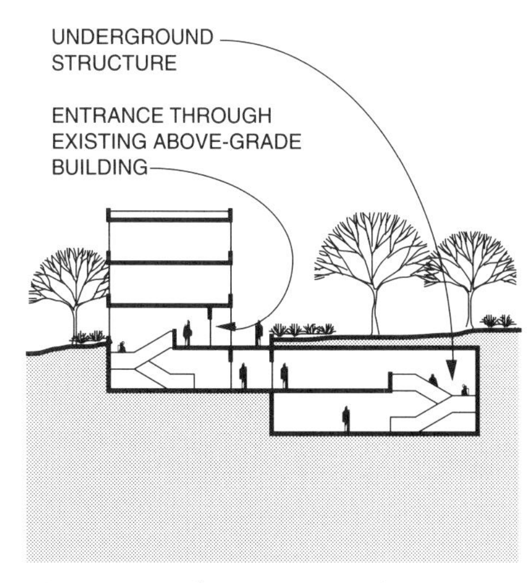

Figure 7-20: The entrance to this underground structure occurs through an adjacent existing above-grade building.

Figure 7-21: One entrance to the library addition at Cornell University is through the existing above-grade library. The transition between the two buildings occurs in a glass-enclosed stairway which helps in maintaining orientation and provides a connection to the outdoors. (Architect: Gunnar Birkerts; photographer: Timothy Hursley)

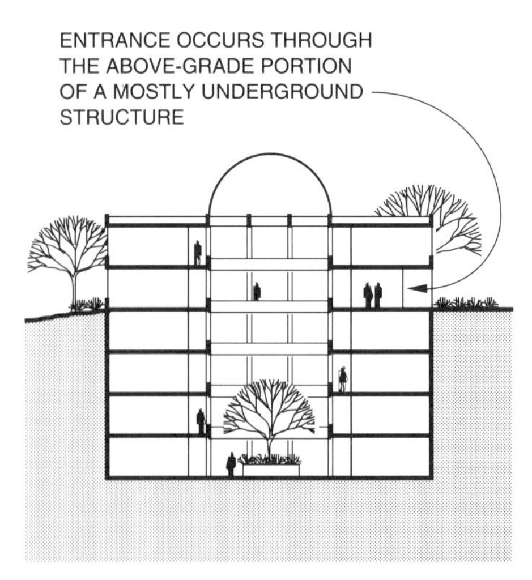

Figure 7-22: With a structure partially above and partially below grade, the above-grade building mass can be entered in a conventional manner.

facility into the underground facility. One successful example is a glass-enclosed stairway at the Cornell library addition, which orients people to the location of both facilities during this transition. Another approach is to create an entrance space with distinct lighting, color, and sound to make the transition.

For independent underground facilities that include above-grade masses, opportunities exist not only to create a legible entrance and distinct building image, but also to connect the surface and subsurface environments with multilevel open spaces. A distinctive above-grade mass at the Civil and Mineral Engineering Building at the University of Minnesota mainly houses the upper level of a four-story-high laboratory that serves as a building atrium.

PATTERN 7-7: OPEN STAIRWAYS, RAMPS, AND ESCALATORS

Place stairways, ramps, and escalators in open multistory spaces to enhance orientation and improve the transition from above to below grade.

An important design objective with underground facilities is to create a graceful transition to lower levels while offsetting associations with darkness and confinement. In addition, it is during this downward transition that the opportunity exists to maintain a connection between the above- and below-grade environments. Stairways, ramps, and escalators all can easily be placed in large open spaces. Orientation is enhanced because there is a continuous flow of space from above to below grade, and from exterior to interior environments. Movement is continuous, unlike waiting for an elevator, and people are in visual contact with others, which reduces feelings of isolation and creates a more stimulating environment.

There are, of course, practical limits to using certain types of vertical circulation. Ramps can only be used for relatively small vertical drops before they require long horizontal distances and occupy large amounts of space, but they can be perhaps the most graceful (and accessible) transition at the entrance into a shallow building. Stairways are limited to serving up to two to three levels before they become too strenuous for many people to use as major circulation, particularly in the upward direction. Also, using stairways as major vertical circulation into and within a building means that mobility-impaired people are required to use other systems.

Clearly, ramps and stairways are not appropriate as major means of bringing people to deep, isolated facilities, but escalators can serve this function. Very long escalators serve subway stations around the world at depths sometimes exceeding 200 feet. Because

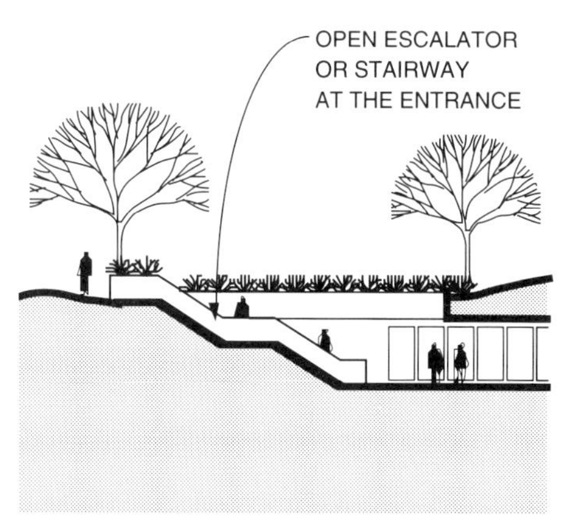

Figure 7-23: The entrance to an underground facility using an open stairway or escalator.

Figure 7-24: This stairway entrance to the Les Halles complex in Paris is placed in a small open courtyard area. The entry transition is enhanced by a series of pools with falling water alongside the stairway. From inside the facility, orientation is improved by views of landmarks on the surface.

there is little effort on the part of the riders and there is a continuous flow of movement, the transition into and out of an underground facility using escalators can be smooth and graceful.

While there are many economic and functional considerations related to vertical circulation systems, the heart of this pattern is the quality of openness that ramps, stairways, and escalators can have when placed in large central spaces. It is precisely the confining and disconnected experience of entering an enclosed stair tower or elevator that is to be avoided. In his design for the Hong Kong and Shanghai Bank Building in Hong Kong, Norman Foster divided the building into five-story zones within which all major vertical circulation occurs on escalators. This design approach was specifically intended to encourage communication between employees and avoid the isolation and compartmentalization that occur in buildings served only by elevators (Doubilet and Fisher 1986).

When escalators must descend to deep isolated facilities such as subway stations, it is often not feasible to place them in a large atrium-like space. Thus, the experience of descending on an escalator in a long narrow tube can evoke some of the worst feelings of claustrophobia and entrapment. In this sense, for some people, seeing the true depth of a subway station through a long narrow tube may be a much more negative experience than descending on an elevator where the spatial relationships are not perceived as well. Similar to entering through a long horizontal tunnel, a long escalator shaft should be designed to enhance spaciousness and provide stimulation through the use of lighting, artwork, sound, and other interior design elements. A spacious, well-lighted transition space at the bottom of the escalator will help give a sense of arrival and spatial relief.

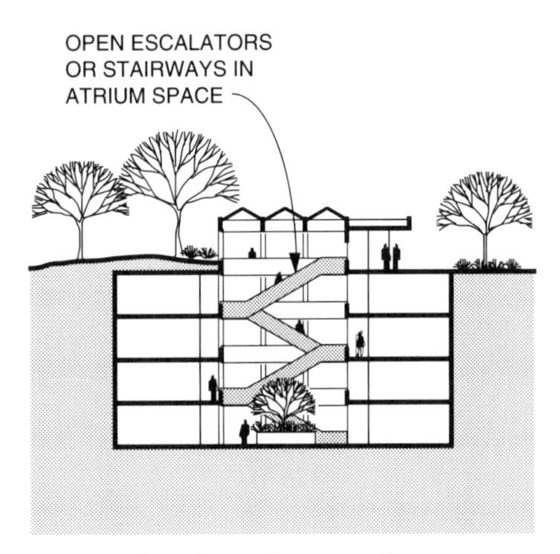

Figure 7-25: An underground structure using open escalators in a multistory atrium space.

Figure 7-26: Escalators and stairways located within large interior atriums and near major circulation spaces help avoid feelings of confinement and improve orientation as well.

PATTERN 7-8: GLASS-ENCLOSED VERTICAL AND INCLINED ELEVATORS

Figure 7-27: Glass-enclosed inclined elevators are commonly used adjacent to escalators in Scandinavian subway stations. These help in maintaining orientation and improve security as well.

Place glass-enclosed elevators in multistory open spaces to enhance orientation and relieve feelings of confinement. Use glass-enclosed inclined elevators alongside escalators to improve accessibility, orientation, and security.

While ramps, escalators, and stairways can provide open, graceful transitions into underground facilities, elevators are likely to be present in all buildings and may be the primary means of vertical circulation in many deep multistory structures. A clear asset of elevators is their accessibility for all people. The inherent problem with elevators, however, is the manner in which they spatially disconnect the surface entrance level from the spaces elsewhere in the building. Perhaps in a conventional above-grade building this is a minor issue, at least when the overall form and organization of the building is easily understood. Additionally, windows are likely to reorient the person in space once arriving on a given floor.

In an underground facility, however, there is likely to be less understanding of the overall form or even that the building is underground. While elevators are familiar parts of the everyday building environment, visitors to public underground buildings are often confused by simple things like the floor numbering system. Questions are raised such as: should floor numbers be negative below grade? or should they increase or decrease with depth? The experience of entering the confined space of an elevator, descending to a below-grade level, and then getting off on a floor with no spatial connection to the above-grade environment seems to have the potential to exacerbate problems of orientation and has

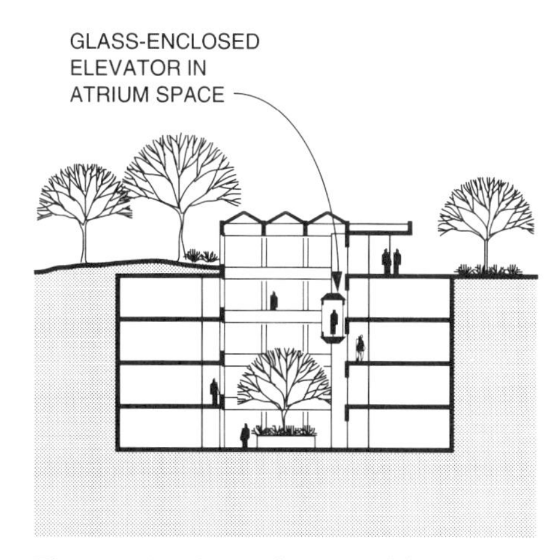

Figure 7-28: An underground facility with a glass-enclosed elevator in an atrium space.

few redeeming characteristics to ease the downward transition into the building. Moreover, there is no continuous movement and less opportunity (or inclination) for visual and verbal communication with others passing through the building.

One design approach that clearly helps this problem of orientation in conventional elevators is the use of glass-enclosed elevators in multilevel open spaces. In addition to having a great sense of spatial orientation and movement while entering and circulating, the glass enclosure relieves the spatial confinement within the elevator. Visible moving elevators also create dynamic activity within the building—an important goal of interior design in underground facilities.

Figure 7-29: Glass-enclosed elevators help maintain orientation and offset feelings of confinement while entering.

In facilities where creating large atrium-like spaces is not feasible, the downward transition using conventional enclosed elevators must be regarded as only one segment of the entire entry sequence. The confining, disorienting aspects of the elevator ride can be relieved by arriving in a transition space on each floor that is carefully designed to have qualities of spaciousness and a distinct character, and that serves to orient the person within the building (see Chapter 8: Layout and Spatial Configuration).

Another design approach to vertical circulation in underground facilities is the use of glass-enclosed inclined elevators. These elevators are commonly used to provide accessibility to mobility-impaired people in subway systems with deep stations—Stockholm and Helsinki are notable examples. In deep subway stations, there are typically two means of entrance available—long escalators in inclined shafts, and conventional elevators in vertical shafts. While accessibility can be provided with vertical elevators, they are often located away from the main entry sequence and for this reason may be less secure as well as more disorienting. Glass-enclosed inclined elevators run adjacent to the bank of escalators. The same entry sequence is used for all people and the glass-enclosed elevators relieve the feelings of confinement and disorientation found in conventional vertical elevators.

CHAPTER 8

by John Carmody

Layout and Spatial Configuration

Design Issues and Problems

This chapter addresses the overall facility plan, its circulation system, and the arrangement, size, and shape of spaces within the facility. In most cases, designing the layout and spatial configuration within a facility represents the most fundamental set of decisions that shape an underground building. The interior layout is developed concurrently with the exterior image and entrance design discussed in the previous chapter. The overall arrangement, size, and shape of spaces sets the stage for all interior design concepts presented in subsequent chapters.

Figure 8-1: A typical problem in underground, windowless buildings is orientation. With no reference to the outside environment, people are easily confused in complicated and sometimes monotonous corridors of many urban subway systems and commercial developments.

Compared with a conventional above-grade building, making an underground facility acceptable to people often requires a fundamentally different approach in designing the building layout and spatial configuration. Simply applying well-known above-grade layout and spatial configuration patterns to an underground building is likely to result in a deficient environment that will not be perceived as equivalent. It is usually not enough to compensate for these deficiencies with "good" interior design alone. Sensitive use of color, lighting, and furnishings can certainly enhance the interior environment, but the basic size, shape, and arrangement of spaces will usually precede and then be refined in concert with more detailed interior design. Generally, the layout of most underground facilities must be inwardly oriented. It must use techniques to overcome disorientation and it must compensate for

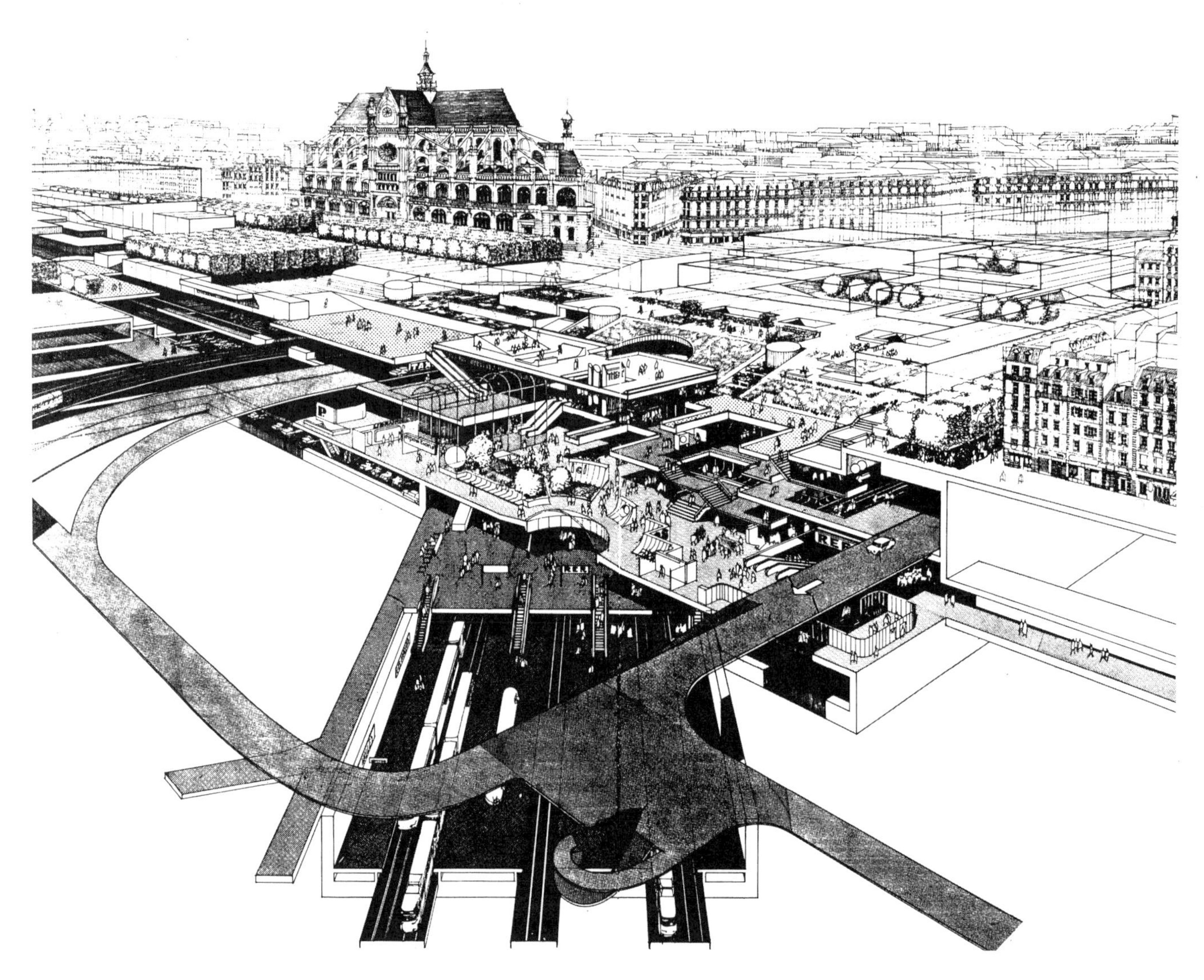

Figure 8-2: This drawing of the Les Halles development in Paris illustrates the complex geometry often found in urban underground facilities. This complexity and the inability of people to visualize the overall form and layout contribute to problems with spatial orientation.

lack of connection to the exterior environment. The key design problems related to layout and spatial configuration are:

1. Because the overall mass and configuration of the building is not visible and the lack of windows reduces reference points to the exterior, there can be a lack of spatial orientation within underground facilities.
2. Without windows to the exterior, there can be a sense of confinement.
3. Because there are no windows, there is a loss of stimulation from the natural and manmade environments on the surface.
4. To compensate for window absence, interior glass walls are used in some underground facilities; however, people may feel that their privacy is invaded if they can be viewed by others.

Lack of Spatial Orientation

Designing an environment so that people can maintain spatial orientation and find their way is a basic requirement in all buildings. Disorientation is not only an inconvenience—it is potentially quite stressful. In *The Image of the City*, Kevin Lynch emphasizes this negative impact on people:

> *. . . let the mishap of disorientation occur and the sense of anxiety and even terror that accompanies it reveals to us how closely it is linked to our sense of balance and well-being. The very word lost in our language means much more than geographical uncertainty: it carries a tone of utter disaster. (Lynch 1960)*

Lynch emphasizes the importance of "legibility" in the design of a city, which he defines as "the ease with which its parts can be recognized and can be organized into a coherent pattern."

> *The need to recognize and pattern our surroundings is so crucial, and has such long roots in the past, that this image has wide practical and emotional importance to the individual . . . a distinctive and legible environment not only offers security but also heightens the potential depth and intensity of human experience. (Lynch 1960)*

While Lynch is primarily addressing the design of cities in his discussions of legibility and forming mental images, the same concepts can be applied to individual building design. The spaces, corridors, and architectural elements of a building can be analogous to plazas, streets, and landmarks in a city. In his book, *Wayfinding in Architecture*, Romedi Passini explains how architectural form and space can help or hinder a building's legibility. One key is designing an environment with "imageability," a term that refers to "the ease with which a place can be mentally represented." These mental images then can be incorporated into an overall cognitive map to maintain orientation (Passini 1984).

Passini suggests that forming a good mental image of a place is facilitated by three factors. First, and most important, the internal organization principle of the facility must be detectable. This refers to understanding the overall system—for example, that the street pattern of a city is a grid, or that all stores in a shopping center face a single multistory atrium. Arranging an underground layout with a clear, understandable organizing principle is essential. Many examples exist of convoluted labyrinths of underground passageways in urban areas that are virtually impossible to comprehend, requiring visitors to rely completely on signs to find their way. According to Passini, certain major underground commercial developments in Montreal are avoided by people who fear getting lost.

The second factor that facilitates imageability is that the external organization principle of the facility must be visually accessible and express the building's contents. Basically, this means that by seeing and comprehending the overall form and volume of a building, one can develop an exterior image that helps people maintain orientation. Passini states that "an object-image can be retained and also permits certain inferences about the inside. At a glance, the three-dimensional form of an above-grade structure can convey a lot about function and overall geometry." It is very helpful when the exterior form and interior layout correspond and are mutually reinforcing (Passini 1984). Passini describes one underground complex in Montreal (La Cité) where four city blocks are interconnected beneath the streets. In this complex, people

Figure 8-3: In the underground Law Library at the University of Michigan, problems of confinement and lack of spatial orientation are overcome by using open, multilevel interior space. Being able to see through the glazing provides a connection to the outdoors and a view of a familiar landmark to help maintain orientation. (Architect: Gunnar Birkerts; photographer: Timothy Hursley)

have no coherent perception of its overall volume, which leads to confusing images. There is no sense of where the edges of the facility are and what form they take. Obviously, in most underground facilities the opportunity to see the overall form from the exterior is limited or nonexistent.

Finally, the third factor facilitating imageability, and therefore orientation, is spatial correspondence. By this Passini means that relationships between spaces, particularly indoors/outdoors and aboveground/underground, are articulated and visually accessible. Cognitive maps must work as a continuous network in which parts are connected, not fragmented. Again, at La Cité in Montreal, Passini describes the total lack of correspondence between the environments above and below ground. There is no sense of whether one is beneath a building or a street, nor any penetrations to the surface to make visual connections. With deep isolated underground facilities, making visual connections between interior and exterior space may be impossible; however, in shallow underground facilities, courtyards that create some continuity between the surface and subsurface can significantly enhance orientation.

The first factor of imageability—understanding the internal organizing principle of a building—takes on added importance in underground facilities since the other factors—forming an exterior image and making visual connections between above and below grade—may be impossible to apply. While a very clear, understandable building layout may be essential to compensate for the lack of other visual axes that aid orientation, it should not be assumed that the layout of an underground building must be so simple that it is monotonous and uninteresting. Much like the layout of a memorable, stimulating city, a desirable building layout should be legible but also incorporate a level of complexity that provides a varied, rich experience.

While the focus of this discussion is on the physical layout and arrangement of space as a means of improving orientation in underground buildings, a system of signs and other interior design elements must complement and reinforce a clear internal organizing principle. Passini has found that people appear to process wayfinding information in two main ways. First are people who approach the problem in a linear fashion and seem to rely mainly on signs. The second group is dependent on developing a spatial understanding of the setting. To maximize the legibility of an environment for the majority of people, both the organization of architectural space and sign systems must be clear. Further discussion of sign systems appears in Chapter 9.

Confinement and Lack of Stimulation

Equally important to the problem of disorientation in underground facilities are the problems created by a lack of windows and connection to the exterior environment. As described in Chapter 5, many researchers have identified the major benefits of windows such as provision of environmental information, sensory stimulation, contact with the outside world, relief from claustrophobia, relaxation by permitting a change of focus for the eyes, as well as daylight. Conversely, the lack of windows can result in feelings of confinement and produce a boring, monotonous environment (Collins 1975; Wotton 1981; Heerwagon 1990).

These fundamental problems in underground buildings must be considered at several levels of design, from overall plan to the choice of interior furnishings. While a wall mural or aquarium may provide visual interest, and patterns of light and color may create a spacious feeling, the overall layout and arrangement of spaces within a building creates the major opportunities to compensate for a windowless environment. Except in the case of a hillside structure with relatively conventional opportunities for view windows, underground buildings must be inwardly oriented.

By creating larger spaces inside the building, arranging spaces to overlook other spaces, and developing long interior views, the designer of an underground facility can begin to compensate for the spatial relief that occurs with windows in a conventional building. But it is not sufficient simply to increase corridor widths or room ceiling heights. Nor is it necessarily effective to use glass partition walls and place rooms around public courtyards or along corridors. The benefits of windows are multifaceted, and creating interior views may only compensate for certain attributes. Several design issues arise in creating an inwardly oriented building plan:

1. What is the content of the interior views, and do they have sufficiently complex and dynamic characteristics to be equivalent to a conventional exterior view?
2. What sizes of spaces and interior view length are sufficient to compensate for window absence?
3. Can spaces be arranged to create long interior views without also creating inefficient spatial arrangements and circulation?
4. Can glass partitions be used to create interior views without also making people feel exposed and that their privacy has been invaded?

Each of these basic design questions must be considered by the designer quite carefully or attempts to compensate for window absence may only result in a sterile and possibly inefficient interior environment that draws attention to its lack of equivalence to a building benefiting from conventional windows and views. While these questions must be addressed, there are no absolute rules about desirable view content, or ideal spatial sizes and arrangements. Some research as well as the evidence of generally perceived successful examples begin to outline some design directions in these areas. This information is presented in conjunction with the appropriate patterns that follow in this and later chapters.

Maintaining Privacy

The final issue listed above—maintaining privacy in an inwardly oriented building—seems to deserve special attention. Perhaps the most obvious and frequently applied design technique in a windowless building is the use of interior glass partition walls. In theory, building occupants can overlook some activity within the building and get the spatial relief provided by a long view. Likewise, people circulating through an underground building can view the life within the building while circulation corridors and other public areas are made to feel more spacious with transparent visual boundaries. In spite of the apparent benefits of interior glass partitions, it is not uncommon to find glass that has been covered with shades or other opaque material which effectively negates the value of the interior window (Heerwagon 1990).

To effectively design interior glass partition walls for the benefit of people, the functions and spaces open to public view must be carefully selected. In addition, spaces must be arranged and interior window openings designed to permit view without creating feelings of intrusion. Judith Heerwagon (1990) has suggested that windows can be placed into four basic categories that reflect fundamentally different conditions of visual access (the desirable view out by the occupant) and visual exposure (the undesirable view in by strangers).

Heerwagon refers to the basic windowless condition—low visual access and exposure—as "the cave." Other conditions include "the goldfish bowl"—high visual access and exposure, and "the interrogation room"—low visual access and high visual exposure. The condition where there is high visual access and exposure occurs frequently in windowless buildings and is acceptable between public areas (i.e., between a corridor and reception area). However, high visual exposure is very unacceptable to people in more personal settings (private offices, hotel or hospital rooms). The ideal condition for these spaces is high visual access with low visual exposure.

Design Objectives for Layout and Spatial Configuration

1. Create an interior layout that is easy to understand, thereby enhancing orientation as well as emergency egress.
2. Arrange space to create a distinct image within the building to compensate for the lack of image outside.
3. Develop a layout and spatial configuration that contributes to creating a stimulating, varied indoor environment to compensate for a lack of windows. Create a stimulating environment from the point of view of people occupying the facility as well as people passing through.
4. Provide visual connections between the interior and exterior environments whenever possible.
5. Arrange spaces and building circulation to enhance a feeling of spaciousness through the facility by providing extended interior views as much as possible.
6. Design each space to enhance a feeling of spaciousness by manipulating room size and shape.
7. Arrange spaces to protect privacy as much as possible.

Design Patterns: Layout and Spatial Configuration

This section presents several design approaches for the layout and spatial configuration of underground facilities that meet the design objectives stated previously. The intention is to present the basic pattern or concept, discuss its characteristics, and illustrate it with a representative drawing and/or photograph. This does not imply that the pattern should be replicated in this exact manner. Many diverse design responses can be developed based on the objectives and approaches presented here. (See Chapter 6 for a discussion of how to place these patterns into a larger context.)

The patterns discussed here are intended to complement those related to exterior and entrance design (Chapter 7). Internal vertical circulation systems (stairs, elevators, escalators) that occur near the entrance can be correctly regarded as part of the entry sequence as well as part of the building interior circulation. These major vertical circulation elements are discussed in Chapter 7 as part of the entrance sequence since these elements relate so strongly to the need for a graceful downward transition into the facility. However, they are also an integral part of the patterns related to building layout in this chapter.

In addition to complementing the exterior and entrance patterns in Chapter 7, design approaches discussed here must be integrated with patterns related to interior design elements (Chapter 9), lighting (Chapter 10), and life safety (Chapter 11) in order to enhance their effectiveness.

Layout and Spatial Configuration Patterns

8-1: A System of Paths, Landmarks, Activity Nodes, and Zones

8-2: Building with Hillside Exposure

8-3: Sunken Exterior Courtyards

8-4: Interior Atrium Spaces

8-5: Building Thoroughfares

8-6: Short, Lively Passageways

8-7: Zones of Distinct Character

8-8: Interior Windows Overlooking Activity

8-9: Hierarchy of Privacy

8-10: Complex Room Shapes and Interconnected Spaces

8-11: High and Varied Ceilings

PATTERN 8-1: A SYSTEM OF PATHS, LANDMARKS, ACTIVITY NODES, AND ZONES

In order to improve orientation and provide a stimulating environment, arrange the layout of an underground building (or an interconnected group of underground facilities) into a system of paths, zones, activity nodes, and landmarks similar to the elements that form the public spaces in a city.

In most cases, underground buildings are experienced primarily from the interior. With limited connection to the surface, it becomes important that the circulation system within the building is understandable to help people maintain orientation. Beyond being clear, though, the layout of the building should create a distinct image or a sequence of distinct images that further aid in forming mental maps of a facility as well as making the experience of passing through the facility more stimulating. To achieve this, the layout of an underground facility should be viewed like the plan of a city rather than a building. Traveling through the public areas of the building should not be similar to passing through a series of enclosed monotonous corridors and

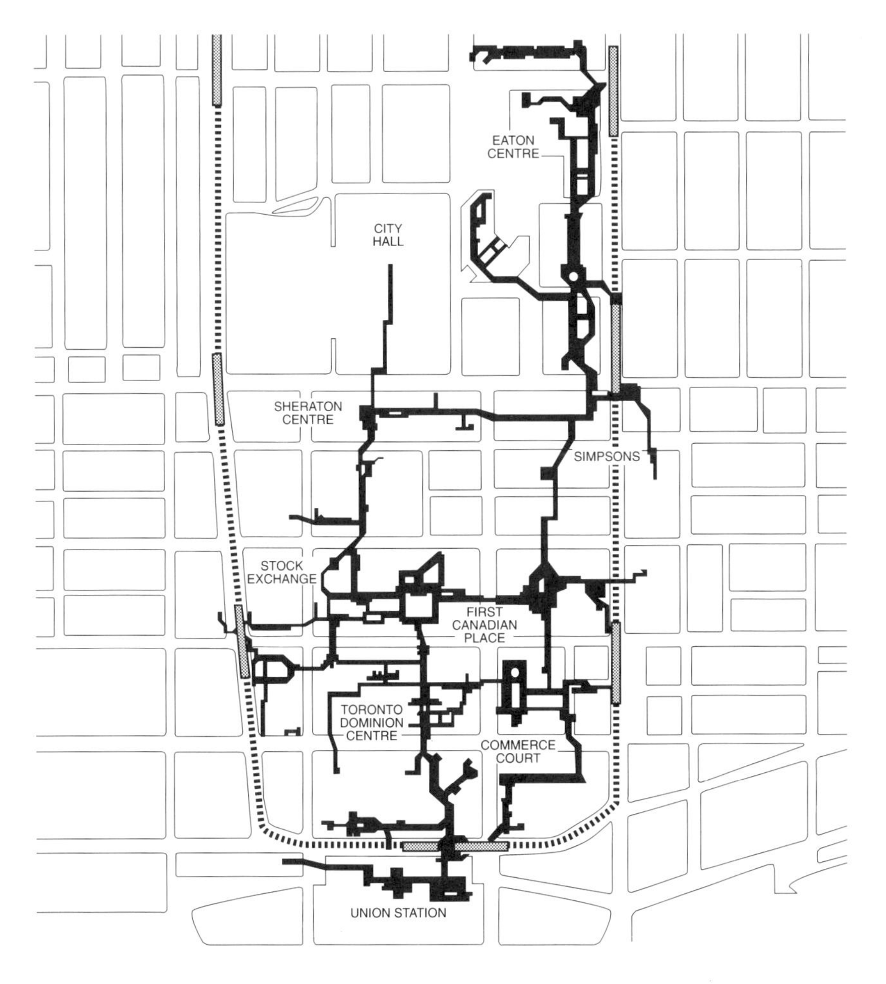

Figure 8-4: In Toronto, Canada, a network of underground corridors and commercial activities extends throughout the downtown area. Similar to downtown Montreal, large atrium spaces in the center of many of the blocks serve as landmarks and activity nodes along the complex layout of pathways.

Underground Pedestrian Mall System
Subway Station
Subway Line

Figure 8-5: In this underground shopping complex in Montreal, several corridors (paths) lead to this open space which serves as both a landmark and an activity node in the overall underground pedestrian system.

elevators. Instead, it should be more like a stimulating, memorable city where there is a legible system of paths (or streets) that are lively and distinct in character. Within the city (building), notable, special features establish variety while enhancing image and orientation.

In *The Image of the City*, Kevin Lynch identifies the five elements that improve imageability: paths, landmarks, nodes, districts, and edges (Lynch 1960). Romedi Passini has taken Lynch's analysis for cities and applied it to buildings or complexes of buildings (Passini 1984). According to Passini, the public paths of a city are analogous to corridors, promenades, and vertical circulation in a building. Lynch defines a landmark as "a rather simply defined physical object: a building, sign, store or mountain." In a building complex, landmarks can be a particular shop, a sculpture, a decorative element, or a space itself such as an atrium. Nodes refer to "intensive foci" and "strategic spots" in a city that imply activity centers and goals or destination points. At a smaller scale, indoor squares and important circulation intersections have a similar function. Lynch's districts are zones of a city "which are recognizable as having some identifiable character." Within a building complex, Passini suggests that zones with distinct functional or design characteristics can be viewed as districts. In some cases, a floor within a building functions as a separate district. Edges, the last of the five elements identified by Lynch, are linear boundaries or barriers. In an underground facility, the perimeter could be regarded as an edge; however, it is often not visible. Thus, this last element seems to be less applicable to the interior environment than the others.

The underlying intent of this pattern is not only to create many distinct, memorable elements within an underground building, but also to organize these elements into an overall system. In *A Pattern Language*, Christopher Alexander et al. address the problem of disorientation and conclude that "a person must be able to explain any given address within a building, to any other person, who does not know his way around in one sentence" (Alexander et al. 1977). For example, in an underground building one might say: "Enter the pavilion on the west end of the plaza, descend on the escalator to the main concourse level, proceed to the central atrium space, and find the doorway facing the fountain in the atrium." The building must be conceived as a hierarchical system of elements that can be named and described in a logical sequence (i.e., main entrance pavilion, main concourse, central atrium, doorway). Alexander et al. refer to this pattern as "nested realms of circulation" and describe it as follows:

> *Lay out very large buildings and collections of small buildings so that one reaches a given point inside by passing through a sequence of realms, each marked by a gateway and becoming smaller and smaller, as one passes from each one, through a gateway, to the next. Choose the realms so that each one can be easily named, so that you can tell a person where to go, simply by telling him which realm to go through.*
> *(Alexander et al. 1977)*

Figure 8-6: As people follow this below-grade concourse in the underground pedestrian network in Toronto, Canada, they arrive at Eaton Center. Similar to landmarks within an above-grade street system, the multistory atrium and fountain are notable features that enhance orientation in the underground environment.

Creating a system of paths, zones, nodes, and landmarks is an appropriate approach not only for individual underground buildings, but also for large building complexes as well as interconnected groups of facilities. In addition, an overall system of circulation and spatial organization within an underground facility must be regarded as an extension of similar systems occurring in the above-grade environment.

This concept of organizing an underground environment in a similar way to a city is most easily visualized in underground developments with circulation systems that are, in fact, on the scale of a city, such as Montreal and Toronto. Although both underground cities have areas that are not very legible to people, there are portions that function quite well as a hierarchical system. In Montreal, for example, several downtown blocks have a named complex, often with a central atrium and a distinct design theme. As one passes through the subsurface corridors (paths) connecting these places, there is a sense of arrival at each complex that is reinforced by the atrium itself and other landmark architectural elements.

This analogy between city and building interior not only implies a well-organized circulation system, but also a decision to concentrate the life of the building (i.e., common areas, areas of social interaction) adjacent to or within these public realms. Otherwise, the potentially stimulating, vital character of atrium spaces and passageways will be absent.

This pattern is the broad fundamental organizing pattern to make the layout and spatial arrangement of underground, windowless space more legible and lively for people. Many of the patterns that follow in this chapter describe the key spatial elements (such as courtyards, interior atriums, passageways, and distinct zones within a building) that are components of the overall system.

PATTERN 8-2: BUILDING WITH HILLSIDE EXPOSURE

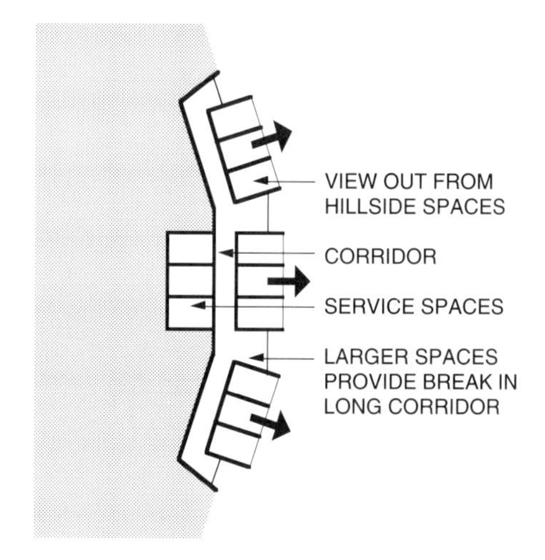

On sloping sites, build underground facilities into hillsides so that interior spaces have a maximum exposure to sunlight and exterior views.

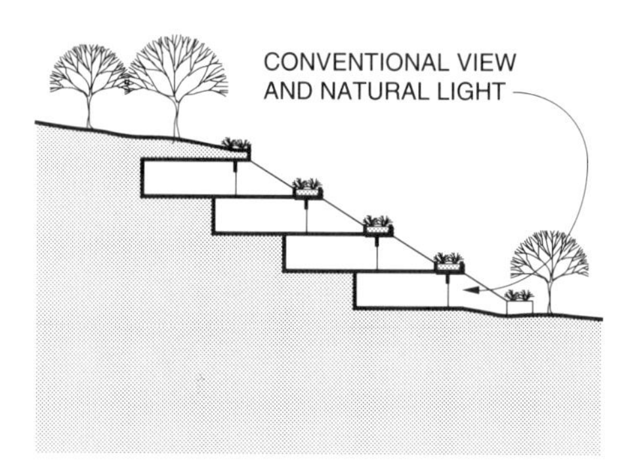

Figure 8-7: Schematic plan and section of a hillside structure that is elongated to maximize windows. Long corridors should be broken up with spaces that provide light and view.

For near surface underground facilities, a site with a sloping terrain presents the opportunity to set the building into a hillside. Multilevel structures that step back to fit into the slope are often referred to as "terraced." Naturally, any spaces that are located along this exposed hillside facade of the building can have windows with light and view characteristics identical to an above-grade building. These conventional windows presumably overcome problems that are normally associated with underground buildings such as confinement, lack of stimulation, and even orientation for the occupants. Compared with less visible underground structures, terraced buildings also provide a distinct exterior image and opportunities for a conventional horizontal entrance (see Pattern 7-1).

Placing a building into a hillside has implications for the overall building layout. Unlike a conventional above-grade structure with exposure and window opportunities on all sides, a terraced building has only one exposed side. If the desire is to maximize windows in all occupied spaces, then the resulting building layout is often a linear configuration with a row of rooms served by a single-loaded corridor. This configuration is sometimes referred to as "elevational." While this type of layout may not be compact and efficient in terms of circulation, it may be justified based on the numerous benefits associated with windows.

In many cases, however, only some spaces are placed along the exposed facade while others are on the inside of the corridor, thus resembling any other underground, windowless space. Most

Figure 8-8: Terraced housing on a sloping site affords the opportunity for windows with conventional distant views. (Photographer: Olivier Huet)

buildings contain some service functions that need no windows. For occupied spaces, however, the choice of which spaces receive windows and which are windowless depends on the function of each space and the relationship required between spaces in the building. Generally, two objectives will be desirable in applying this layout pattern: (1) create periodic open spaces with windows along the corridors, which are likely to be lengthy, and (2) explore spatial arrangements that permit natural light and view to be perceived from occupied spaces not immediately adjacent to the exposed facade.

The terraced design approach is most often applied to housing and other smaller scale functions where a majority of the spaces can be exposed to the exterior. The concept of a terraced building, however, can also be applied as a component of a larger structure that may extend several levels below grade. The exposed, terraced portion can serve as the entrance area and include functions that will benefit most from light and view.

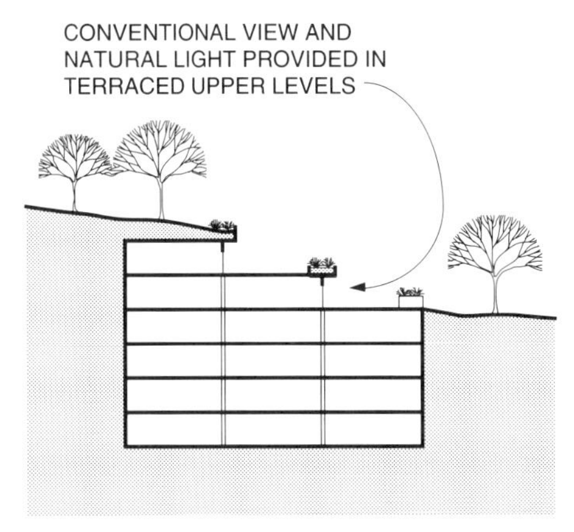

Figure 8-9: The terraced concept can also be applied to the upper portions of large multistory underground facilities.

PATTERN 8-3: SUNKEN EXTERIOR COURTYARDS

Figure 8-10: Sunken courtyards provide views, sunlight, and connection to the outdoors while improving orientation within the building. (Pusey Library, Harvard University; architect: Hugh Stubbins and Associates; photograph: © Steve Rosenthal)

On a flat site, utilize sunken exterior courtyards in underground facilities to provide sunlight, view, a connection to the outdoors, and to improve orientation within the facility. Design the courtyard to maximize sunlight penetration, utilize plants and other natural elements, and make the courtyard accessible to people.

Sunken exterior courtyards provide numerous benefits for people in near surface underground buildings. In terms of orientation within an underground facility, sunken courtyards provide a visual connection between surface and subsurface. If the dimensions of the courtyard are sufficient, landmarks such as surface buildings may be seen from below. In addition, the courtyard itself is usually such an amenity and is so distinct from the otherwise windowless areas of the building that it becomes a major landmark that aids in orientation. The spaces surrounding and overlooking a sunken courtyard are likely to feel conventional and can easily avoid the problems of confinement and lack of stimulation found in underground space. A sunken courtyard may also serve as part of the entry sequence for an underground facility.

While virtually any sunken courtyard will be viewed as an amenity in an underground facility, there are many examples of empty, cold, unused, concrete courtyards that fail to become the positive feature they could be. The successful design of a courtyard must address several issues: (1) What is the appropriate size in relation to depth to create a feeling of space and light? (2) What elements are desirable in the courtyard to enhance the quality of the view? and (3) What activities can occur in the courtyard to give it life and vitality?

To determine an appropriate size for a sunken courtyard, the designer must examine its intended functions. If the courtyard is intended to be the central amenity and image of the facility, then maximizing its size is a priority. On the other hand, if the only purpose is visual relief by permitting the eyes to focus at infinity, then a minimum width of 5 meters is adequate (Mahnke 1987). If another function of the courtyard is to provide views of above-grade landmarks from within the underground facility, then sight lines must be determined based on the height and location of the landmarks as well as the depth and width of the courtyard.

Finally, if a purpose of the courtyard is to bring sunlight into the building, then local sun angles must be calculated to determine the degree to which sunlight will actually penetrate the courtyard. A reasonable goal may be to have sunlight cover half the floor of the courtyard at noon on the winter solstice (December 21 in the northern hemisphere). This type of approach results in increasing the courtyard width as the depth increases and as the location is further from the equator. Sunlight will also make the courtyard more appealing for people to spend time there and will enhance the growth of plant materials within the courtyard.

Research on the content of views through conventional windows concludes that desirable characteristics are: (1) complexity of information content, (2) information about sky, horizon, and ground, (3) natural rather than urban scenes, and (4) dynamic rather than static images (Collins 1975).

Other research related to hospital and prison settings suggests that views with nature have restorative and relaxing qualities (Heerwagon 1990). One study in particular by Masao Inui concludes that views of greenery from a window appear to provide more feelings of spaciousness than views of buildings. Inui also found that a certain amount of sky in the view produced more feeling of spaciousness than full facade views (Inui 1980). Based on these studies, the extensive use of plant materials in sunken courtyards appears desirable for a number of reasons. Since views into courtyards are restricted, not distant, and the enclosure is entirely of hard building materials, plants tend to soften and naturalize the view. Moreover, plants will reinforce the image of the courtyard as a connection to the natural above-grade world.

Human activity in a courtyard will always make it more interesting to look at and will provide the benefits of an outdoor space for building inhabitants. To encourage activity, furnishings for sitting, eating, meeting or other appropriate functions must be provided. Use will also be enhanced by the degree to which the courtyard is accessible and a natural extension of the building circulation and public areas. Main circulation paths adjacent to the courtyard and multiple entrances to the courtyard are desirable. This will enable people to see and walk through the courtyard while circulating in the building.

With respect to the overall layout of an underground facility, a sunken courtyard is likely to be a key feature of the overall design and may be the central element in the overall organization of the building. Referring to Lynch's key elements that contribute to improving imageability, a sunken courtyard is a landmark or may contain landmarks, and it may also be an activity node.

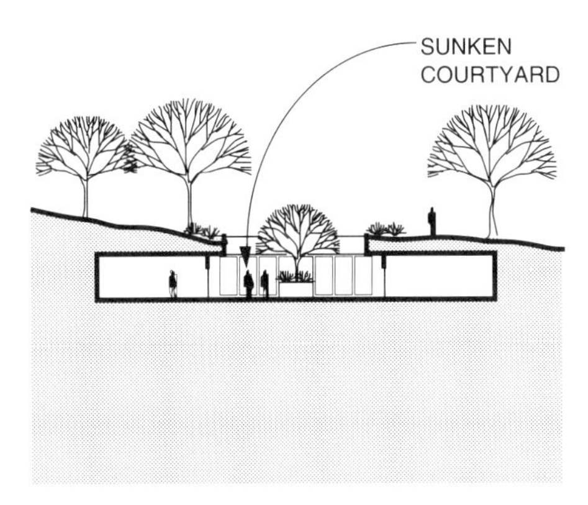

Figure 8-11: An underground building with a sunken courtyard.

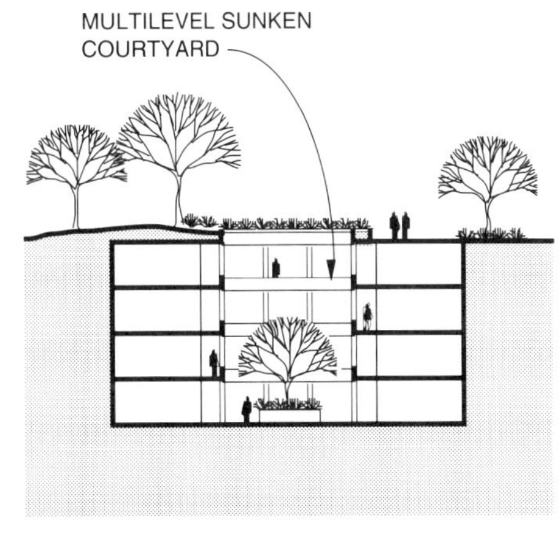

Figure 8-12: Sunken courtyards may be used in deep multistory structures. However, spaces over four to five stories high are likely to be covered interior atriums.

PATTERN 8-4: INTERIOR ATRIUM SPACES

Create multistory interior atrium spaces within underground facilities to provide extended views, visual stimulation, a sense of orientation, sunlight (in some cases), and a focus of activity within the building.

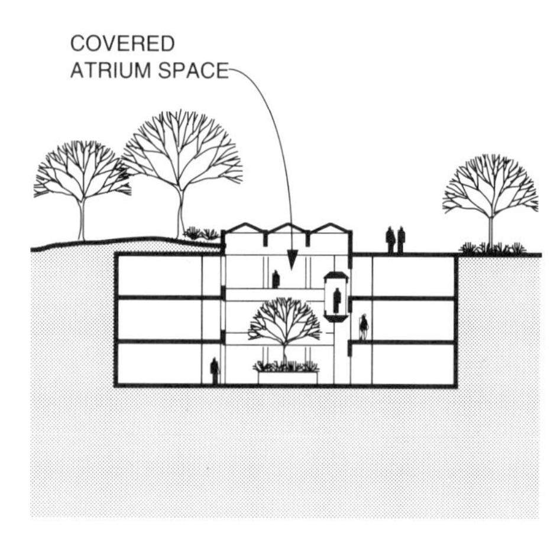

Figure 8-13: A shallow cut-and-cover underground building with a multistory atrium space.

The term *atrium* generally refers to an interior or covered courtyard space. Several characteristics associated with atrium spaces (although they are not present in all cases) are: (1) they are naturally lighted from above, (2) they contain some elements associated with the exterior environment such as plants, pools, and benches, (3) they are accessible to people and are an area for social activity and relaxation, (4) they are more than one story high and often the full height of the facility, and (5) they are surrounded by smaller spaces with windows and/or balconies. An atrium can be used in any type of underground facility—near surface or deep cavern—and is not dependent on a certain type of terrain. Sometimes atriums connect the above- and below-grade floors of a building complex.

An interior atrium in an underground building is one of the most powerful and versatile design patterns available. With respect to orientation and image, the atrium space often is the central landmark within an underground building and establishes

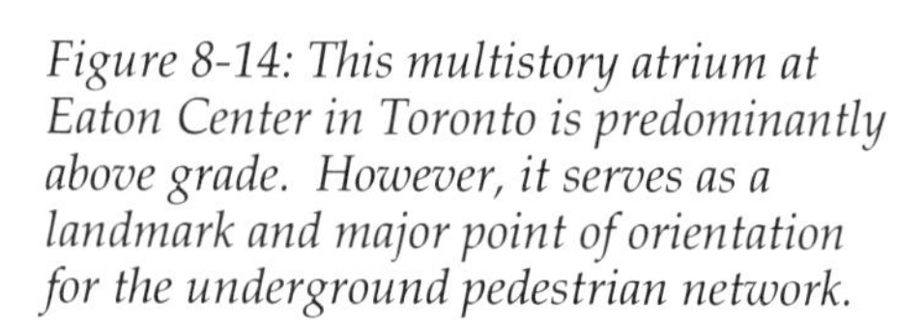

Figure 8-14: This multistory atrium at Eaton Center in Toronto is predominantly above grade. However, it serves as a landmark and major point of orientation for the underground pedestrian network.

the major image of the facility. In his study of wayfinding problems in several underground complexes in Montreal, Romedi Passini found that buildings containing a central open space are generally well understood. "Such an opening . . . gives visual access to the different floors of the building and allows one to sense at least part of the building volume. A single perspective of the space contains much information that in a closed floor arrangement has to be organized from a number of separate experiences of individual floors. Visual information is easily accessible, the legibility of the space is enhanced" (Passini 1984). With respect to Lynch's imageability terminology, an interior atrium can be part of a major circulation path, it can be an activity node, and it can contain landmarks or be a landmark itself.

Since a multistory atrium is likely to be by far the largest space within an underground building, it provides a major means of relieving feelings of confinement. Long views are available and smaller spaces actually can overlook floor levels below. In addition to providing a large space, an atrium can be a source of varied, stimulating views of people, activities, and natural elements. In designing an interior atrium space, key questions arise that are similar in nature to those discussed for exterior sunken courtyards: (1) What is the appropriate size to create a feeling of spaciousness? (2) What elements are desirable to enhance the quality of the view? and (3) What activities can occur in the atrium to give it life and vitality?

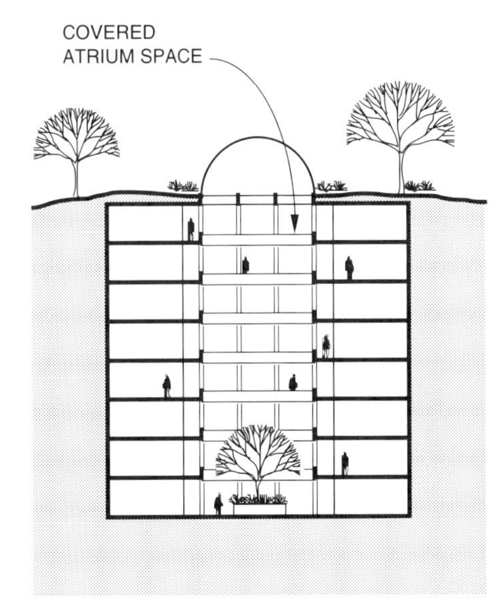

Figure 8-15: A multistory atrium can extend from the surface many stories in deep cut underground structures.

With respect to the size of an atrium, a minimum distance of 5 meters is desirable to let the eyes relax by focusing to infinity (Mahnke 1987). In contrast to sunken exterior courtyards, however, the direct penetration of sunlight may not be an important criterion for determining the overall shape of the atrium. Natural light is desirable but is likely to be supplemented by artificial light. In addition, the design of skylights overhead may include devices that reflect light further into the atrium (Hane 1989; also see Pattern 10-2).

While a multistory atrium of any size is likely to provide welcome relief in a windowless structure, there is a relationship between width and depth that may affect the perception of spaciousness. For example, a 20-meter by 20-meter atrium may appear quite spacious in a two-level facility where the floor height is 6 to 10 meters. However, the same dimensions applied to an atrium extending down 50 meters or more would create a space that is very much like a shaft rather than an open space. One important factor in creating long views and a feeling of spaciousness is the degree to which the walls of the atrium are solid or transparent. If glass partition walls surround the atrium, views will be extended beyond the atrium boundaries and reveal life and activity within the building. This visual exposure must be balanced against the need for privacy by occupants.

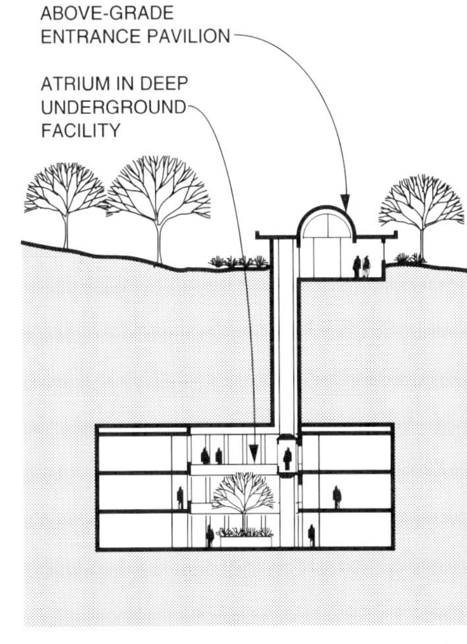

Figure 8-16: An atrium without natural light can be the central organizing space within deep isolated structures.

As stated in Pattern 8-3 for exterior courtyards, desirable conventional views have the characteristics of (1) complexity of information content, (2) information about sky, horizon, and ground, (3) natural rather than urban scenes, and (4) dynamic rather than static images (Collins 1975). Views with natural elements have restorative and relaxing qualities (Heerwagon 1990), and views of greenery appear to provide more spaciousness in interiors than views of buildings (Inui 1980). This suggests that one effective approach in atrium design is to approximate a natural setting as much as possible, such as a completely glass-covered space filled with plants, pools of water, and other natural features and with maximum natural light. An advantage of an indoor rather than outdoor courtyard is that a summertime environment can be maintained throughout the year.

In addition to or partially in place of a simulated natural environment, an atrium can also contain human activity that is stimulating to occupants who overlook the space and others passing through. In effect, the atrium can be the "town square," that place where the life and vitality of the building is evident.

While lively interior atrium spaces are common in successful commercial settings, interior courtyards can be dead places in many facilities. To avoid this, the atrium should be designed to encourage its active use. Major circulation paths should pass adjacent to or through the atrium, and if the building program allows, appropriate functions can be placed there (i.e., eating, relaxation, or meeting spaces). The layout of the atrium space itself and its furnishings should encourage social interaction and use. Seating must be provided, but it must be arranged so that people are not overly exposed and uncomfortable. Seating along the edges of the atrium or protected by trees or other architectural features will be used more than furnishings placed in the center of a large, visible open area. Pattern 8-9 addresses issues related to the design of spaces overlooking the atrium.

Figure 8-17: An atrium within a small building creates spaciousness and also provides natural light and interior views. (Firestone Library, Princeton University; architect: Koetter, Kim & Associates; photograph: © Jeff Goldberg / Esto)

PATTERN 8-5: BUILDING THOROUGHFARE

Figure 8-18: A thoroughfare within an underground building is analogous to a pedestrian street on the surface. This multistory major corridor in the Smithsonian underground museum and office complex is open and lively. (Architect: Shepley Bulfinch Richardson and Abbott)

Rather than using conventional corridors alone, create a major thoroughfare through an underground facility. Make it wider and higher than a normal corridor (multistory if possible), and provide places for sitting and social interaction similar to a lively exterior street.

According to Kevin Lynch (1960), paths are one of the major elements that make cities more imageable. A street pattern, for example, is a major part of the organizing principle for the city. It is the network that connects landmarks and open spaces; buildings and their entrances are found by traveling the streets. In many cases it is also the place where social interaction occurs, in effect where the people and life of a city are visible. The path or street becomes the view area or open space for people in buildings adjacent to the street.

If we accept the concept that the interior of an underground facility must be designed using the elements of a city to make it legible and stimulating for people, then the paths within the building must be thought of as streets, not as conventional interior corridors. While corridors perform the minimum function of providing paths of circulation through a building, they are usually confining, monotonous spaces. Because corridors are required on each level and must lead to every space, it is easy for the movement and vitality of the people traveling through a building to be dissipated. Extensive networks of corridors and elevators tend to compartmentalize and separate people within a facility, reducing stimulation, orientation, and feelings of spaciousness.

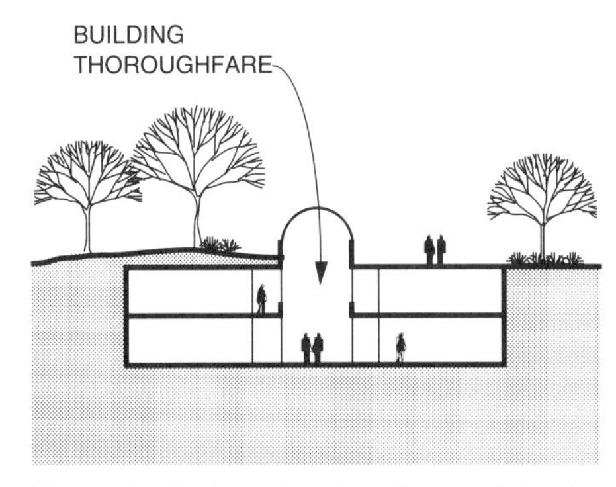

Figure 8-19: A pedestrian thoroughfare in an underground building. A multilevel thoroughfare may be similar to a long, extended atrium.

In *A Pattern Language*, Christopher Alexander et al. (1977) address the same problem of creating interior pathways that do not lose the vitality of exterior streets. "When a public building complex cannot be completely served by outdoor pedestrian streets, a new form of indoor street, quite different from the conventional corridor is needed." While Alexander et al. are referring to above-grade structures, most of the characteristics of the "Building Thoroughfare" are appropriate for major circulation paths within an underground facility. They advise the following:

Figure 8-20: An underground thoroughfare in Williamson Hall at the University of Minnesota improves orientation for visitors and creates activity within the building. (Architect: BRW Architects)

> *Place each thoroughfare in a position where it functions as a shortcut, as continuous as possible with the public street outside, with wide open entrances. And line its edges with windows, places to sit, counters, and entrances which project out into the hall and expose the building's main functions to the public. Make it a wider than normal corridor – at least 11 feet wide and more usually 15 to 20 feet wide, give it a high ceiling, at least 15 feet, with a glazed roof, if possible, and low places along the edge. If the street is several stories high, then the walkways along the edges, on the different stories, can be used to form the low places (Alexander et al. 1977).*

Essentially, to create an effective building thoroughfare, it must be wider and higher (often multistory) than a normal corridor, it must provide places for sitting and social interaction (Alexander's low places on the edge), and it must reveal the life within the building as much as possible. Interior glass partitions lining the thoroughfare reveal activities within the building while enhancing view and spaciousness in both directions. The thoroughfare can be further enlivened and legibility enhanced by creating a distinct entrance for each significant function occurring along the path. Thoroughfares are intended as major arteries of the circulation systems, and cross or lead to secondary paths. They also should connect major spaces and landmarks (sunken courtyards, or interior atriums). A wide, lively multistory thoroughfare can become a linear-shaped interior atrium with its powerful ability to open up an underground building spatially and create a strong, understandable image.

PATTERN 8-6: SHORT, LIVELY PASSAGEWAYS

Eliminate long, windowless corridors as much as possible and replace them with short, lively passageways.

Typical corridors in many modern buildings are long, narrow, and monotonous. In an underground building, using typical corridors for circulation reinforces feelings of confinement and an understimulating environment. Due to the lack of visual cues to the outside (an occasional window or a glimpse into a space with a window), underground corridors can also be disorienting. In the previous pattern (Pattern 8-5), it was suggested that major circulation arteries within underground facilities should be designed as thoroughfares—an indoor street larger than a conventional corridor.

As much as possible, it is desirable to eliminate other corridors so that all spaces in the building can be entered directly from the thoroughfare or perhaps from atrium spaces connected by thoroughfares. Obviously, this will not always be possible and secondary passageways intersecting the major thoroughfares will be required. Several design techniques will improve these passageways. First, they should be as short as possible. Christopher Alexander et al. (1977) suggest that 50 feet is a maximum length beyond which a corridor begins to feel dead and monotonous. Second, whenever possible, passageways should occur alongside sunken courtyards or interior atriums that often provide natural light and open up the space to the point where it no longer feels like a corridor. Third, interior windows along the

Figure 8-21: Long, windowless corridors reinforce feelings of confinement and lack of stimulation in underground buildings.

Figure 8-22: Alcoves with displays improve this corridor through the underground Pusey Library at Harvard University. Elsewhere in the building, major corridors pass adjacent to a sunken courtyard and larger interior spaces providing spatial variety and stimulation. (Architect: Hugh Stubbins & Associates; photograph: © Steve Rosenthal)

passageway will provide a sense of spaciousness as well as glimpses into the activity within the building. Finally, when appropriate for the building function, passageways can be widened in places and include seating areas. In some cases a passageway within a secure complex of rooms can be lined with bookshelves, displays, or other elements that give the space color, occasional activity, and a dual function.

Other issues related to the design of passageways such as room arrangements and privacy versus view using glass partitions are discussed in Pattern 8-8: Interior Windows Overlooking Activity.

PATTERN 8-7: ZONES OF DISTINCT CHARACTER

Figure 8-23: The Les Halles underground complex in Paris contains large areas of commercial activity, community recreational facilities, and a major subway station. Each of these functional areas is separate and has a distinct architectural character. In this photo, the transit area is characterized by a large central space with massive concrete structural forms. Long open stairways and escalators connect to the surface and other parts of the complex.

Within large underground facilities (or interconnected groups of facilities), create zones of distinct character to enhance orientation and provide a more stimulating interior environment.

In his analysis of cities, Lynch (1960) identifies "districts" as one of the key elements that enhance the ability to form mental images and thus improve orientation and wayfinding. A district is defined as "medium to large sections of the city . . . which are recognizable as having some identifiable character." Continuing the analogy between city and underground facility, a district is similar to a zone within a building complex. Large building complexes often contain zones that are distinguished by function—for example, a complex may contain apartments, offices, a hotel, shops, theaters, and a transit station. The inherently different appearance of some of these functions and the type of activity they generate create zones of distinct character in many cases.

Within an underground facility, zones of distinct character will certainly enhance the ability to differentiate areas and contribute to better orientation. Zones do not have to be based on functional separation as in the example above. It may be necessary or desirable to mix functions, the building may be a single function, or it may be made up of functions not inherently different in character from each other. Zones may be distinguished by their location (the west end or the lower level), or they may be associated with a building feature (around the atrium with the waterfall in it). The point here is to develop a layout and spatial configuration in conjunction with detailed architectural elements that define and reinforce zones of distinct character. The zones should have meaningful names and clear boundaries with identifiable gateways or entrance transitions.

Figure 8-24: The shopping area of the Les Halles complex is organized around an exterior sunken courtyard. This courtyard serves as a central landmark for the network of shopping corridors that surround it, resulting in an image that is distinct from other zones of the complex.

In addition to being a device for improving orientation, establishing zones of distinct character can humanize a building by giving parts within the building their own identity. Christopher Alexander et al. (1977) suggest that "the more monolithic a building is, and the less differentiated, the more it presents itself as an inhuman, mechanical factory . . . the more it prevents people from being personal, and from making human contact with the other people in the building." This suggests that buildings should have not only relatively large zones of distinct character, but also within these zones, subzones representing specific work groups that could, for example, have an office entrance with a distinct character from others in the building.

PATTERN 8-8: INTERIOR WINDOWS OVERLOOKING ACTIVITY

Use interior windows within underground buildings to overlook areas of activity and create long interior views.

The use of interior windows is an integral part of previous patterns in this chapter. The benefits of an interior atrium space (Pattern 8-4) are maximized when it is surrounded by smaller spaces that overlook it. Likewise, building thoroughfares (Pattern 8-5) and short lively passageways (Pattern 8-6) rely on interior windows to communicate information about the functions and activities within a building while relieving feelings of confinement and monotony in corridors. This pattern complements these larger scale patterns by focusing on the design issues related to interior windows between individual spaces in an underground facility.

Interior windows represent one of the most obvious techniques to alleviate confinement and provide stimulation in an underground, windowless building. Conventional exterior windows clearly increase feelings of spaciousness in rooms, and creating extended views on the interior begins to provide similar benefits.

Determining the optimal size and shape of interior windows depends on several factors. Research on conventional exterior windows has produced a few general guidelines concerning windows and feelings of spaciousness. Several studies indicate that the presence of windows increases perceived room size

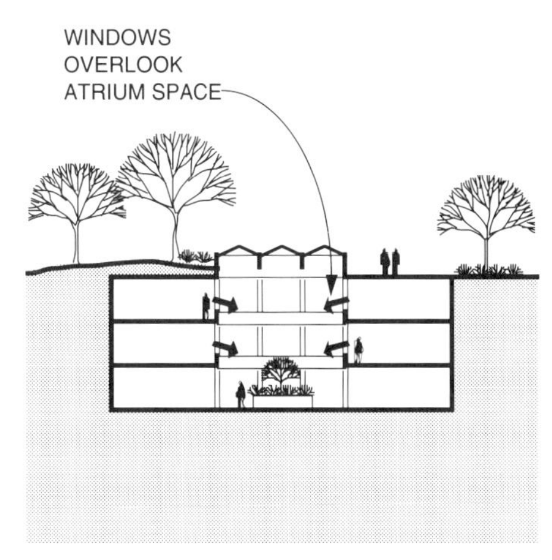

Figure 8-25: An underground building arranged so that smaller spaces with interior windows overlook an active central atrium space.

Figure 8-26: In this underground building at the University of Minnesota, offices and public corridors overlook the activity in the bookstore below. (Williamson Hall; architect: BRW Architects)

(Collins 1975; Kaye and Murray 1982). Inui and Miyata (1973) found that increased window size results in an increased perception of spaciousness. Placing windows on the short wall of a rectangular room feels more spacious than placing the same window area on the longer wall (Imamoglu and Markus 1973). Research on window shape is less clear. Imamoglu and Markus (1973) found that a set of smaller, individual windows gave a greater feeling of spaciousness in a square room while a continuous band of windows gave a greater feeling of spaciousness in a rectangular room. There is no agreement on whether horizontal or vertical window shapes produce a greater feeling of spaciousness (Collins 1975).

Figure 8-27: It is desirable for interior windows overlooking atrium spaces to be large in order to maximize a sense of spaciousness and provide a complete view of close range objects and activities.

Several studies have addressed the desirable total window area in a room. In a study by Keighley (1973), building occupants were dissatisfied with a window area limited to 10 percent of the external wall but their satisfaction increased when this was raised to 20 percent, and 30 percent or more was even better. Ne'eman and Hopkinson (1970) found that 50 percent of the people interviewed were satisfied with a 25 percent ratio of window to wall area, while 85 percent became satisfied with a 35 percent ratio. Other researchers seem to support this 20 to 40 percent range as desirable (Collins 1975; Wotton 1981). Many studies, however, point out that a variable such as window area cannot be examined in isolation. Satisfaction with a space and its window view is affected by other factors such as the view content and the design of the room itself. Common sense would indicate that window size and shape will also be influenced by the distance and position of the viewer in relation to the window.

While these research findings suggest a few guidelines, they mainly address conventional exterior windows. These differ from interior windows in that views are likely to be more distant outside, there is likely to be more light entering exterior glazing, and exterior views may often be considered more desirable than interior views. Because an interior view may be darker and considered not equivalent to an exterior view, a larger area of interior glazing may be required to relieve feelings of confinement. In effect, it may be necessary to overcompensate. Some researchers suggest that larger windows are required for viewing closer scenes and objects (Ne'eman and Hopkinson 1970). Distant views require a smaller cone of vision to be seen completely and they are not seen in as a great a detail as near views. This reinforces the idea that larger interior windows may be required than would be considered adequate for outside windows since interior views are usually at close range.

The effectiveness and desirability of interior windows is related not only to geometric variables but also to the content of the view (Patterns 9-3 and 9-4) and how well privacy is maintained (Pattern 8-9).

PATTERN 8-9: HIERARCHY OF PRIVACY

Figure 8-28: Private offices with interior windows overlook a semi-private group work area. People are uncomfortable and tend to cover interior windows if private spaces can be directly viewed from public spaces.

When interior windows are used in underground facilities, preserve a sense of privacy by arranging spaces so that the most private areas cannot be viewed from public realms.

A key problem with interior windows is maintaining privacy. Judith Heerwagon refers to the condition where there is high visual access and high visual exposure as the "goldfish bowl" (Heerwagon 1990). This goldfish bowl condition is acceptable and even desirable between public areas (such as a major corridor and a reception area, or an atrium and a restaurant), but it represents an uncomfortable and intrusive condition for more private space (i.e., a hotel room, an office, or a hospital room). Heerwagon has suggested that the ideal condition is one of high visual access with low visual exposure.

Lining public corridors and lobbies with windows looking into more private spaces will result in unacceptable visual exposure. For private functions like personal offices, this requires substantial screening to the point where the window becomes almost nonexistent. Heerwagon notes how people in this condition cover the interior windows completely with blinds or curtains to preserve their privacy (Heerwagon 1990). A solution to this is to identify a hierarchy of privacy which includes very private spaces (personal offices, for example), then semi-private spaces only accessible to a limited group (a clerical area, a common library, or lounge), and finally public spaces (corridors and lobbies). Then the plan can be arranged so that interior windows are not placed between private and public areas, but only between private/semi-private areas and

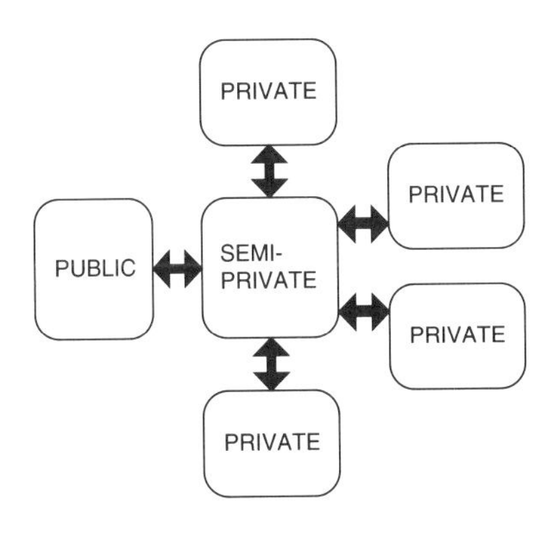

Figure 8-29: Diagram of room arrangement that preserves a hierarchy of privacy while using interior windows.

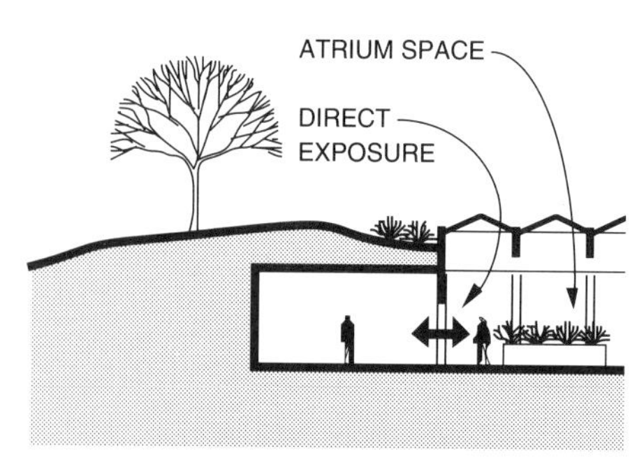

Figure 8-30: In single-level facilities, a careful arrangement of spaces is necessary to maintain a hierarchy of privacy. Direct exposure to public areas (shown above) is most acceptable for other public functions such as a shop or a reception area.

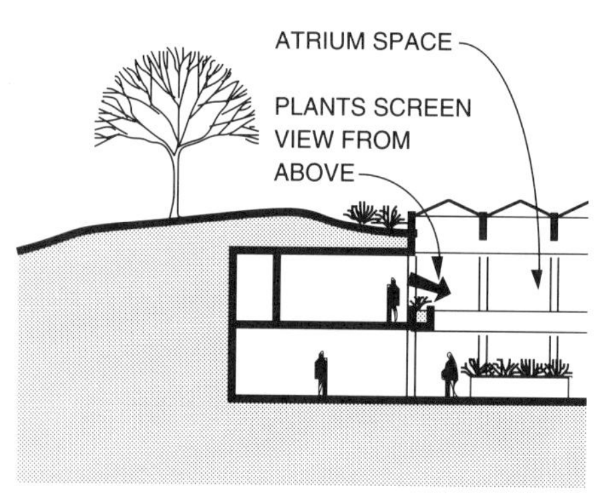

Figure 8-31: In multilevel facilities, more private activities can overlook public areas from above. Plants, blinds, and other screening devices can provide further separation without completely losing the benefits of the windows.

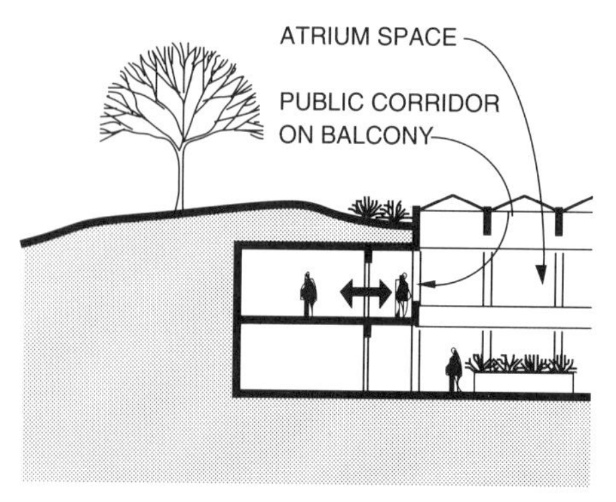

Figure 8-32: In multilevel facilities with balconies serving as public corridors, individuals in the smaller spaces along the balconies can be viewed at close range. When privacy is invaded in this manner, people sometimes cover the interior windows and negate their benefits.

then semi-private/public areas. There may be more than three degrees of privacy, and the individual functions and activities must be examined carefully to determine the acceptability of exposure within a particular facility.

With respect to layout, this hierarchical approach suggests groups of smaller private spaces around a semi-private central common space that can be entered from the public realm. In a sense this is similar to the rooms of a traditional house organized around a central courtyard that is the common space of the family but not open to the public. When applied to a nonresidential setting, this type of organization (individual spaces around a common space) can enhance group interaction and identity. Even in a relatively small cluster of spaces, the central area can be designed to be an attractive view, and screening elements, such as plants, partial blinds, or changes in floor level, can increase privacy without completely sacrificing the view.

Multilevel atriums present the opportunity to bypass this hierarchical arrangement and permit private spaces to overlook public areas directly. Interior windows overlooking an atrium space or a thoroughfare from above are one of the most desirable conditions possible since the viewer can look down on a relatively large area of public activity (high visual access), but is at a distance from the public area and can be seen only partially from below (low visual exposure). Screening devices like plants or setting the window back from the edge can provide further privacy. If the atrium or thoroughfare is relatively narrow (less than 20 meters), then a feeling of exposure may arise from being directly viewed by people in other spaces across the open space. Again appropriate screening devices may be required.

A different and much less desirable condition occurs when interior windows are placed between spaces and publicly accessible balconies that surround and overlook atrium spaces. Although there is potentially a long view into a multistory space, there is a much greater degree of visual exposure since the public can directly view building occupants at close range.

PATTERN 8-10: COMPLEX ROOM SHAPES AND INTERCONNECTED SPACES

Make individual spaces (or groups of interconnected spaces) more geometrically complex in order to increase the perception of spaciousness in underground buildings. Subdivide large simple volumes into interconnected, smaller spaces using lofts, alcoves, and half-height walls, for example. Arrange spaces so they are only partially enclosed and permit long views into adjacent spaces without being able to see the entire volume at a glance.

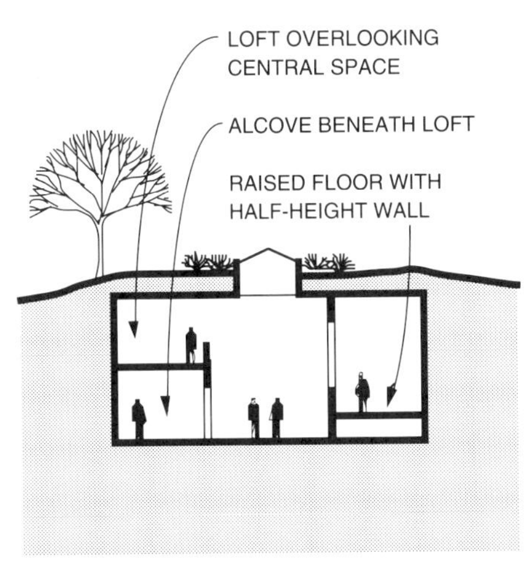

Figure 8-33: A space that is subdivided into smaller partially enclosed spaces is perceived as more spacious than a large simple volume.

The focus of this pattern is on the geometric characteristics of individual spaces within a building and how they can be designed to enhance spaciousness. This refers basically to room size and shape, although it necessarily addresses the boundaries between adjacent spaces as well.

Naturally, all other things being equal, a longer and wider room will be perceived as more spacious than a smaller one. Usually, though, it is not practical to significantly increase floor areas for functions simply because they are underground. Therefore, it is useful to understand what geometric characteristics of spaces lead to a perception of greater spaciousness. First, the shape of a room influences the perceived volume of a space. A rectangular room is generally perceived as having a greater volume

Figure 8-34: Spaces with more complex geometry and ambiguous boundaries tend to seem more spacious than simple volumes that can be seen at a glance. (Williamson Hall, University of Minnesota; architect: BRW Architects)

than a square room with an equal height and floor area (Menchikoff 1975). This effect increases as the rectangle becomes elongated up to a two to one ratio of length to width. There is some evidence that highly compact symmetrical spaces will be judged as less spacious than irregular, elongated ones (Ankerl 1981).

Beverly Tiedje (1987) suggests that complexity in room shape is an attribute with several facets that all lead to an impression of increased spaciousness. If a room is complex it takes longer to view and comprehend. One must travel through the space experiencing it dynamically, and it cannot be seen as a whole entity from any one point of view. Rappoport and Kantor (1967) indicate that humans prefer ambiguous, complex patterns in their visual fields. They hypothesize that "there is an optimal, perceptual rate which enables one to explore, to unfold gradually, to see, to give meaning to the environment."

The desirability of some complexity in the shape of interior spaces suggests that spaces should be formed so that they cannot be seen and comprehended at a glance. This implies spaces of irregular shape, spaces with partitions or other elements that prevent a complete single view of the space, but spaces that still let one see there is space beyond. This also implies the subdivision of a large single space into a central space with smaller alcoves or possibly lofts if the space is high enough. Varied ceiling heights and portions of raised floors further differentiate the space (see Pattern 8-11).

Inherent in this idea of creating distinct smaller spaces within a larger one is that these spaces remain at least partially open to each other. An alcove or loft will not enhance spaciousness and add to the complexity and interest of the environment if it is completely closed off. A half-height wall, a railing, or a row of columns will give a sense of enclosure but permit the space to flow beyond these boundaries. Interior windows, described in Pattern 8-8, can be used between spaces to provide a sense of partial enclosure as well. While the context of this pattern is an individual space within a larger facility, most of the concepts apply equally to a group of rooms. It is desirable to create similar ambiguous boundaries between spaces where appropriate, resulting in extended long views and a complex, stimulating, and spacious environment underground.

To enhance the feeling of spaciousness, creating a complex geometry should be used in conjunction with other design techniques. Ceiling height is addressed in Pattern 8-11. Chapter 9 suggests design techniques related to color, pattern, materials, and furnishings, while Chapter 10 addresses lighting.

Room A:

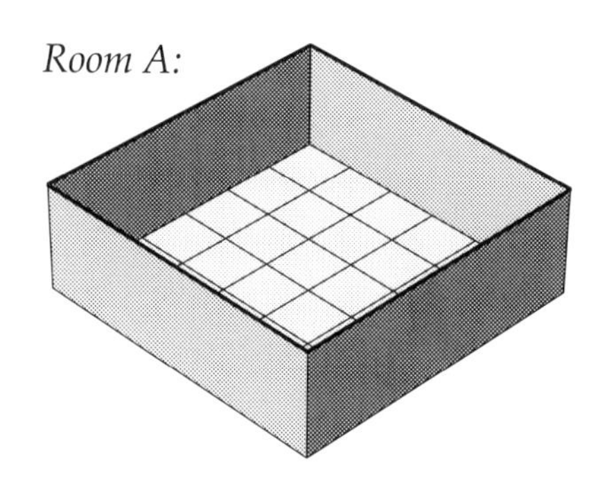

Room B:

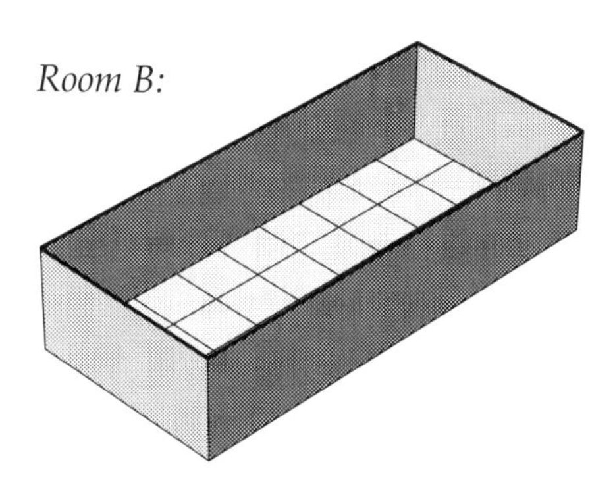

Room C:

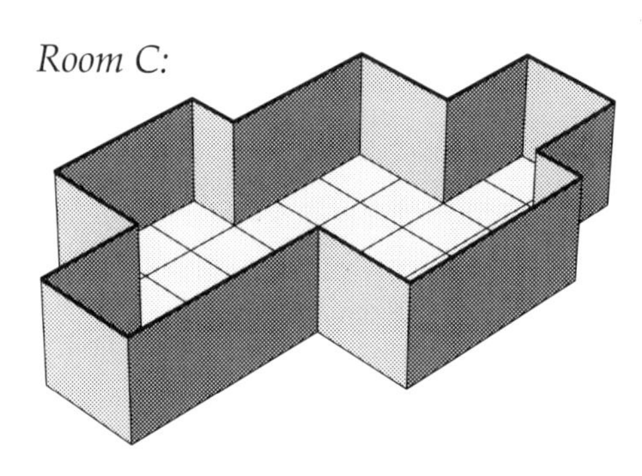

Figure 8-35: Several aspects of the geometric configuration of a space can affect the perception of spaciousness. A rectangular room (B) is perceived as more spacious than a square room (A) of equal floor area. Some evidence suggests that a more complex shape (C) which provides long interior views is perceived as more spacious than a simple shape (A or B) where the whole volume can be seen at a glance.

PATTERN 8-11: HIGH AND VARIED CEILINGS

Figure 8-36: In a windowless underground school, a pyramid-shaped ceiling with a skylight relieves feelings of confinement.

In underground facilities, make ceilings higher than in conventional buildings to enhance a feeling of spaciousness. Vary ceiling heights to reflect the different function and character of each space within a building and to create a stimulating interior environment.

Increased ceiling height is sometimes utilized as a technique for enhancing feelings of spaciousness in an underground facility. According to Menchikoff (1975), height dimensions are more often overestimated than horizontal dimensions, which implies that increasing the ceiling height in a room will have an impact on perceived spaciousness that is greater than a similar increase in other room dimensions. The effect of increased ceiling height on improving feelings of spaciousness is reflected in a study by Cochran and Urbanczyk (1982), which found that people needed more personal space when ceiling height was reduced. In a similar study, Savinar (1975) found that increased ceiling height reduced feelings of crowding even though floor space remained constant.

While higher than conventional ceilings may generally appear to be desirable to improve spaciousness, it is clear that not all spaces should have equally higher ceilings. Appropriate ceiling height is related to room width and length as well as function—a more public space requires a greater height to maintain comfortable social distance, while a more private, intimate space requires a lower ceiling to ensure privacy.

Christopher Alexander et al. suggest that while geometric proportion and social context are related to ceiling height, there is no absolute relationship to determine the optimal size. They maintain it is the variety in ceiling heights within a building that is important, not the absolute height in any particular space. "Vary

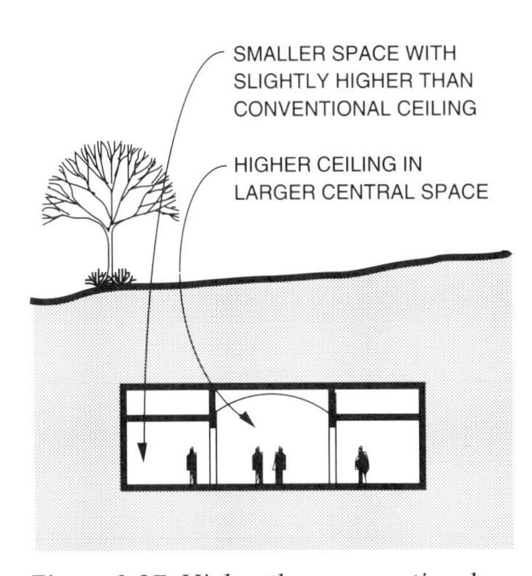

Figure 8-37: Higher than conventional ceilings increase a feeling of spaciousness in underground facilities. Varied ceiling heights create a more complex and stimulating interior environment.

the ceiling heights continuously throughout the building, especially between rooms which open into each other, so that the relative intimacy of different spaces can be felt. In particular, make ceilings high in rooms which are public or meant for large gatherings . . ., lower in rooms for smaller gatherings . . ., and very low in rooms or alcoves for one to two people . . ." (Alexander et al. 1977).

Another aspect of ceiling design is its shape (i.e., flat, sloped, vaulted). One study suggests that sloped ceilings are more "friendly" than flat ones (Wools and Canter 1970). While ceiling heights appear to have a significant influence on the perception of spaciousness, which suggests greater than conventional height is generally advisable, it is also apparent that variety in ceiling height and shape can be used to help provide the complexity and stimulation needed in underground environments.

Changing floor levels can differentiate interior space much like changing ceiling height, resulting in a more complex and thus more spacious environment. Raising a portion of the floor can enhance spaciousness in another manner. This occurs because an object that is farther away appears higher against the horizon, so the raised area appears more distant.

Figure 8-38: In relatively small underground offices, spaciousness is enhanced by higher than conventional ceilings and interior windows.

CHAPTER 9

by John Carmody

Interior Design Elements and Systems

Design Issues and Problems

Interior design in its broadest sense can include virtually any aspect of the interior environment of a building. In this book, the focus is on design techniques to enhance underground and often windowless facilities to make them more acceptable for people. Therefore, this chapter addresses a selection of interior design elements and systems that are particularly important in this

Figure 9-1: Interior design can be used to offset many of the negative associations with windowless, underground space. In the underground Smithsonian museum and office complex, interior elements such as fountains, plants, artwork, and mirrors contribute to a stimulating, positive environment. (Smithsonian Museum of African and Eastern Art; architect: Shepley Bulfinch Richardson and Abbott; photographer: Nick Wheeler / Wheeler Photographics)

context. In Chapter 8, Layout and Spatial Configuration, the arrangement, size, and shape of spaces within the facility were addressed. In effect, Chapter 8 establishes the enclosure on which interior design elements and systems are then applied.

Interior design typically includes predominantly visual elements such as the use of color and pattern, materials, furnishings, graphic design, artwork, and other notable elements such as plants and fountains. These are all addressed in this chapter, but in addition, special techniques for providing views within the interior environment are presented. These techniques, which attempt to provide an alternative to conventional windows, are sometimes referred to as surrogate windows. Other non-visual aspects of the interior environment are also included, such as sound and smell, air movement, temperature, and quality. One notable interior design element is missing from this list—lighting. Lighting (both natural and artificial) is of such importance in underground buildings that it requires its own chapter, which follows. Nevertheless, it is an integral part of many of the interior design elements and systems discussed here.

In conventional buildings, the general goals of interior design include providing functional, comfortable, and attractive spaces. Because of some of the negative attributes and associations with underground, windowless environments, the designer must not only achieve these general goals, but must consciously attempt to offset particular negative perceptions. The key design problems related to the interior of underground buildings can be summarized as follows:

1. Without windows to the exterior, there is a loss of stimulation from and connection to the natural and manmade environments on the surface.
2. Because there are no windows, there can be a sense of confinement.
3. In underground space there are often associations with coldness and dampness.
4. Underground spaces are sometimes perceived to have poor ventilation and air quality even though they are mechanically ventilated in a manner similar to most above-grade buildings.
5. Underground space sometimes connotes less desirable or lower status space.
6. Without connection to the surface providing visual reference points, there can be a lack of spatial orientation in underground space. With respect to interior design, this is a problem to be addressed with effective signage.

Throughout this book the problems of lack of stimulation, lack of connection to nature, and feelings of confinement all due to the absence of windows are major recurring design issues. It is in the small-scale, subtle interior design choices where these issues seem to become a dominant factor. Achieving the general goals of providing a stimulating, "natural," and spacious environment

Figure 9-2: The use of plants, water, and natural light enhances the interior environment in this underground office building. (Mutual of Omaha Building; architect; Leo A. Daly; photographer: Paul John Brokering)

without windows requires a more precise understanding of how these qualities are perceived by people.

Stimulation and Variety

A stimulating and varied interior environment has many components. It involves the visual aspects of the space—shape, size, color, texture, furnishings, and artwork, for example—as well as the acoustic, olfactory, and thermal aspects of the environment. Moreover, an interior is a place of human activity, not a static visual image. This implies that other important aspects of a stimulating environment include the movement and activity of people, and the changes in the environment over a period of time. A related issue is the ability for people to adjust or change aspects of their environment, which enhances satisfaction because people have some control.

Given the lack of stimulation inherent in a windowless space, providing variety in the environment is an important goal, but it is not necessarily desirable to maximize stimulation in all spaces. Clearly every function has its particular requirements for privacy, noise level, and decor. A reasonable, comfortable amount of variety in the environment must be viewed as a balance point on a spectrum between extreme understimulation and extreme overstimulation. Frank and Rudolph Mahnke (1987) describe this in their review of the psychophysiological effects of color and light:

> *Exposure to overstimulation can cause changes in the rate of breathing, pulse rate, and blood pressure; increase in muscle tension; psychiatric reactions of various types; and probably*

compounded medical consequences, such as increased susceptibility to infection, coronary disease and ulcers ... Persons subjected to understimulation showed symptoms of restlessness, excessive emotional response, difficulty in concentration, irritation, and in some cases, a variety of more extreme reactions.

This suggests that the designer should seek a moderate amount of stimulation and variety in the environment, but within a predictable framework.

Nature as a Model

This quest for a moderately varied environment leads many researchers to identify nature as an ideal model. Faber Birren (1983) states:

> *In response to environment, people expect all of their senses to be moderately stimulated at all times. This is what happens in nature and it relates not only to color and changing degrees of brightness, but to variations in temperature and sound. The unnatural condition is one that is static, boring, tedious, and unchanging. Variety is indeed the spice – and needed substance – of life.*

Anita Olds (1985, 1987) writes:

> *When the environmental stimulation and movement are predictable, yet involve moderate degrees of change and contrast, the nervous system can function optimally and the person experiences a sense of 'being comfortable.' Nature is often perceived as a 'healer' precisely because of the soothing qualities of*

Figure 9-3: In Montreal, Canada, each subway station is designed differently, but most utilize colorful artwork and high-quality materials. In this station, the interior environment is enhanced by natural light and the large volume of space.

'difference within sameness'... Natural elements, such as babbling brooks, gentle breezes, and sunlight dancing on leaves, are always undergoing fairly predictable yet fascinating changes. They prevent boredom, as subtle fluctuations in their movement periodically reawaken all the senses.

The obvious implication is to attempt to replicate the essential qualities of patterns from the natural environment in the design of windowless, underground environments. A second related implication is actually to use elements from nature within the interior environment. Natural elements such as plants, water, and rocks embody the quality of desirable visual complexity, and also evoke direct associations with the natural world. Actual natural elements, their use in artwork, or even projected views of natural settings have been shown to have relaxing and restorative effects on people (Ulrich 1983, 1986; Wohlwill 1983). All of these techniques for establishing connections with the natural world in underground interiors are presented in the patterns that follow.

Confinement

The feeling of confinement associated with underground, windowless buildings implies that interiors should be designed to feel "spacious." Creating spaciousness in interiors will be made easier when the building layout provides large spaces, high ceilings, views through interior windows to atriums or courtyards, and a flow between spaces as described in Chapter 8. Enhancing spaciousness, however, has many aspects beyond simply making spaces larger and creating long interior views. The quality of spaciousness can be created with visual illusions involving light, color, pattern, and texture, and it is also influenced by the arrangement and design of furnishings within a space. Tiedje (1987) believes the ability to move freely affects perceived spaciousness, and Imamoglu (1986) states that a spacious room must be appealing, well planned, and have space freedom. Thus, spaciousness is more than perception of visual size—it is related to aesthetics, how well a space functions, and whether it feels cramped or cluttered. In effect, a smaller, attractive, well-organized, uncluttered room can feel more spacious than a larger room without these qualities. In the patterns that follow, several aspects of the interior environment are discussed with respect to creating spaciousness; however, they must be considered as part of an integrated whole design approach, not just as an isolated optical illusion. Otherwise, other factors will overshadow their effectiveness at increasing spaciousness.

Images of Cold, Damp Spaces

Caves are generally regarded as cold, damp, and poorly ventilated, and manmade underground structures such as tunnels, mines, and many unoccupied basements have similar qualities. Windowless underground spaces that are to be occupied by people can be mechanically ventilated, heated, cooled, and dehumidified just like most conventional buildings with or without windows. Nevertheless, it is the associations with these qualities that present

Design Objectives for Interior Elements and Systems

1. Create a stimulating indoor environment to compensate for a lack of windows. Environmental stimuli should be varied, integrated, and balanced to avoid overstimulation as well as understimulation.
2. Provide connections with the natural world.
3. Create a feeling of spaciousness.
4. Create a feeling of warmth to offset associations with cold, damp underground environments.
5. Provide fresh air and thermal comfort.
6. Use interior elements that are perceived as high quality to compensate for the negative status associated with below-grade space.
7. Provide a clear, attractive system of signs and maps (if necessary) to facilitate orientation.

design concerns for underground space. This implies careful design of the mechanical system; however, there are implications for many other aspects of the interior environment, particularly those that can influence the perception of warmth and dryness. Other issues related to mechanically ventilated environments may deserve particular attention underground. These are lack of thermal variation, need for individual control, and predominance of mechanical noise in an otherwise silent environment.

Lower Status

In addition to the actual or perceived physical shortcomings of underground space, it can simply be viewed as inferior or second-class space. As James Wise (1984) points out:

> *Much of this may be due to the cultural conditioning we receive, with its rich symbolism of life's rewards and their directional contexts. Affective and evaluative connotations of 'above and below' suffuse our language, and relative height is a strong indicant of status and social power. It is not unreasonable to hypothesize that social and cultural expectations, as well as sensory ones, need to be compensated for in other ways if they are violated in a move to an underground work setting.*

Thus it can be argued that the quality of interior design elements in underground spaces (i.e., furnishings, materials, and artwork) should be higher than for those found in an equivalent above-grade space to compensate for the perceived lack of status and other amenities.

Spatial Orientation

Finally, the lack of spatial orientation in underground facilities has been discussed extensively in Chapters 7 and 8. The exterior and entrance design, as well as the interior layout of an underground building, can be designed to give people a clear understanding of the overall organizing principles of the design. In a building with many distinctive well-designed central spaces, orientation and wayfinding may occur quite easily and naturally. This architectural legibility, however, must be complemented and reinforced by a system of signs and perhaps maps and graphic symbols. An effective system of signs is important in any underground building because some people simply choose to rely on signs regardless of the design, but clear signage is essential in environments that are complex and do not inherently lend themselves to easy understanding.

Design Patterns Related to Interior Elements and Systems

This section presents several approaches for the design of interior elements and systems in underground facilities that meet the design objectives stated previously. The intention is to present the basic pattern or concept, discuss its characteristics, and illustrate it with a representative drawing and/or photograph. This does not imply that the pattern should be replicated in this exact manner. Many diverse design responses can be developed based on the objectives and approaches presented here. (See Chapter 6 for a discussion of putting these patterns into a larger context.)

The patterns discussed here are intended to complement those related to exterior and entrance design (Chapter 7), as well as layout and spatial configuration (Chapter 8).

In addition to being complementary to the patterns in Chapters 7 and 8, design approaches discussed here must be integrated with patterns related to lighting (Chapter 10) in order to enhance their effectiveness.

Interior Design Patterns

9-1: Colorful, Warm, and Spacious Environment

9-2: Line, Texture, and Pattern

9-3: Natural Elements and Materials

9-4: Sculpture and Manmade Artifacts

9-5: Warm, Uncluttered Furnishings

9-6: Mirrors

9-7: Alcoves and Window-like Recesses

9-8: Paintings and Photographs

9-9: Transmitted and Reflected Exterior Views

9-10: Clear System of Signs and Maps

9-11: Well-ventilated, Comfortable Environment

PATTERN 9-1: COLORFUL, WARM, AND SPACIOUS ENVIRONMENT

Figure 9-4: Colorful flags provide warmth and stimulation at the entrance to underground offices within a Kansas City mined space development.

Use color to provide visual stimulation, warmth, and to enhance spaciousness in underground environments.

Color is a powerful element in interior design that can affect the overall attractiveness and acceptability of an environment. It can also be applied in a space to create feelings of warmth and spaciousness—two key issues in underground design.

In an extensive review of color-related research, Rikard Kuller states that the presence of color gives rise to positive evaluations of the environment while the absence of color is generally considered to be negative. While there are many studies of color preferences and mood associations with colors, Kuller states that hue, lightness, and chromatic strength will not affect the pleasantness of the interior space in any consistent way (Kuller 1981). In effect, it is the presence of color that seems desirable, but any number of color schemes can potentially be successful.

The presence or absence of certain colors in underground space may have a special significance. Some negative reactions to working in underground facilities occur in spaces with unfinished gray concrete walls (Sterling and Carmody 1990). This may be attributed to the association with undesirable basement space, but its cold and colorless character is most likely a factor. The effect of color depends on many factors and it must be viewed in the context of the overall environment, which typically consists of many colors in combination.

One possible use of color in underground environments is to help offset the associations with coldness and dampness.

Figure 9-5: Brown-colored, richly textured bricks add warmth to this corridor in the Montreal subway system. In many cases underground corridors are simply left unfinished with gray concrete walls that feel cold and reinforce images of low-quality basement space.

Generally, many colors with longer wavelengths (i.e., red, orange, yellow, brown) are considered to be associated with warmth, while those with shorter wavelengths (i.e., blue and green) are considered to be "cooler." These associations seem to be consistent with research findings. In one set of experiments, occupants of a blue-green room felt that 59°F was cold, whereas the occupants of a red-orange room felt cold only after the temperature fell to 52° to 54°F (Itten 1970). Similar results were found in a Norwegian study where people tended to set the thermostat four degrees higher in a blue room than in a red room (Porter and Mikellides 1976). In another study subjects were placed in a stark chamber, while others were placed in a chamber with red carpet, wood walls, and acoustical ceiling tiles. Although the temperature was 74°F in both spaces, subjects felt significantly warmer in the space with warm colors and texture (Rohles and Wells 1977). A further reason for utilizing warmer colors underground is that colors such as yellow and tan seem to connote dryness while cooler blue-green colors are associated more with moist or damp conditions (Mahnke 1987). It has also been suggested that warm, natural earth tones are a good choice for underground space because they invoke outdoor associations (Wise and Wise 1984).

Another important use of color in underground environments is to create a feeling of spaciousness. A widely believed rule of thumb states that warm colors (red, for instance) advance toward the viewer, while cool colors (i.e., blue) recede. Thus, the conclusion often drawn is that blue or green surfaces will create a greater feeling of spaciousness than red or orange. The perception of depth related to colors, however, is much more complicated and other factors can make this rule of thumb untrue. To understand this, it is first necessary to identify the three main attributes of color: hue, saturation (or chroma), and value (or lightness). Hue is determined by the wavelength of a color—it is the characteristic that distinguishes one color from another (i.e., blue, green, yellow, red). Saturation, or chroma, designates the purity of a color—it is the amount that a color varies from a gray color. A highly saturated color is strong and intense with no gray. Lightness, or value, is the quality that differentiates a dark color from a light one. This is a measure of how much light is reflected from its surface. A fourth term, brightness, can sometimes be confusing since it means the intensity of a light source or luminous sensation when describing light, but it means highly saturated when describing color (Mahnke 1987).

Contrary to the previously mentioned rule of thumb, some researchers have concluded that hue does not have a strong effect on the perception of distance (Wise and Wise 1987; Tiedje 1987). Spaciousness is enhanced by increasing lightness of the enclosing surfaces. High value colors reflect more light, and lighter spaces are generally perceived as larger and more open. In addition, saturated (high chroma) colors appear closer than less saturated, grayer colors. Thus, the perceived depth or distance to a color is relative to the color of the surfaces around it and the properties of the light falling on it. Enhancing spaciousness using lighter colors on enclosing surfaces will be most successful with higher levels of illumination directed on these surfaces (see Pattern 10-5 in Chapter 10).

Figure 9-6: Brightly colored fabric on the seats in this underground classroom improve the interior. Wood covering the walls adds texture and a connection to the natural world.

Because a spacious design approach with color is not necessarily restricted to a particular set of hues, there seems to be no inherent conflict in designing a space to be both warm and spacious. Even if the designer chooses to use light, cool colors on walls and ceilings to enhance spaciousness, warm-colored furnishings and artwork may be used to offset associations with coldness. It is important to remember that color is only one component of the visual environment and its use is multifaceted. Although color can be used to create effects of warmth and spaciousness, the greatest psychological effect associated with color may simply be that it is stimulating and attractive. Frank and Rudolph Mahnke (1987) warn against using a single color in a space to create a particular effect:

> *Taking all research collectively, it is safe to conclude and suggest that color variety is psychologically most beneficial...there must be colors in changing degrees of brightness, temperature, and chromatics, and the complement of the dominant color should be present to some extent. Maximum favorable color effects depend on variety and contrast, within reason.*

PATTERN 9-2: LINE, TEXTURE, AND PATTERN

Figure 9-7: Diagonal lines applied to the floor of this Stockholm subway station draw attention to long diagonal views and thus enhance a feeling of spaciousness.

Use applied lines, patterns, and textures on enclosing surfaces in underground facilities to enhance spaciousness and create visual interest. Vertical lines on walls increase the perception of ceiling height, while diagonal lines on floors make spaces seem larger. Surfaces with patterns and textures composed of finer elements seem farther away than those with bolder elements.

Surfaces within a space have many possible attributes including color, texture, and applied line and pattern. All these characteristics can contribute to the creation of a more varied, stimulating space, and they can also enhance the perception of spaciousness. Line, pattern, and texture actually can increase spaciousness in two ways. First, patterns and textures make an environment more complex, with more visual information to explore, and this tends to make a space actually seem larger because it cannot be comprehended at a glance. Second, because lines suggest direction while patterns and texture suggest scale due to the size of the repetitive elements, they can influence the perception of distance and therefore spaciousness.

In a survey of techniques to increase spaciousness, Beverly Tiedje identifies several design strategies (Tiedje 1987). First, the application of line enhances size in the direction of the application. Thus, vertical lines on walls make the ceiling appear higher. This approach is particularly effective because people overestimate vertical dimensions, exaggerating the effect even further. Horizontal lines increase width and decrease height, an effect that seems less desirable than increasing height in underground space. Diagonal lines are particularly space enhancing; they suggest dynamic movement and draw attention to long diagonal views in a space. Diagonal patterns applied to floors are particularly effective in making the space appear larger.

A second technique to enhance spaciousness is to apply patterns to surfaces in order to make them recede. Generally, a smaller, finer pattern size and spacing appears farther away than larger, bolder elements. Also, less distinct objects or surfaces appear farther away. This presumably occurs because distant objects are not as clear as close ones in an actual three-dimensional view. Thus, a ceiling with large, bold elements will appear lower than one with a finer pattern. Tiedje suggests manipulating the pattern effect by decreasing the pattern spacing on the upper portion of a wall near the ceiling. A similar optical illusion could be created by decreasing the pattern size and spacing along the edges of a tile floor or carpet.

Texture on surfaces has some of the same effects as applied line and pattern. For example, vertical ribs formed in a concrete wall can increase the illusion of height, while the size and spacing of texture in stucco or plaster can make a wall appear nearer or farther away. Texture, however, is three dimensional and in some cases can be used to create a higher level of visual interest than lines and patterns. For example, complex patterns of light and shadow can result from lighting a heavily textured surface. Textures can also connote warmth and stimulate other tactile associations (see Pattern 9-3).

Using texture, applied line, and pattern in interior design to enhance spaciousness must be done in moderation. The designer must avoid too much visual pattern and seek a balance between overstimulation and understimulation.

Figure 9-8: The vertical lines created by the texture of the concrete walls and balconies in this underground building make the space seem higher, thus helping to alleviate feelings of confinement. (Architect: BRW Architects)

PATTERN 9-3: NATURAL ELEMENTS AND MATERIALS

Use natural elements and materials in underground spaces to create visual stimulation, warmth, and a feeling of quality, as well as to evoke associations with the natural world. Green plants, pools and fountains of water, and materials such as wood or stone are effective. Where possible, expose rock walls in underground caverns to highlight their rough-textured, natural characteristics.

Using natural elements and materials in underground facilities is perhaps one of the most obvious, but also one of the most powerful, techniques for creating a positive environment for people. Many of the negative associations with underground windowless spaces are related to the lack of connection with the natural world on the surface. Furthermore, in seeking design approaches to create a stimulating, comfortable artificial environment, nature is often identified as the ideal model. It is not only the visual aspect of nature that is appealing, but the overall sensory experience including sounds, smells, and the tactile associations with highly textured natural materials.

Experience with creating artificial environments in space, particularly Soviet space stations, has confirmed the importance of natural and naturalistic images and elements. While several weeks or months in a space vehicle is a considerably more extreme experience than visiting or working in an underground facility a few hours a day, it is interesting to note the value placed on projected views of nature scenes. The Soviets actually accompany these visual sequences with natural sounds (birds and rushing water) and provide music to create an illusory nature experience. Researchers suggest that the evocation of natural images and associations may be more important than the actual reproduction of the objects themselves (Gurovskiy et al. 1986).

Figure 9-9: The use of green plants and natural materials are common and effective techniques for enhancing the interior of underground environments. In this deep underground office area, plants are placed beneath artificially lighted skylights and wood is used extensively for finishes and furnishings. (Graduate student offices in the Civil and Mineral Engineering Building at the University of Minnesota; architects: John Carmody and Mike Melman)

Figure 9-10: This waterfall in the atrium of an underground building in Toronto provides a connection with nature. The movement of falling water is visually fascinating and produces a sound that is both soothing and stimulating.

The use of natural elements themselves and natural materials are part of the typical palette of the interior designer. The use of green plants, for example, is one of the most common and effective techniques for enhancing the interior environment. One study concluded that plants made a significant contribution to the perceived quality of a space (Laviana, Mattson, and Rohles 1983). While they had a positive influence on people's evaluation of the interior environment, they did not appear to have an effect on the perception of spaciousness, nor did they affect thermal comfort. Large plants are frequently one of the main visual features of an interior atrium space. Even in very limited enclosures, however, plants can be clustered into centrally visible areas with higher illumination to create a focal point and the illusion of an exterior courtyard. Plants have the desirable quality of being complex in form and partially transparent and thus can be used as screens between spaces while leaving the perception of space extending beyond. They can also be used with lighting to create naturalistic, varied patterns of filtered light and shadow.

Another powerful natural element that can be used in the interior environment is water. In a study to determine the most preferred elements in visual scenes, natural landscapes with vegetation and particularly water had the most positive influences on subjects' emotional states (Ulrich 1981). In the interior environment, analogous views of large bodies of water can be replicated in artwork or slides. Pools, fountains, and waterfalls are commonly created in interior atrium spaces with positive results. In addition to being visually attractive, fountains and falling water provide movement and sound. Falling water embodies the natural quality of being fascinating yet predictable, helping to strike a balance between overstimulation and understimulation. The sound of rushing or falling water not only evokes natural associations, it also interests and soothes at the same time. In an atrium with plants and falling water, the sound of birds chirping can further reinforce the sounds associated with the natural environment.

Figure 9-11: Rock walls are left exposed in this underground swimming pool in a cavern in Norway. The rock is lighted from above which emphasizes its rough texture.

In addition to plants and water, the use of certain "natural" materials to improve the underground environment is an effective strategy. It is worth considering, however, what exactly is meant by "natural" and what constitute the desirable qualities of a natural material. Although there is no established definition, the qualities of so-called "natural" materials are: (1) they are taken from the natural world and processed minimally, (2) they are irregularly textured, and (3) they are colored in warmer tones. Wood, more than any other material, seems to fit this definition since the pattern and texture of wood grain is so distinct, its natural colors are warm, and it was once alive. Rock and soil are also clearly from the natural world. Natural rock walls or rough textured stone applied to an interior are distinctly recognizable as being in a natural state. Brick and tiles made from clay have been shaped and processed and thus may be identified as "natural" in some cases and not others. For example, an irregular or rough textured brick wall of earth-tone colors definitely appears natural, while a brightly colored, smoothly glazed brick wall may not. Some fabrics, particularly those using natural fibers with rough hewn textures and earth-tone colors, may be regarded as natural materials.

Natural materials can be important in determining whether an underground environment is perceived as being cold or warm. As noted above, natural materials seem to be colored in warm tones, but they also have associations with being warm or cold to the touch. Generally, textured surfaces are associated more with warmth than smooth surfaces. In this respect, most natural materials fall into the more textured category. However, there are also learned associations with the thermal properties of materials. For example, wood and fabrics conduct heat away from skin less rapidly than metal or concrete, therefore they evoke greater feelings of warmth. Natural stone, bricks, and tiles present a paradox in this sense in that they can connote warmth with their natural appearance and color, but also can connote a coldness to the touch compared with wood or cloth.

Natural elements such as plants and water, as well as natural materials such as wood and brick, are often more expensive than the most common interior finishes such as sheetrock. Thus, they communicate not only a visual richness but, in some cases, a higher quality environment. This may be an important factor in compensating for the perceived lower status of underground space.

All the natural materials discussed here are commonly used in many types of conventional facilities with one exception. Some types of underground construction present the opportunity to expose the rock walls and roof that form the enclosure. Exposing rock walls has been a successful design technique for many types of underground facilities. In some cases, the irregular texture of the rock has all the powerful qualities of other natural materials—it is from nature, and it is visually fascinating with its very rough, irregular and sometimes colorful appearance. Unlike any other natural material, however, it is an honest expression of the actual enclosure of the underground facility. Rather than creating a comfortable artificial environment by using "natural" elements from the surface, exposed rock surfaces emphasize the unique (but natural) quality of being underground that cannot easily be replicated anywhere else. Some of the finest examples are found in Norway and other Scandinavian countries where sections of the granite rock walls are exposed, but much of the ceiling and other wall areas are finished in wood. This sets off the sections of rock as if they are sculptures or natural settings to be viewed in place of an exterior view. This effect is enhanced by indirect lighting from above that emphasizes their texture. In some cases rock walls are painted white to reflect light. In other cases, the actual rock is either not attractive or must be covered by a sprayed-on layer of concrete for structural reasons. Although this coating lacks the completely natural color and texture of the rock, the rough hewn shape of the cavern enclosure is often preserved.

Figure 9-12: In many underground facilities the natural rock walls are exposed. These irregular, highly textured walls are visually interesting and emphasize the unique nature of being underground.

PATTERN 9-4: SCULPTURE AND MANMADE ARTIFACTS

Incorporate sculpture and other manmade artifacts into the design of underground spaces. Sculpture can provide a focal point and may introduce color, texture, movement, sound, natural materials, or symbolic manmade elements.

The use of sculpture in underground spaces has the potential to enrich the environment in many ways. Usually, sculpture is a focal point, such as an isolated art object in contrast with its surroundings, although it may be seamlessly integrated into the overall environment.

The range of objects that fall under the category of sculpture can best be represented by some examples. The most traditional placement of sculptural objects is within wall recesses or in a central location such as an atrium or sunken courtyard, much as they would be displayed in a museum. In some cases, the fountain, pool, or waterfall in an atrium or courtyard space either contains sculpture or is itself a sculptural object. Suspended sculptures can give a dynamic quality and sense of depth to multistory atrium spaces. An object such as a mobile that moves in a slow, natural pattern with the air currents can be more stimulating than static objects, and yet the motion is not distracting but soothing like trees wavering in the breeze.

An intriguing and powerful use of sculpture in underground space can be found in the 800-foot-long pedestrian concourse at O'Hare Airport in Chicago. A multicolored neon sculpture is constantly changing overhead as people pass through the

Figure 9-13: In this long underground corridor at O'Hare Airport in Chicago, stimulation is provided by a multicolored neon sculpture overhead. The neon tubes flash on and off in patterns synchronized to music. (Architect: Murphy / Jahn Architects)

underground corridor on moving conveyors. A mirrored ceiling reflects the neon tubes so that they appear suspended in a much higher space. The visual stimulation of color, form, and movement is further enhanced by the sound of musical tones that seem to correspond with the changes in the sculpture. The resulting effect of this multimedia use of sculpture is quite stimulating but also pleasant and relaxing, not overloading.

A particularly interesting design approach in underground environments is to utilize archeological structures and artifacts that are encountered during construction. In the construction of subways in Mexico City and Rome, such structures were encountered unintentionally but incorporated into the station designs. During excavation of the underground addition to the Louvre in Paris, the original foundation walls around the fortress were revealed and have now been incorporated into an archeological exhibition. Artifacts and sculptures not necessarily found in the actual construction can also be used to create images with archeological associations that seem uniquely suited to an underground setting. In the Kungstradgarden Station in Stockholm, archeological artifacts are used and sculptural figures appear to emerge from the rock walls of the station.

Figure 9-14: Sculptural figures appear to emerge from the rock walls of this Stockholm subway station.

PATTERN 9-5: WARM, UNCLUTTERED FURNISHINGS

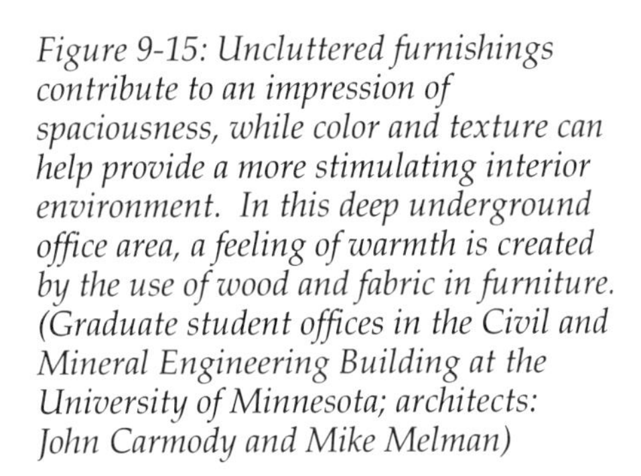

Figure 9-15: Uncluttered furnishings contribute to an impression of spaciousness, while color and texture can help provide a more stimulating interior environment. In this deep underground office area, a feeling of warmth is created by the use of wood and fabric in furniture. (Graduate student offices in the Civil and Mineral Engineering Building at the University of Minnesota; architects: John Carmody and Mike Melman)

Select furnishings that are not massive in design with materials and colors that provide warmth, texture, a sense of quality, and associations with nature.

In an underground building, furnishings can affect the perception of spaciousness and warmth as well as the overall quality and comfort in a given space. Spaciousness is affected by the amount and distribution of furnishings, as well as their design. Clearly, overfurnishing a space will make it appear more cluttered and less spacious. It has also been determined that if a given amount of furniture is evenly distributed throughout a space, it will appear more spacious than if those same furnishings are concentrated in one area (Titus et al. 1977). The design of individual pieces of furniture can also contribute to a perception of spaciousness. A large, overstuffed chair may be warm and comfortable, but it will also appear massive and occupy more space than a lighter weight, more open chair design. Of course, color and texture of furnishings will have an impact on whether they appear massive or not (see Patterns 9-1 and 9-2).

The materials used in furnishings are important in creating a feeling of warmth in a space—particularly since people come in direct contact with them. Generally, more rough-textured surfaces are warmer to the touch than smoother surfaces and they contribute to a more stimulating environment both tactually and visually. Specific material uses such as metal for armrests on chairs will feel and appear colder than wood or fabric, for example. The selection of appropriate materials in furnishings can contribute not only to a feeling of warmth, but also to the perception of quality and status—other important issues in underground space. In a previous pattern (9-3), the positive associations with natural materials such as wood and fabrics were identified. Using these materials in furnishings complements and reinforces these overall design themes.

A particularly important type of furnishing in many workplace settings is the movable partition. In addition to the impact of their color and material on the interior design, the height and extent of room dividers have a potentially powerful impact on the feeling of spaciousness. In Chapter 8 it was suggested that the walls or boundaries between spaces be partially transparent and ambiguous to enhance spaciousness by creating long views, complexity so a space cannot be seen at once, and the hint of extended space beyond the immediate space. Following this approach, partitions should not be so high that they appear to subdivide the space into small, individual compartments. For example, 7-foot-high partitions in an 8-foot-high space would appear to diminish severely any feelings of spaciousness. On the other hand, while minimizing partition height would generally make a space appear more open and create more extended views, the people working within the cubicles may feel less privacy and more crowded. In fact, visually borrowing surrounding space through the use of low partitions does not seem to compensate for reduced floor area, at least in office settings (Brill et al. 1983).

While partitioning a space into compartments would appear to make it seem less spacious, subdivision of a single large space does make it more complex to explore and understand, which tends to make it seem larger. If high ceilings (10 feet or more) are used in underground space (as recommended in Chapter 8), then 5- or 6-foot-high partitions may not seem as enclosing as they do in a space with a lower ceiling. This problem of privacy versus openness appears to be mainly a concern with office workstations where a degree of privacy and concentration is required. In many other situations, i.e., reception areas, libraries, and lounges, relatively low partitions are desirable (if partitions are required at all) for spaciousness since complete privacy is not essential.

PATTERN 9-6: MIRRORS

In confined underground spaces, use mirrors to reflect light and to create a feeling of spaciousness.

The use of mirrors in underground, windowless interiors can have a great effect on the perception of spaciousness. Mirrored walls and sometimes ceilings are a well-known technique for creating the illusion that there is space extending beyond the actual surface of the mirror. Unlike using a painting with an exterior view to create the illusion of depth beyond the wall surface, a mirror is optically correct from any angle and the view changes as one walks around the space. Basically, the form of objects, their color, and the amount of light are not significantly altered by a high-quality flat mirror, resulting in an extremely realistic illusion. In addition to appearing to extend the view, mirrors actually lighten space since they are highly reflective and can make surfaces appear transparent, reducing the massiveness of columns or other architectural elements.

Perhaps the most common use of mirrors to create spaciousness is simply to place them on an entire wall of a space, creating the illusion that the space is doubled in size. An extraordinary example of this approach is applied in a windowless above-grade

Figure 9-16: A seven-story-high mirror on one wall of a narrow atrium considerably expands the perceived space in this windowless above-grade building.

Figure 9-17: In the Les Halles underground shopping complex in Paris, mirrors placed along the upper wall make the ceiling appear higher and give the impression of space extending beyond the actual wall surfaces.

building in Minneapolis, Minnesota. A seven-story-high mirrored surface on one wall of a narrow atrium considerably expands the apparent size of the space.

Mirrors in interior spaces can also be placed at angles to direct a view around a corner, again creating longer views. Spaciousness is enhanced because there is a glimpse of spaces beyond that cannot be seen completely, thus adding to the complexity and visual interest of the space. In a library in Minnesota, a large mirror is set at an angle so that a view of an exterior sunken courtyard is reflected deep into an interior underground space. Mirrors also can be placed along soffits or even encase structural elements to create sometimes confusing illusions of transparency and lightness as well as the appearance of space beyond.

PATTERN 9-7: ALCOVES AND WINDOW-LIKE RECESSES

Use alcoves and window-like recesses in the walls of underground spaces to create visual interest and enhance spaciousness. Place plants, sculpture, or other objects of interest in the alcoves and light them indirectly from above.

Figure 9-18: An alcove using indirect lighting to create the impression of daylight.

In windowless spaces, it is desirable to provide elements in the interior environment that have some of the qualities of an actual window view. These visual qualities include providing stimulation and a connection to the outside world, as well as enhancing spaciousness. Sometimes referred to as "surrogate windows," these design techniques can include alcoves or wall recesses containing objects of interest, pictures or photographs, or even projected or transmitted views of the exterior or other scenes. This pattern addresses the first set of techniques—alcoves and window-like recesses in walls. Subsequent patterns describe the other techniques.

An alcove or recessed area in a wall is a three-dimensional indentation of the wall surface. It may be nearly the size of the entire wall or it may be a small niche. In some cases a recessed wall area may have a glass window over it similar to a commercial display window. While an alcove seldom if ever creates the illusion that it is an actual window with an exterior view, its depth breaks the plane of the wall and suggests space beyond the surface.

Figure 9-19: In this underground office building naturally lighted alcoves containing plants are a simple means of providing surrogate windows. (National Arts Education Center; architect: The Benham Group, Oklahoma City)

Figure 9-20: An alcove containing sculpture is the focal point in a St. Petersburg subway station. The landscape painting behind the sculpture in the alcove creates the illusion of an outside window view.

Successfully creating an alcove that enhances the interior environment depends on the contents of the alcove and its lighting. Plants and rocks in an alcove provide a connection with nature and may even give the illusion of looking into a small courtyard. This effect is enhanced by a bright, hidden light source in the ceiling of the alcove. Light that is the color of natural light can appear to be a skylight, and the higher level of light at the perimeter of a room tends to make it appear more spacious. A fish tank set into a wall recess with lighting from above can also serve as a point of visual interest and give a sense of depth beyond an interior wall. The movement and color of fish along with the natural associations with water, plants, and rocks can make it a very appealing feature of a windowless environment. Manmade objects, such as sculpture, artifacts, or even the display of two-dimensional artwork in alcoves or wall recesses, can provide visual stimulation and enhance spaciousness. Particular types of flat artwork and its effects are discussed in Pattern 9-8. A related design approach is to backlight translucent panels (such as stained glass or paper partitions), either within an alcove or simply along the wall plane (see Pattern 10-4).

Some alcoves or wall recesses may not actually contain anything of visual interest. They may simply exist to break up the wall plane or in some cases to create the illusion of a window. For example, a light well above eye level may appear to be a view up into an overcast sky. This type of wall recess must be above eye level or the illusion will be lost because it will be obvious there is no view (Hopkinson and Collins 1970). Rather than simply being viewed from the room, larger, deeper alcoves can also be used as workspaces or sitting and meeting areas. This leads to a more visually complex and differentiated space which appears more spacious and interesting (see Pattern 8-10). A series of alcoves can also be used to create the illusion of a series of window niches when viewed obliquely (see Pattern 10-3).

PATTERN 9-8: PAINTINGS AND PHOTOGRAPHS

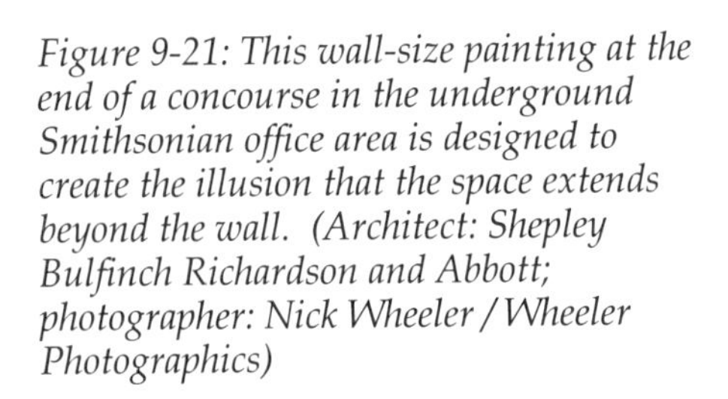

Figure 9-21: This wall-size painting at the end of a concourse in the underground Smithsonian office area is designed to create the illusion that the space extends beyond the wall. (Architect: Shepley Bulfinch Richardson and Abbott; photographer: Nick Wheeler / Wheeler Photographics)

Use paintings and photographs to provide color and visual interest in underground spaces. Select paintings or photos with natural elements—notably water, trees, and mountains—and scenes that create the illusion of extended views to enhance a feeling of spaciousness.

Paintings and photographs on the walls of an underground, windowless space can provide color, beauty, and visual stimulation just as they can in any interior environment. The size, depth of field, and content of a painting or photograph can also affect other important issues in underground design such as spaciousness and connection with the outside (and natural) world. Creating a sense of spaciousness is most strongly related to the perspective or depth of field in a painting. A wall-size mural that appears to extend the space of a room can be an effective optical illusion. A notable example of such a painting is found at the end of a concourse in the below-grade Smithsonian Museum offices. On the end wall of a long, narrow space, a one-point perspective clearly draws the eye into the painting and beyond the plane of the flat wall. Presumably a mural-size photograph could create a similar effect.

Of particular interest in relation to artwork in windowless spaces is the question of content. Since one problem associated with underground environments is lack of connection with nature, are pictures of natural settings the most desirable? In observing workers in windowless offices, Robert Sommer noted his amazement at the frequency that workers hung landscape pictures and posters on the walls (Sommer 1974). Another study found that people in windowless offices used twice as many items of wall decoration than those in windowed offices, and that nature themes dominated (i.e., pictures of trees, flowers, landscape scenes, gardens, animals, and birds). In fact, 75 percent of the posters in the windowless offices had no buildings, people, or manmade artifacts compared with 58 percent for the windowed group (Heerwagon and Orians 1986).

Several reviews of existing research on views conclude that there is an emerging consensus supporting not only preferences for views of natural settings, but also the belief that they have relaxing and restorative effects on people (Ulrich 1979, 1986; Coss et al. 1989; Heerwagon 1990; and Wise and Rosenberg 1988). Often cited are the beneficial effects on hospital patients in post-operative recovery of natural views versus views of buildings (Ulrich 1984). Also, prisoners with views of natural settings reportedly experience fewer stress-related sicknesses (West 1986). Ulrich (1981) also found that slides of natural landscapes with vegetation, and particularly water, positively influenced subjects' emotional states.

In an effort to identify appropriate visual images for the decor of a space station, NASA researchers investigated subjects' preferences and reactions to viewing a diverse set of slides (Coss et al. 1989). They concluded that "subjects preferred photographs and paintings with the greatest apparent depth of field, irrespective of picture topic. This indicates the opportunity to look outside a confined environment is a very desirable attribute that can be simulated by spacious photographs and paintings of landscapes." Soviet experiences in space reinforce this preference for visual images from nature.

From these various studies on desirable views and images, preferred features emerge: scenes depicting water or moist vegetation, and scenes with apparent depth of field, especially distant mountain ridges with low hills and sparse trees in the foreground. Landscape views that provide a sense of "mystery" with partially occluded backgrounds are more fascinating to

Figure 9-22: In Stockholm subway stations artists have painted designs directly onto the exposed rock caverns.

observers (Ulrich 1981, 1984). It is also suggested that views of spacious park-like settings will elicit more pleasant emotional responses than other landscape scenes such as dense forests or deserts. This is based on the theory that such scenes are similar to ancient habitat preferences on the African savannah that continue to persist within the human species (Orians 1980).

While natural landscapes appear to be preferred and beneficial compared with other visual images, abstract paintings also have the power to influence feelings of spaciousness, provide visual stimulation, and establish connections with the natural world. A remarkable set of examples of paintings in underground settings can be found in Stockholm subway stations where completely abstract as well as naturalistic elements are painted directly on the rock walls and ceilings. Likewise, photographic or painted images of people, animals, or manmade settings with positive associations can enhance the interior environment. Unlike windows, however, all photographs and paintings are static. Opportunities to change artwork over time and for people to select art for their own spaces are likely to be effective.

Figure 9-23: A landscape painting is placed behind this conventional window in an underground house. The light intensity changes during the day, and a fan blows when the window is opened. This approach raises questions about the desirability of creating obviously false illusions.

Visual images in the interior environment need not be static. Projected slide images or high-definition video images can create a "surrogate window" that is quite dynamic. These approaches are discussed in Pattern 9-9.

An issue of concern in using artwork or other techniques to create the illusion of a window is whether or not they will appear "fake." A large wall painting, or even a mirror, designed to extend the feeling of space can create an optical illusion that may mislead or even confuse the observer initially, but once understood will not necessarily be regarded negatively as a trick. Likewise, a landscape painting will evoke positive associations with nature, even though it is never mistaken for an exterior view. In some cases, however, designers of underground environments attempt to imitate windows directly with more negative results. An example of this is the design of a completely underground house where a conventional exterior window with curtains is placed in the blank wall. Just outside is a painting of a landscape. When the window is opened, a fan commences to blow the curtains and as night approaches, the lighting over the painting dims. None of these elements above is necessarily objectionable, but their obviously theatrical application seems to draw attention to what is missing—in effect, that one is in a false, artificial environment pretending to be something else.

PATTERN 9-9: TRANSMITTED AND REFLECTED EXTERIOR VIEWS

Provide exterior views to isolated underground spaces by reflection with optical devices or by transmission with video systems. High-quality video systems may also enhance the interior by providing visual images, information, and entertainment that is not related to the immediate building exterior environment.

The final category of so-called "surrogate windows" are systems that actually provide a view of the exterior either optically with lenses and mirrors or electronically with video transmission. Even though an underground space may be quite isolated from the surface, a view can be reflected through a narrow shaft or video cables can easily be run to any location. The advantage of these systems compared with other interior views is that they can provide current information about the immediate exterior environment—weather conditions, changes in light, and activity.

A simple reflected view device exists in the Fort Snelling Visitor Center in Minneapolis, Minnesota. Office workers sitting at desks two levels below grade see a large angled mirror set into a wall recess that provides an image reflected off another mirror above. It is similar to a simple periscope, but the exterior view can be seen from virtually any seated position in the rooms. A more complex periscope device is used in the Civil and Mineral Engineering Building, also in Minneapolis (Carmody and Sterling 1983). The view is provided to an office area over 30 meters below grade through a series of lenses with angled mirrors at the top and bottom of the shaft. Here, the designers chose to maximize the depth or three-dimensional aspect of the image but at the expense

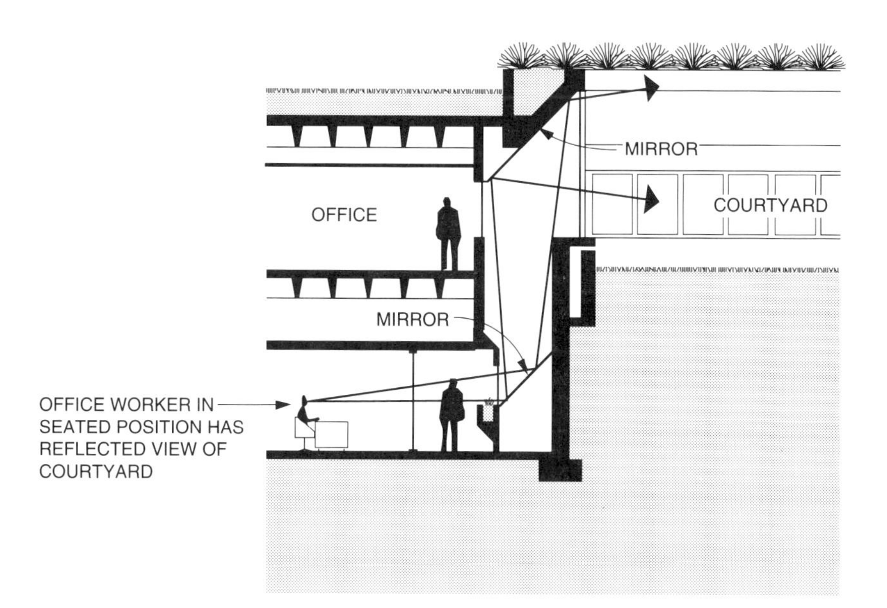

Figure 9-24: Workers in this underground office building in Minnesota can see outside using angled mirrors that work like a simple periscope. (Architect: BRW Architects)

of only seeing it from one position. Thus it lacks the feeling of a window that is seen from different places in a room and is used more like a periscope on a submarine. People must go to the viewing position to receive information about the exterior.

If an exterior view of the immediate surroundings is in fact a desirable enhancement to the windowless environment, then video transmission presents another technological avenue. Unlike an optical system that is likely to be fixed in position, a video camera on the surface could be rotated by remote control to provide a variety of views from the surface. Video technology has been widely used for security purposes but seldom to act as a "surrogate window." These systems are limited in that the video image on a typical monitor is not large compared to a window, it does not have extremely high resolution, and it has a two-dimensional look to it. In addition, the depth and clarity of a high-quality optical image are lacking. However, improved technology may soon be able to provide a larger scale high-definition video image that is very realistic.

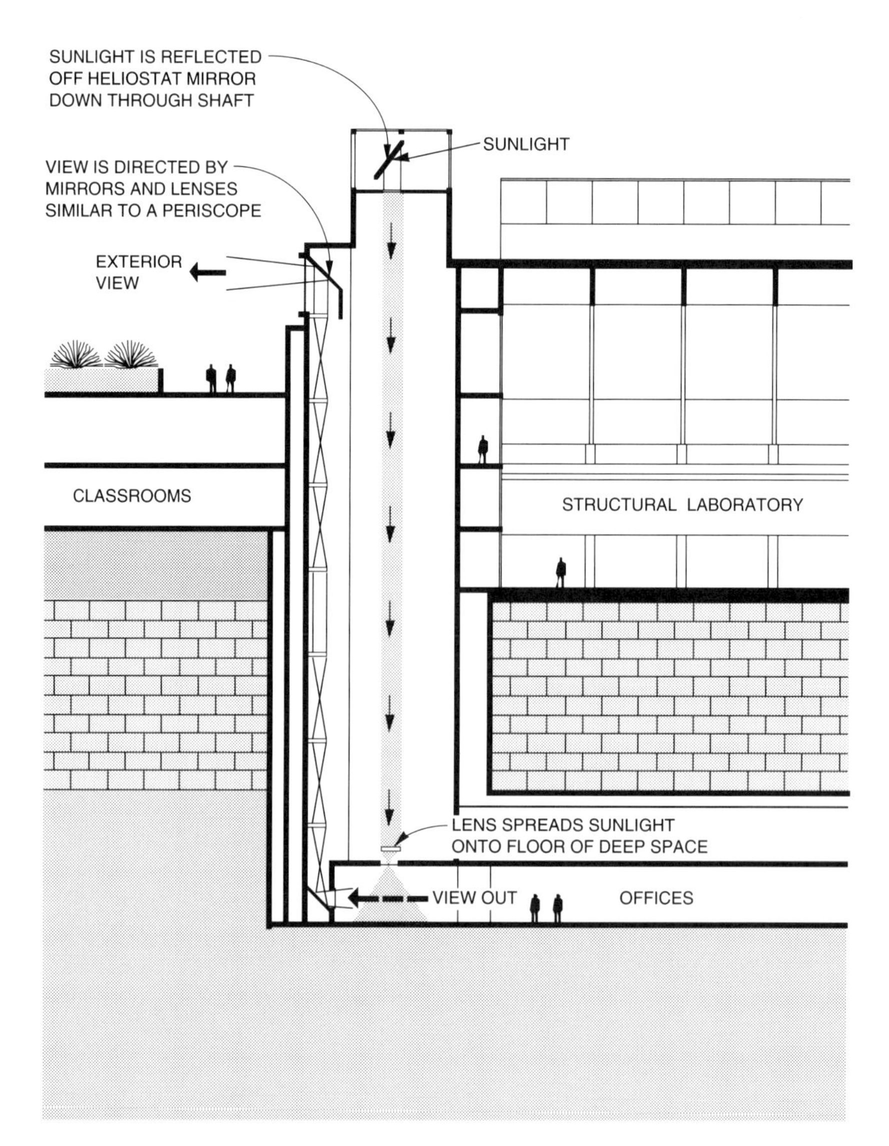

Figure 9-25: In the Civil and Mineral Engineering Building at the University of Minnesota, a periscope-like device provides outside views to offices over 30 meters below grade. Also shown in the drawing is a system that relects sunlight down a shaft to offices in deep mined space (see Chapter 10).

The use of high-quality video technology to provide a surrogate window raises other possibilities that go beyond simply providing an exterior view of the outdoors above the building. Video transmission from other locations is possible, as well as tapes of entertainment, information, or desirable natural views such as the ocean or mountain scenery. Unlike other visual devices, video has the added dimensions of sound and movement as well as the potential for continuous change. If the purpose of this video view window is to provide either relaxing or stimulating images rather than information from the outside environment, then projected slides are another medium that could be used in a similar manner.

In some work settings, the computer screen is the predominant visual focus for people. If computer screens become larger and higher in resolution and are used to provide information in video images, photographic images, and animations, the line between the computer screen and a video view window as described above begins to blur. In effect, with the potential for more communication to occur through the computer, the screen becomes the person's window to the world. This type of use is not restricted to the workplace.

This approach of providing views, information, and possibly entertainment through transmitted or projected images raises a number of questions: (1) Can these images actually appear realistic enough to have the desirable effects associated with windows? (2) What types of images produce what effects, and when do they become distracting? (3) What is the impact of sound, movement, and continuous change on the desirability of these images? and (4) What is the appropriate use of the technology?—i.e., a continuous background of a soothing natural landscape, or a special projection room where a sequence of images can be selected to provide a mental break on occasion.

Some researchers are beginning to explore the use of video and other viewing technologies in everyday settings (Wada and Sakugawa 1990). Soviet factories sometimes utilize "psychological relief rooms" that provide fatigued workers with 10-minute simulations of wilderness settings using music and large back-illuminated slide images (Mel'nikov 1978). Similar techniques of providing illusory nature experiences have been used in Soviet space stations and may be applied in the U.S. space program (Clearwater and Coss 1991). As both optical and video technology continue to develop, the opportunity to create realistic visual images in the interior environment may become a powerful tool for designers.

PATTERN 9-10: CLEAR SYSTEM OF SIGNS AND MAPS

Figure 9-26: In Tokyo subway stations large photographs of the buildings just above the exit help people maintain their orientation.

In all underground facilities, provide a clear, complete system of signs and maps to assist in wayfinding and maintaining spatial orientation.

An important aspect of interior design is the system of signs, graphics, and maps that people use to find their way in a building. Spatial orientation is a particular problem in underground facilities because many of the normal visual cues provided by windows (i.e., a glimpse of the ground plane, the sky, or surrounding landmarks) are missing. Moreover, the exterior form and extent of the building are often not clear, leading people to feel they are in a labyrinth of convoluted passageways. These problems can be alleviated to some extent by following the patterns in Chapters 7 and 8, which are intended to make the layout and organization of an underground building as clear as possible. But even in well-organized, legible buildings, clear signs and maps are necessary to reinforce and assist people.

Romedi Passini (1985), who has analyzed problems in orientation and wayfinding in complex underground facilities in Montreal, notes the importance of effective signage:

> *Signs and maps, it appears, are not second class supports for badly designed settings, but information systems which complement information obtained from other environmental sources. Signs in particular are relied upon by a large segment of the population which finds it difficult to mentally represent complex indoor settings. A given sign ... has a good chance to be perceived only if it occurs at a moment when such information is sought.*

The key problems with many sign systems are: (1) the information is not accessible, (2) the information is unclear or ambiguous, and (3) the information cannot be distinguished in an overloaded visual environment.

The following guidelines will assist in designing a system of signs to aid orientation and wayfinding (Passini 1984, 1985):

1. The signs pertaining to wayfinding must be visually accessible from relevant circulation routes.
2. The signs must be sufficiently differentiated from the general background.
3. The signs must have consistent design features so they can be easily recognized, particularly in complex settings.
4. The signs must be in consistent and predictable locations, particularly in complex settings.
5. The wayfinding signs must be differentiated from other types of signs such as advertising.
6. The message on signs must be sufficiently large to be read from a distance, particularly from an obvious point where a decision must be made.
7. The information on signs must be visually structured in small packages of three or four components.
8. Identification and directional signs should be easily distinguished from each other.
9. Sign messages must be unambiguous so they can only be read with one meaning.
10. Well-known terms should be used. (In one Montreal complex, "floors" were referred to as "sections" leading to considerable confusion.)

Maps can provide an overview of the facility and assist people both in finding an appropriate route to their destination as well as giving them an understanding of the overall organizing principle of the building. Just like sign systems, maps must be designed and located to avoid the following problems: (1) inaccessibility, (2) ambiguous, unclear information, or (3) too much information leading to overload. The following guidelines will assist in designing useful maps in an underground setting (Passini 1984, 1985):

1. Maps must be visually accessible from the relevant circulation routes.
2. Maps must be aligned with the surroundings so people do not have to make complicated mental rotations to orient themselves.
3. The information must be packaged according to content. For example, major destination and functional zones (i.e., offices, commercial, parking) should be distinguished.
4. Information must be packaged in small units of not more than three to four names to facilitate reading at a glance.

Figure 9-27: In this Helsinki underground shopping and transit complex, a large compass on the floor is intended to assist people in wayfinding.

5. Messages must be unambiguous so they can only be read with one meaning.
6. Maps should not be overly complicated. Information not required for wayfinding should be minimized.
7. Maps should emphasize the key recognizable elements that contribute to forming a strong image of the facility: key circulation paths, activity nodes, landmarks, zones, and the overall boundaries of the building.

In addition to using conventional signs and maps, other graphic devices that aid orientation in underground environments can be used. Subway stations in Stockholm, Helsinki, and Osaka have compass patterns set into the floor indicating the cardinal directions. Signs near exits from Tokyo subway stations sometimes include wall-size photographs of the above-grade scene just outside that particular exit. Not only do the photographs help passengers visualize where the exit will lead, they also are a visually attractive addition to otherwise very plain interior spaces.

Particularly in an underground setting where spatial orientation is a potentially greater problem, effective systems of signs and maps are important but must be part of an overall design that is easily understood. As Passini (1985) notes:

> *Wayfinding design does not only concern itself with signs and maps, but includes also the conception of space and the use of architectural elements. We should be thinking of wayfinding from the very beginning of the design conception. . .*

PATTERN 9-11: WELL-VENTILATED, COMFORTABLE ENVIRONMENT

Design the mechanical system in underground buildings to provide a high level of thermal comfort, an acceptable humidity level, and adequate ventilation to overcome air quality problems. To compensate for images of stuffiness, coldness, and dampness underground, make ventilation air movement perceptible and provide slightly warmer, dryer, and better-ventilated space than is typically designed.

In any space, the heating, ventilating and air-conditioning (HVAC) system is designed to meet several objectives. The temperature must be maintained within a comfort range—usually taken as an air temperature of 73° to 78°F and a relative humidity between 40 and 60 percent (Flynn et al. 1988). The comfort range varies depending on the level of activity, the density of people, duration of occupancy, sex and age of occupants, and the geographical location of the building. Recent studies on the detrimental health effects of various biological pathogens have increased support for lowering acceptable humidity levels to 20 to 35 percent, particularly in the heating season when colder walls cause condensation that enables biological growth. Feelings of thermal comfort are also influenced by air movement and the radiant heat flow that occurs when room surfaces are warmer or cooler than the air temperature. In addition to heating and cooling, the ventilation system mixes fresh air with recirculated air to replenish oxygen, as well as to remove odors and other pollutants.

In most cases, underground spaces naturally maintain a more moderate temperature than the surface environment. This effect increases with depth to the point where underground temperatures will be virtually constant year round. For example, in Minneapolis, Minnesota, the ground temperature at depths greater than 25 feet is a close to constant 50°F, and slightly higher than the annual average outdoor air temperature. This characteristic, along with very limited infiltration and solar heat gain, tends to conserve heating and cooling energy. However, openings to the surface increase heat losses and gains while the need to provide fresh air and reduce humidity requires energy expenditure to maintain comfort. Ultimately, most underground buildings occupied by people are designed with conventional HVAC systems that are intended to maintain desired temperature, humidity, and ventilation.

Figure 9-28: In windowless environments it may be advisable to provide visible ventilation ducts and a noticeable level of air movement to avoid complaints about stuffiness and air quality.

A critical question in HVAC design for underground spaces is whether they require any special attention or unique design approaches to deal with the perceived psychological and physiological concerns. Three key issues are often the source of complaints in actual underground buildings and also seem to contribute to the negative imagery of underground space. These are (1) coldness, (2) dampness, and (3) stuffiness, lack of adequate ventilation, or poor air quality. While a conventional HVAC system is technically capable of providing heat and controlling humidity within acceptable ranges, in practice they sometimes fail (Sterling and Carmody 1990). In some cases, heat is radiated away

Figure 9-29: In this 100-foot-deep manmade rock cavern the temperature is relatively moderate and constant throughout the year, however humidity levels can be quite high. This space, shown here under construction, is currently utilized for offices and laboratories at the University of Minnesota. In order to provide healthy, comfortable conditions in a space like this, the mechanical system must be designed to respond to these unique conditions.

from people to the colder surfaces of a cavern or underground enclosure in spite of the air temperature being maintained in the comfort range. In other cases, the ambient humidity may be higher than that normally encountered in a conventional building because the conventional process of air-conditioning may not sufficiently regulate the humidity levels for underground structures. Underground structures (which may have a heat loss to the ground year round) typically require a higher ratio of humidity removal to actual cooling than do surface structures.

To alleviate the feeling of coldness due to radiant heat loss, the interior air temperature can be raised or the wall temperature can be increased by placing insulation between the interior surface and the cold ground. To alleviate persistently humid conditions, the building should be sealed as much as possible from surrounding ground moisture sources, and then an HVAC system should be designed that can provide well-controlled dehumidification on demand.

Lack of adequate ventilation can occur because of poor mechanical system design. Being tightly sealed, underground buildings do not have the forgiving quality of permitting fresh air to enter through infiltration. While HVAC systems can be effectively designed to ventilate underground spaces, the perception of stuffiness may be as important as the actual conditions. Without operable windows, people may feel they have less fresh air with effective interior mixing available, and the option of opening a window is clearly missing, undermining their sense of control. In addition to providing fresh air and removing pollutants and odors, it may be necessary to ensure that the ventilation is perceptible and can be controlled in individual spaces. One example of the need for perceptible ventilation is a windowless factory where workers complained of stuffiness. While the system in fact was providing adequate ventilation, workers felt confined in a windowless plant where they could not feel a breeze. After ribbons were attached to the ventilation supply grills that visibly demonstrated the air flow, the complaints became negligible (Gilmer 1966). Table 9-1 gives the subjective evaluations associated with background air motion. Because there is a need to compensate for images of stuffiness, as well as coldness and dampness, it may be advisable to provide slightly warmer, dryer, and better ventilated space underground than is required in a conventional setting. Providing controls for these conditions in individual spaces not only ensures a better quality environment for the occupants, it also increases their satisfaction precisely because they have some control.

Placing people in deep, isolated underground spaces may require a fundamentally different approach to ventilation. Extending fresh air supply ducts from the surface to spaces 100 meters deep or more may be difficult and costly. At substantial depths it may be appropriate to rely principally on recirculated air with effective filtration and oxygen supply similar to the systems found in spacecraft or submarines.

Another possible design approach is to create intentionally some variation in the thermal environment. Gerlach (1974) has suggested that temperature variations of a few degrees help alleviate boredom and tedium, thus maintaining alertness and productivity. This concept fits into the overall goal of seeking moderately stimulating variation in all aspects of underground environments.

A final intriguing aspect of the indoor environment in relation to air is its smell. While a basic function of an HVAC system is to remove odors to create a neutral background, recent research has

Table 9-1: Evaluations of background air motion.

Air Speed at Head Level (feet per minute)	Subjective Evaluation
less than 15	Complaints about stagnant air when other atmospheric conditions lie in the comfort range
15-25	Favorable; basis for *effective temperature (ET) chart*
25-50	Favorable when atmospheric conditions lie in the comfort range; summer comfort range: 71-73 ET
50-100	Subtle awareness of air movement, but generally comfortable when temperature of the moving air is at or slightly above room air temperature; summer comfort range: 75-77 ET
200-700*	Increasingly drafty conditions; increasing complaints about the adverse effects of *wind* in disrupting a task, an activity, or personal composure

* There are some preliminary indications that localized and intermittent introduction of moderate velocity room temperature air at head level will induce temporary stimulation in an occupant who is involved in long-term activities or work tasks.

Source: Flynn et al. 1988.

suggested that certain scents or aromas can be injected into the environment through the HVAC system with notable effects on people. Lemon, jasmine, and lavender fragrances have been utilized in office environments in Japan, resulting in increased productivity for certain tasks and more positive evaluations of the indoor environment (Hashimoto et al. 1989). Particular scents are associated with reducing anxiety and inducing alertness or relaxation. The scents are injected intermittently and at a barely perceptible level, which avoids the problem of losing sensitivity to the smell during continuous exposure.

Researchers at Warwick University in England have used smells with positive associations to induce feelings of relaxation. Ocean smells combined with the sound of waves produced a relaxing effect on some subjects. It is believed that smells are crucial factors in determining moods, and once a person associates the ocean smell with relaxation, a brief exposure can reduce anxiety (Nuttall 1988). The olfactory environment is clearly a potentially important component of the overall interior, but it is a relatively new area requiring further research and exploration. In underground environments, the use of fragrances that elicit associations with nature and natural environments may be an effective design technique.

CHAPTER 10

by John Carmody

Lighting

Design Issues and Problems

While lighting is only one of many considerations in the interior design of a building, it takes on a fundamental and multifaceted importance in the design of underground spaces. Associations with darkness are frequent in underground imagery, and lack of windows and natural light are among the most commonly cited drawbacks of below-grade facilities. If underground spaces are designed to be positive, healthy environments for people, both natural and artificial light will play a significant role. Light is the medium for all visual experience and thus is integral to creating perceptions of spaciousness, providing definition and character in spaces, as well as simply providing light to facilitate the performance of activities and tasks.

In the design of underground environments, providing natural light may fundamentally shape the entire building layout. For example, creating naturally lighted sunken courtyards and atriums may be the major organizing principles of the facility. On the other hand, it simply may not be possible to provide natural light to deep isolated spaces by conventional means. In either case, artificial lighting must be designed to alleviate a number of negative associations with underground facilities. The key design problems related to lighting in underground buildings are:

1. Windowless spaces lack the stimulation and connection with nature provided by outside views and sunlight. Conventional uniform, overhead artificial lighting contributes further to a monotonous interior environment.
2. Because there are no windows, there can be a sense of confinement underground.

Figure 10-1: Conventional, uniform overhead fluorescent lighting is monotonous, does not define space, and does a poor job of rendering objects in three dimensions.

3. Underground space is often associated with darkness and coldness.
4. Most artificial lighting lacks the characteristics of sunlight, which raises physiological concerns in environments without any natural light.

The Desire for Natural Light

Except for certain functions where it is clearly unwanted, such as in theaters or laboratories, natural light seems to be regarded universally as an enhancement to any interior space. This value is reflected in *A Pattern Language* by Christopher Alexander et al. (1977): ". . . buildings which displace natural light as the major source of illumination are not fit places to spend the day." Although sunlight is an inconsistent light source that can contribute to problems of glare, overheating, and lack of adequate illumination, it is nevertheless preferred by people in many settings (Collins 1975). Three studies of office workers found that daylight

Figure 10-2: The desire for natural light is a fundamental issue in underground design. Skylights significantly enhance the underground Firestone Library at Princeton University. (Architect: Koetter, Kim and Associates; photograph: © Jeff Goldberg / Esto)

is strongly preferred as a superior source of illumination (Wells 1965; Markus 1967; Manning 1965). There is also a widespread desire for sunlight in residential buildings (Hopkinson 1967; Bitter and van Ierland 1967; Holm and Roessler 1972). In a hospital setting, 90 percent of the patients found sunlight desirable; however, 62 percent of the hospital staff thought it to be a nuisance (Longmore and Ne'eman 1974). This latter finding reflects the functional differences of a patient's room where the sunlight is a pleasant feature to be enjoyed, and an operating room, for example, where control of heat, glare, and illumination is essential.

This apparent preference may reflect not so much the absolute superiority of sunlight as an illumination source, but the deficiencies of most artificial lighting. In most cases people do not utilize natural light as a sole source of illumination but view it as an important complement to artificial lighting. In one study, people who worked over 20 feet from a window significantly overestimated the contribution of daylight to their overall illumination (Wells 1965). Even though the contribution of daylight was extremely low, preconceived attitudes and desires for natural light influenced their perception of its importance.

The desire for natural light in buildings raises some important questions in the design of underground space:

1. What are the precise attributes of natural light that make it preferred to most artificial light?
2. What are the physiological impacts of natural versus artificial light?
3. Can the qualities of natural light be obtained only through conventional windows and skylights, or can natural light transmitted through fiber optic cables, for example, produce similar benefits?
4. Can the qualities of natural light be replicated with artificial light so that it is perceived as equivalent?

The discussion that follows attempts to further define the first two questions. Some of the design patterns in this chapter are based on the hypothesis that natural light transmission systems as well as artificial lighting can be designed to offset at least partially the lack of natural light. It is important to emphasize that providing or simulating natural light has many facets and potential advantages. For example, lighting can be a powerful tool in solving problems such as creating spaciousness, warmth, and visual stimulation in a windowless environment.

Lack of Stimulation and Connection with Nature

One recurrent problem associated with windowless underground environments is lack of stimulation or variety. This is reinforced by overhead uniform fluorescent lighting which seems to predominate in nonresidential interiors. With this lighting there is no differentiation of space, no patterns of light and dark, and the overhead light source does a relatively poor job of rendering objects and faces so they can be seen clearly. In contrast, natural light

Figure 10-3: *Sloped glazing over office areas in this underground building are designed so that natural light penetrates to the lowest level of the multistory space. (Williamson Hall, University of Minnesota; architect: BRW Architects)*

typically enters a room from the side, producing horizontal lighting that renders objects more dramatically and clearly.

Natural light, through the slow continuous motion of the sun and the periodic influence of clouds, provides relief from monotony, information about weather and time of day, and contact with the outside world (Collins 1975). Even if the window or skylight cannot be seen, sunlight penetrates a space in a manner that brings the natural world indoors. The previous chapter suggests that nature is a good model for moderate yet fascinating stimulation within a predictable framework. Sunlight clearly has these characteristics and complements other interior elements (for example, falling water, plants, or sculpture).

Whether or not it is possible to provide sunlight in underground interiors, artificial lighting can be designed to create variety and stimulation in a number of ways. These include varying color, intensity, direction, and overall patterns of light and shadow. Other aspects of creating variety are providing change over time, and individual control of lighting.

Darkness, Cold, and Confinement

Darkness represents one of the fundamentally negative associations with underground space. Entering a cave or tunnel represents departure from light and nature and entry into a place of darkness and the unknown. Poorly illuminated basements that are not designed primarily for use by people often reinforce the dark image of underground places. Darkness can create an enjoyable sense of mystery but more commonly creates fear of the unknown, a somber mood, and dissatisfaction with an environment since visual clarity is diminished. Although patterns of light and dark may be desirable to create diversity and define spaces, providing a well-lighted interior in general will be beneficial to offset negative associations with darkness and underground space.

Other associations with windowless underground spaces are coldness and feelings of confinement or claustrophobia. Sunlight is often associated with warmth and its presence clearly will help offset images of coldness. Warm-colored artificial light also may alleviate this problem in some settings. Offsetting feelings of confinement involves the geometry of spaces, colors, furnishings, and materials. Light plays an important role in reinforcing various design techniques to enhance spaciousness in interior environments and can itself be a powerful tool in manipulating the perceived boundaries of space.

Physiological Concerns of Light

In addition to the many psychological associations with light, there are significant concerns related to its physiological effects. As Richard Wurtman (1968) states: ". . . it seems clear that light is the most important environmental input, after food, in controlling bodily function." The relationship between light and health is complex and multifaceted, and in many areas only fragmentary evidence exists. Nevertheless, many researchers have concluded that the impact of light on people deserves attention.

> *The human psychological system and the behavior which is linked to it evolved over millions of years. The whole of that evolution took place under the influence of the sunlight spectrum, to which particular light-sensitive and light-modulated organ systems are specifically adapted... We have all been participating in a nearly century-long and completely undocumented and unmeasured experiment on the effects of electrical lighting with deficient spectra. (Spivack and Tamer 1981)*

Sunlight is composed of ultraviolet, visible, and infrared radiation. The visible portion of the spectrum comprises a relatively even distribution of colors (see the adjacent figures). Incandescent light bulbs produce a significant amount of infrared radiation while the visible light is mainly at the red-orange end of the spectrum. The most commonly used fluorescent light bulbs (cool white) are predominantly yellow-green with relatively little ultraviolet radiation. Some fluorescent bulbs, referred to as full-spectrum, are designed to replicate the spectral characteristics of natural light more closely. Certain full-spectrum bulbs also are designed to replicate the ultraviolet portion of the natural light spectrum to provide the presumed health benefits (described below). The most important physiological effects of light are caused by the ultraviolet and visible portions of the spectrum and have been discussed by many researchers (Wurtman 1968; Levin and Duhl 1984; Mahnke 1987; Wurtman et al. 1985).

Ultraviolet radiation is divided into three ranges: (1) UV-A, or near ultraviolet, from 320-420 nanometers, (2) UV-B, or mid ultraviolet, from 280-320 nanometers, and (3) UV-C, or far ultraviolet, from 200-280 nanometers. The most notable health effect of ultraviolet radiation is the synthesis of vitamin D (califeral), which promotes the metabolism of phosphorous and calcium. The UV-B range produces this effect, but because window glass absorbs UV-B it usually is not transmitted even to people in naturally lighted spaces. Vitamin D deficiency may cause rickets, dental caries in children, or brittle bones in elderly people.

The incidence of dental caries was studied in two groups of schoolchildren—one in a school lighted by conventional cool-white fluorescent lamps and the other with full-spectrum fluorescent lamps containing UV-B radiation. The group under cool-white lamps had significantly higher rates of dental caries (Mayron et al. 1975). Earlier studies of dental caries in rats and hamsters under these same two types of light produced similar results (Sharon et al. 1971; Feller et al. 1974). It also was found that elderly patients under full-spectrum fluorescent light containing UV-B radiation exhibited increased calcium absorption while those under cool-white lamps experienced decreased calcium absorption (Neer et al. 1971). This effect was present even when vitamin D supplement was provided through dairy products.

Beyond the enhancement of vitamin D absorption, ultraviolet light has been associated with a broader range of health-related

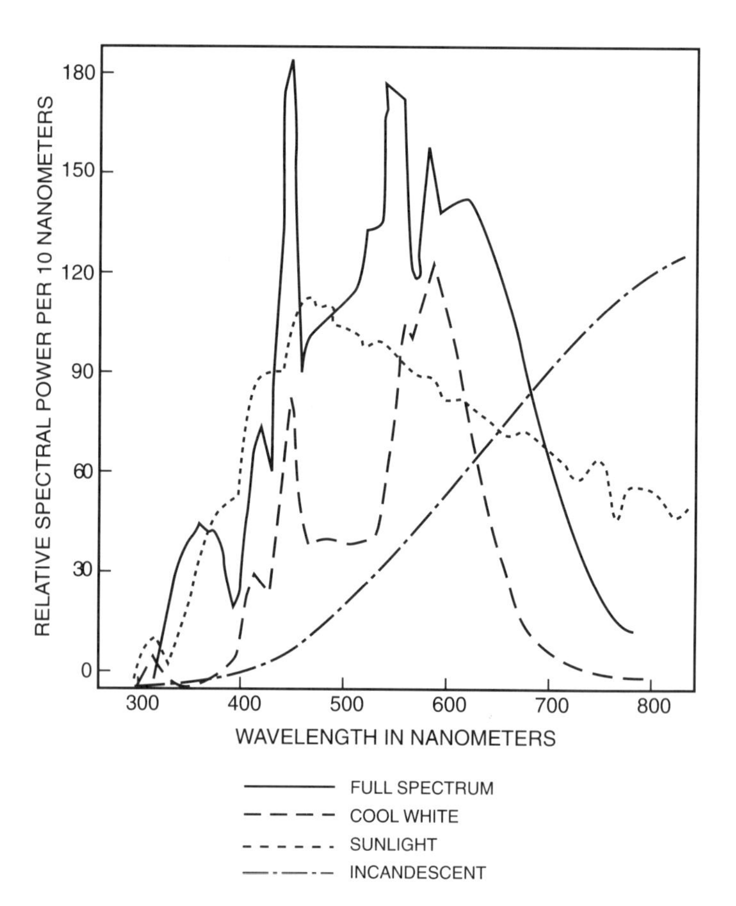

Figure 10-4: A comparison of the spectral characteristics of common light sources – natural light, full-spectrum fluorescent, cool white fluorescent, and incandescent bulbs.

effects by some researchers. Children in the Soviet Union irradiated with ultraviolet lamps in classrooms had a shorter reaction time to light and sound, lower fatigability of visual receptors, and an improved working capacity (Zamkova and Krivitskaya 1966). In addition, Soviet researchers report a reduction in the incidence of disease and an increase in overall immunological responsiveness in children irradiated with ultraviolet light (Dantsig et al. 1967).

While the health-related benefits of ultraviolet radiation appear well founded, overexposure also can cause problems such as skin cancer, photoallergies, and reddening of the skin. These concerns and the general uncertainty due to lack of definitive research have created a cautious attitude in some regarding the intentional introduction of ultraviolet radiation into artificial lighting. The amount of ultraviolet radiation required for vitamin D synthesis is relatively little—it can be obtained through exposure of the face and hands during a 15-minute walk. Yet many people, especially the elderly as well as those in northerly latitudes, do not receive this amount, at least during winter.

Light from the visible portion of the spectrum also has some significant physiological effects. In addition to enabling vision, light that enters the eye influences various biological functions. It affects the production of hormones throughout the endocrine system by influencing the pituitary and pineal glands (Wurtman 1968, 1969; Hollwich 1980). Stress-like levels of certain hormones have been found in subjects exposed to strong artificial light that deviates from the normal spectrum (Hollwich 1980). In a comparison of full-spectrum versus cool-white fluorescent lamps, hyperactive behavior in students was reduced significantly after a 60-day exposure to full-spectrum lighting (Mayron et al. 1974).

Another important impact of visible light appears to be related to the regulation of day/night cycles, or the so-called biological clock. In effect, light synchronizes the biological clock to maintain a 24-hour cycle. Wurtman (1969) has suggested that light suppresses production of the hormone melatonin in the pineal gland. When melatonin is released into the body during periods of darkness, it produces a reduction in alertness, vigilance, and reaction time.

It has been demonstrated that patients suffering from winter-long depression known as SAD (seasonal affective disorder) can obtain relief by exposure to very bright artificial light in the morning and afternoon that effectively extends the daylight period (Lewy 1982). Rosenthal et al. (1985) found that 2500 lux of full-spectrum light for three hours at dawn and dusk had an antidepressant effect on SAD patients. Other symptoms of SAD include decreased physical activity, increased carbohydrate craving, decreased energy level, irritability, and sleep disorders. While only a small minority of patients appear to suffer considerable debilitating effects from SAD, the connection between light and mood may exist to some degree in most people. According to one researcher, "The public response to press stories about winter depression, and the association of winter's dreariness with gloomy moods in ancient literature . . . indicate that sub-clinical winter depression could be quite prevalent" (Smith 1986).

Finally, the spectral characteristics of visible light appear to affect the clarity of vision. In one study, students studying for four-

Design Objectives Related to Lighting

1. Provide appropriate levels of illumination to enhance visual clarity and facilitate all activities. Spaces should be well lighted to offset associations with darkness underground.
2. Provide natural light whenever possible.
3. Design artificial lighting systems to simulate the characteristics of natural light.
4. Use lighting to enhance feelings of spaciousness.
5. Use lighting to create a stimulating, varied environment. Lighting patterns should help define and reinforce social spaces.

hour periods under full-spectrum light experienced better visual activity and less fatigue than students studying under cool-white lamps (Maas et al. 1974).

It is difficult to draw definite conclusions and design guidelines from the research on physiological effects of light. The effects being investigated are complicated and likely to take some time to be fully understood. Moreover, the impact of lighting on people in a particular space is mitigated by the amount of time they spend there and what they do, as well as individual differences in response. Nevertheless, some lighting researchers argue that the relationship between light and health is too important to ignore.

> *There is now abundant evidence that environmental lighting exerts more important effects upon human health and productivity, far beyond its requirements for vision ... Light has perhaps several hundred important effects on bodily functions, but only a few dozen are currently known and even a smaller number really understood. Since these particular biological effects presumably evolved in relation to a particular lighting environment, i.e., sunlight, filtered and reflected by atmospheric constituents, architects, lighting designers and engineers might be well-advised to be conservative about introducing great deviations from 'natural' lighting in designing the lighting environments in which people spend their working hours. (Wurtman 1973)*

Design Patterns Related to Lighting

This section presents several approaches for lighting design in underground facilities that meet the design objectives stated previously. The intention is to present the basic pattern or concept, discuss its characteristics, and illustrate it with a representative drawing and/or photograph. This does not imply that the pattern should be replicated in this exact manner. There are many diverse design responses that can be developed based on the objectives and approaches presented here. (See the last section of Chapter 6 for a discussion of putting these patterns into a larger context.)

The patterns discussed here are intended to be complementary to those related to exterior and entrance design (Chapter 7), layout and spatial configuration (Chapter 8), and interior design elements and systems (Chapter 9).

Lighting Design Patterns

10-1: Natural Light through Windows and Skylights

10-2: Transmitted and Reflected Natural Light

10-3: Artificial Light with Natural Characteristics

10-4: Skylights and Wall Panels with Artificial Backlighting

10-5: Indirect Lighting of Walls and Ceilings

10-6: Dark, Ambiguous Boundaries

10-7: Patterns of Light and Shadow

PATTERN 10-1: NATURAL LIGHT THROUGH WINDOWS AND SKYLIGHTS

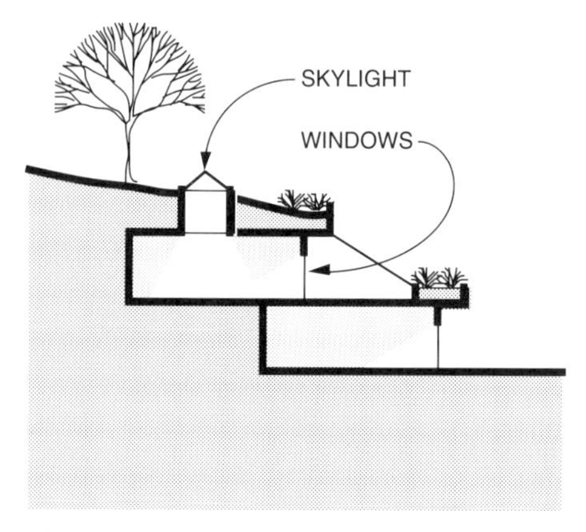

Figure 10-5: A hillside configuration permits natural light to enter through windows and skylights.

Whenever possible, provide natural light through windows and skylights in underground facilities.

In underground buildings near the surface, windows and skylights can provide natural light that significantly alleviates many of the negative characteristics associated with subsurface facilities. The natural light spectrum enhances visibility while daylight provides a calm constant source of illumination without the flickering characteristics of fluorescent lighting. Moreover, sunlight connotes warmth and a connection to the natural world. Sunlight provides information about time of day and the weather, and there is the subtle but constant stimulation created as light patterns change throughout the day.

A sloping site affords the opportunity to set a building into the hillside with at least one facade exposed (see Pattern 8-2). This

Figure 10-6: In the underground library at the University of Michigan, natural light from skylights penetrates three levels deep. (Architect: Gunnar Birkerts; photographer: Timothy Hursley)

Figure 10-7: Even in a corridor, a simple skylight enhances the interior space and provides a connection to the outdoors. (University of Minnesota Student Center; architect: BRW Architects).

configuration permits conventional windows to provide daylight into the spaces along the building perimeter. If the plan is elongated, sunlight may reach most spaces to give the interior a completely conventional character. Skylights can provide natural light to corridors and spaces away from the exposed facade.

On flat sites, skylights can provide natural light to the upper floor of an underground structure. Skylights over atriums or other multistory spaces such as a major building thoroughfare permit the natural light to penetrate further into lower levels of the structure. Then rooms that surround and overlook these multistory spaces benefit from the natural light as well. In a similar sense, an exterior sunken courtyard permits natural light to penetrate into the upper levels of an underground structure. Daylight enters the spaces surrounding the courtyard horizontally through conventional windows.

Providing natural light through these relatively obvious conventional design approaches can be among the most powerful techniques for offsetting negative reactions to underground buildings. Natural light is a welcome enhancement to most spaces, but it is a particularly important attribute of sunken courtyards and multistory atriums since they are frequently the visual focal points and spatial relief for the entire building.

A major limitation of this pattern is that it is only available to structures directly beneath the surface, not to isolated chambers reached by long tunnels or shafts. Even near-surface structures may be limited if the surface use (a road, for example) prevents placement of skylights or courtyard openings. Naturally lighted atriums, however, are not limited to shallow depths of two or three stories—just as they are used to provide space and light within very tall above-grade buildings, designers have suggested extending naturally lighted atriums to depths of 50 meters or more in large underground complexes. The distribution of natural light from all types of windows and skylights can be enhanced by certain reflecting devices discussed in Pattern 10-2.

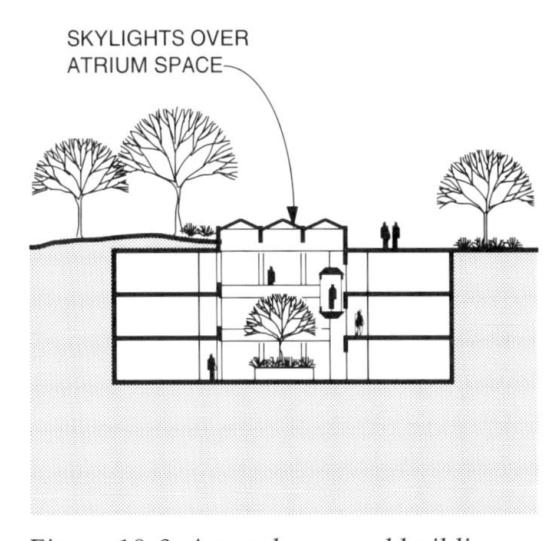

Figure 10-8: An underground building on a flat site using an atrium to provide natural light.

PATTERN 10-2: TRANSMITTED AND REFLECTED NATURAL LIGHT

When natural light enters an underground building through windows and skylights, reflect it off surfaces and other devices to maximize its penetration and distribution in the space. In deeper, more isolated spaces, use systems that transmit or reflect natural light into the building through shafts, conduits, or cables.

When natural light enters an underground building through skylights or windows (as described in Pattern 10-1), it is desirable to maximize the amount of light and distribute that light as much as possible throughout the building. Light-colored wall and floor surfaces reflect natural light from skylights and windows. Techniques such as wide window sills, light shelves, and special lowered blinds can reflect daylight upward toward the ceiling and thus distribute it further into the space. Light distribution will be enhanced by open plans or interior partition walls partially or completely made of glass. These techniques of redirecting natural light further into a sidelit space are useful in buildings with exterior windows exposed on a hillside site or around sunken courtyards as well as in spaces surrounding interior atriums. The use of holographic film on windows to direct the patterns of light passing through is an emerging technology that may have useful applications in underground space.

Utilizing large multistory atriums represents one of the most powerful techniques for creating spaciousness, visual interest, and natural light in an underground structure. Simply covering an atrium with glass, however, can result in overheating and glare problems. In addition, the natural light may reach predominantly the upper floors around the atrium and only penetrate to the lower floors during times when the sun is almost directly overhead. However, people on the lower floors are likely to require at least as much if not more daylight to enhance the interior environment.

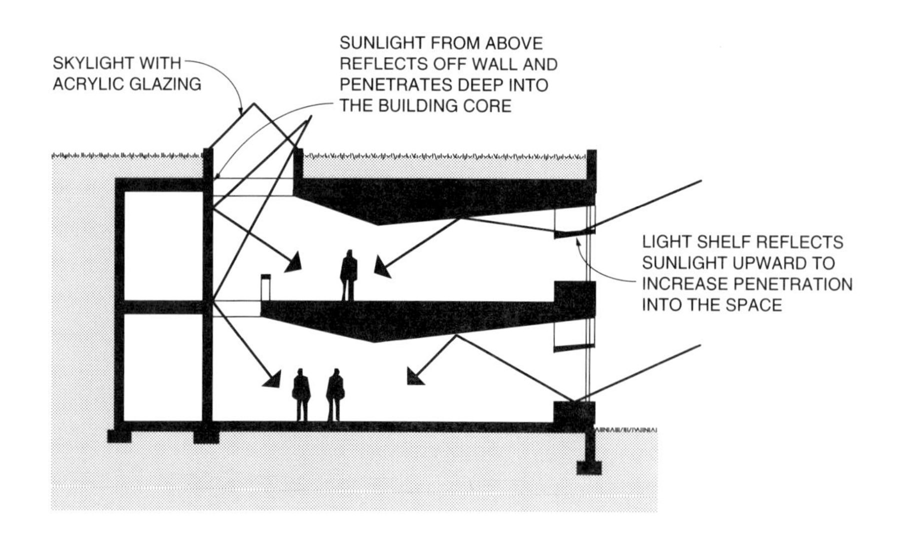

Figure 10-9: Light shelves and glass partition walls increase the penetration of daylight from windows. Light-colored, reflective walls and floors enhance the distribution of daylight from skylights.

Figure 10-10: Stationary reflecting panels on the roof of the Civil and Mineral Engineering Building concentrate and direct sunlight to a multistory space below. A heliostat device that reflects sunlight to spaces 100 feet below grade is housed in the cupola on top of the building. (Architect: BRW Architects)

One solution to this problem is to utilize arrays of stationary reflecting panels that direct light to secondary diffusing panels above the atrium. This approach has been applied to the Civil and Mineral Engineering Building in Minnesota, the Thresher Square Office building in Minnesota, and the 3M Austin Center in Texas. The solar lens reflecting film used in these systems follows the light transmission principles of the Fresnel lens, which directs and intensifies light. The panel systems are designed to capture sunlight at all times of day throughout the year and direct it downward to the atrium floor in a uniform manner. Only a portion of the array is in use at one time. In the Texas installation, the uniform, diffuse light is complemented by a few conventional skylights that provide the contrast and changing patterns of direct sunlight (Tilley 1990).

In the Hong Kong Bank building, natural light is provided to a 10-story atrium by a system of reflecting mirrors. Overhead skylights are not possible since the atrium only occupies the lower floors of the tall building. A large movable reflector panel on the side of the building directs sunlight to an array of mirrors on the atrium ceiling that reflect the light downward.

Another system for enhancing the delivery of natural light to an atrium consists of a series of moving mirrors that track the sun (Hane 1989). With this system, which is installed on a Tokyo office building, the entire array of reflecting surfaces is in position to direct sunlight downward to the atrium floor. During cloudy periods, the system remains stationary.

All the systems described above represent ways of enhancing and directing natural light entering through a window or skylight. In many cases, however, underground spaces are isolated and are only accessible through tunnels or shafts, so natural light from windows and skylights is not possible. Systems have been devised, however, that can transmit sunlight to isolated spaces. In the Civil and Mineral Engineering Building at the University of Minnesota, a rooftop heliostat tracks the sun and reflects a beam of light down a

Figure 10-11: Underground Space Center offices 35 meters below grade in the Civil and Mineral Engineering Building receive sunlight from a rooftop heliostat (see Figure 10-12).

narrow shaft to offices in a manmade cavern 35 meters below (Hane 1989). The heliostat consists of a single 2-meter-diameter rotating mirror enclosed in a glass cupola. In this system, the reflected sunlight is beamed through an open shaft until it passes through a single lens at the bottom, which spreads it into a 3-meter-square lighted area on the floor.

Another potential component of a beamed daylighting system is a light pipe, which is a hollow tube that is totally internally reflective (Whitehead et al. 1986). Natural or artificial light is transmitted to the space through translucent openings in the tube. Although not used with the University of Minnesota heliostat, light pipes have been employed to distribute sunlight from heliostats in other facilities. In addition to distributing natural light within a building, light pipes can be used with artificial lights in a remote location to permit easy lamp replacement and reduced heat gain compared with conventional fixtures. A hybrid system with daylight entering one end of the pipe and artificial light entering the other permits the system to function in all weather conditions and at night. It should be noted that the purpose of beaming daylight to isolated spaces is not necessarily to provide adequate illumination, but in some cases simply to provide a connection with nature by lighting a small courtyard or other point of visual interest.

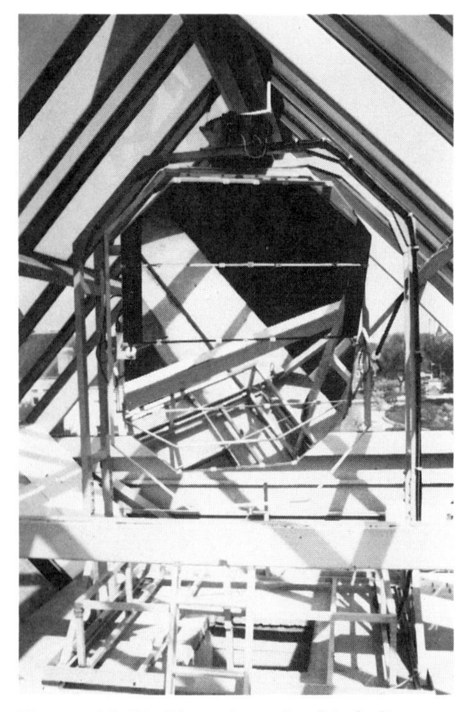

Figure 10-12: The mirror in this heliostat rotates to track the sun and directs light downward through a narrow shaft in the Civil and Mineral Engineering Building (see Figure 10-12).

The use of fiber optic cables is another technique for transmitting daylight to isolated spaces underground. On the surface or rooftop, light enters an acrylic resin capsule that contains a collection system composed of an array of small Fresnel lenses in a honeycomb pattern. These lenses focus the light rays onto the highly polished ends of fiber optic cables. In several applications in Japan, cables transmit natural light to areas of maximum benefit such as plant-filled atriums, displays, or lounge areas (Mori 1988). Unlike the reflecting mirrors, lenses, and tubes described previously, fiber optic cable can be bent and easily placed in small ducts, even in existing buildings. On the other hand, the cost of the cables is considerable compared to the amount of light delivered. Of course, the economics of emerging technologies can change rapidly. An interesting aspect of light transmitted with this system is that both infrared and ultraviolet light are intentionally excluded. While this is regarded as a significant benefit by the developer of this system, it is not consistent with researchers who suggest that appropriate amounts of ultraviolet light are desirable for health.

Transmission of daylight with beamed or fiber optic systems raises some important design issues. Although natural light is being provided, all the characteristics of natural light are not necessarily present. The color and lack of flicker are maintained and the knowledge that the light is natural provides some connection with the outdoors. However, if daylight emerges from a device that appears to be similar to a fixture for artificial light, then the slowly changing, stimulating effect of patterns of sunlight entering a window and crossing a room is lost. Information about the time of day and weather is not provided either, except that the sunlight is either completely "on" or "off."

These factors stress the importance of integrating interior design elements with lighting systems. A shaft of reflected or transmitted sunlight can be designed as a powerful highlight in a visually important area of plants or sculpture, for example, and the illusion of natural light from a window or skylight can be created, if desired.

Figure 10-13: Fiber optic cables receive sunlight from an array of Fresnel lens collectors on the rooftop of a Tokyo office building. Sunlight is transmitted by fiber optic cables to several below-grade spaces in the building.

PATTERN 10-3: ARTIFICIAL LIGHT WITH NATURAL CHARACTERISTICS

Design artificial lighting systems to simulate characteristics of natural light such as its color, lack of flicker, and variation in direction and intensity.

In many underground facilities, it is not possible to provide substantial amounts of natural light. Even when some natural light can be provided, it is unlikely that it can reach all spaces within the building and, in any case, it must be supplemented by artificial light. Since lack of natural light is regarded as a significant shortcoming in windowless buildings, one important approach is to design the artificial lighting system to simulate the characteristics of natural light.

The color spectrum of natural light is the easiest characteristic to simulate with artificial lighting. Fluorescent bulbs that closely replicate the spectrum of natural light simply can replace conventional bulbs of limited or distorted spectrum. Some full-spectrum bulbs are designed to emit ultraviolet radiation similar to that found in natural light to provide the presumed health-related benefits associated with this part of the spectrum. Full-spectrum bulbs hidden to give indirect light or placed above an artificial skylight can give a strong illusion of daylight (see Patterns 10-4 and 10-5). An important advantage of full-spectrum artificial light is that it improves visual clarity compared with conventional cool-white fluorescent bulbs (Flynn et al. 1988). According to Aksugur (1979), daylight fluorescent bulbs (approximately full-spectrum) make spaces appear larger than tungsten filament lamps. Other researchers appear to agree that in general, "cooler" color lamps (full-spectrum) aid in the impression of spaciousness compared with "warmer" color lamps (Watson and Payne 1968). Flynn and Spencer (1971), however, found that color had little effect on perception of spaciousness.

Figure 10-14: In this wndowless control room, an array of lamps above the skylight change color, intensity, and direction throughout the day to simulate sunlight. (Architects: Piera Scuri and Douglas Skene; photographer: Dida Biggi)

While full-spectrum artificial light appears to have numerous benefits for underground environments, it is not clear that it is desirable at all times or under all conditions. According to a study by Kruithof, when illumination levels are high, people prefer light with a cool color temperature, and when illumination is low, they prefer light with a warm color temperature (Mahnke 1987). Also, he reported that objects and surfaces have a normal color appearance under cool light at high intensity and warm light at low intensity. In this context, full-spectrum lighting should be classified as a "cool" light source. In another study, Kuller (1980) demonstrated that the preference for fluorescent daylight tubes (approximately full-spectrum) decreased in the evening. When it was dark outside, occupants found the full-spectrum artificial light became "unpleasant, unnatural, monotonous, cold, and hard."

This suggests that designing artificial light to simulate the characteristics of natural light involves more than changing its color to that of mid-day sunlight. The intensity and color of sunlight changes at dawn and dusk and, of course, the light disappears at night. Some designers have attempted to replicate these diurnal rhythms with artificial light in windowless spaces. Above "false" skylights in an industrial control room, architects Piera Scuri and Douglas Skene (1990) have devised an array of artificial lights that change in color, intensity, and direction throughout the day. At noon, for example, bright full-spectrum light is directed downward while at dusk a reddish glow at lower intensity appears on the western side the skylight. In windowless areas of an airport passenger lounge, the lighting designers change the intensity and color of light to correspond with the diurnal cycle outside (Linn 1988).

Another characteristic of natural light missing with most conventional artificial lighting is the way it enters a space from the side. Natural light from a window "models" interior elements in a manner that creates patterns of light and dark, making objects and faces more clear and more interesting (Wise and Wise 1984).

Researchers indicate that people dislike the modeling effects from conventional overhead uniform lighting systems. Overhead light sources are described as flat and boring, while horizontal light sources are desirable, especially for faces. A preferred range is 0° to 30° above the horizon and 45° from either side (Barton, Spivack and Powell 1972; Canter 1976). Creating this effect with artificial light using alcoves (see Pattern 9-7) has been suggested by Hopkinson (1970):

> *One of the pleasant features of a building with windows is the manner in which sunlight can stream through a window into the room, even though the window itself may be hidden by a return wall or by furniture in the room. This illusion can be created in a windowless enclosure, and it is an illusion which seems to remain even though the artifice is well understood. An extension of this device is to provide a number of alcoves down the length of a windowless space, lit to a very much higher level of illumination with the light of the color which sunlight would be expected to be... These alcoves have the effect of a row of rooms lit by sunlight and so enhance the appearance of the main room.*

Attempts to replicate daylight with artificial light appear to have been successful to some degree; however, creating false illusions can always have a negative impact if not handled carefully. As Jackson and Holmes (1973) note:

> *Much of the window's contribution to the built environment is classed as qualitative – there is a marked difference in the 'feel' of an interior lit from side windows as compared with normal electric lighting... Furthermore, the short term variations add an extra dimension to the daylit interior and undoubtedly contribute to the avoidance of monotony sometimes found under static installations. It is interesting that attempts to produce this effect in electric lighting seem strangely artificial and almost annoying.*

PATTERN 10-4: SKYLIGHTS AND WALL PANELS WITH ARTIFICIAL BACKLIGHTING

Place artificial lighting above translucent skylights and wall panels to create the illusion of natural light entering the space.

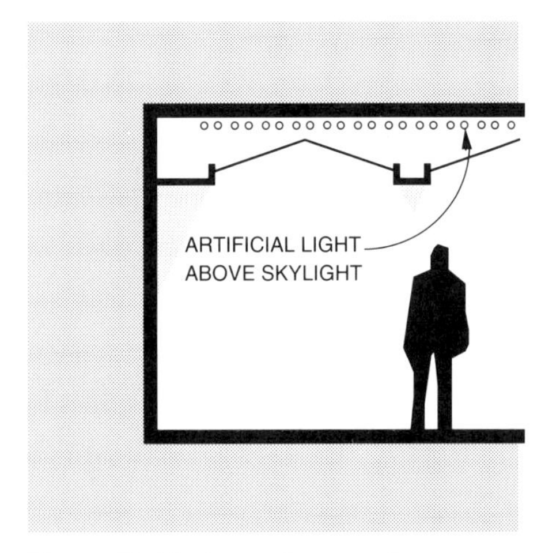

Figure 10-15: An underground space utilizing skylights with artificial backlighting creates the illusion of natural light.

The previous pattern (10-3) suggests that one approach to improve windowless spaces is to use artificial light to simulate the variation in color, intensity, and direction associated with natural light. In addition to replicating these characteristics using conventional light fixtures, the illusion of natural light can be enhanced by placing the artificial light (with natural characteristics) above skylights with translucent panels. If the panels are not flush with the ceiling but project upward, then spaciousness as well as visual interest are enhanced (see Pattern 8-11: High and Varied Ceilings). Since skylights often are translucent but not clear, this illusion can be quite close to reality.

A similar approach can be applied by placing artificial lights behind translucent walls or wall panels. Usually to enhance visual interest, the backlighted wall is composed of glass block or colorful stained glass, making the wall a significant decorative element. One notable example of this technique is found in an underground pedestrian concourse at O'Hare Airport in Chicago. Colorful, backlighted panels line the concourse, and their shapes and patterns are intended to emulate the form of a row of trees. Elsewhere in the same airport, undulating glass block walls, also lighted from behind, line the subway station platform. In traditional Japanese architecture, partitions of wood and translucent white paper divide spaces and sometimes are placed between the interior and exterior. A windowless space with similar partitions lighted from behind may appear similar to a space above grade.

Figure 10-16: The raised pyramidal form of these artificially lighted skylights enhances spaciousness. The flourescent lights above the skylight are the color of natural light and change in intensity during the day to simulate natural light. (Graduate student offices in the Civil and Mineral Engineering Building at the University of Minnesota; architects: John Carmody and Mike Melman)

Figure 10-17: In this train station at O'Hare Airport in Chicago, undulating glass block walls are backlighted in different colors. (Architect: Murphy / Jahn Architects)

One design approach that can be effective is to use translucent wall panels with backlighting to create an illusion of natural light entering through a conventional window. However, even if no illusion is intended, this design technique can enhance a windowless environment in several ways. As previously stated, they can introduce color and artwork to the interior. Also, light from behind translucent panels enters the space from the side. As discussed in Pattern 10-3, light from a horizontal rather than overhead source is preferred for visual clarity and interest when looking at objects and faces. Finally, any backlighted surface appears to have space on the other side of it. Instead of a flat wall, there is the implication of a more complex, ambiguously defined space which contributes to the overall perception of being more spacious (see Pattern 8-10).

PATTERN 10-5: INDIRECT LIGHTING OF WALLS AND CEILINGS

To enhance spaciousness in underground facilities, use uniform indirect lighting on perimeter walls and ceilings.

Figure 10-18: Uniform indirect lighting on walls makes a space appear larger.

Indirect lighting that uniformly washes the walls of a space appears to be a consistently effective technique to increase the perception of spaciousness in a room (Flynn et al. 1988; Boyce 1980). In a series of experiments in 1973, Flynn found that rooms with indirect peripheral lighting were always perceived as more spacious than rooms without it. Spaciousness is enhanced by a higher illumination level and by adding some diffuse overhead lighting to the peripheral lighting. In a similar fashion, indirect lighting of the ceiling makes that enclosing surface appear farther away as well. According to Aubree (1978), indirect lighting of walls and ceiling periphery by fluorescent lamps was preferred over other systems. The soft, diffuse character of indirect light seems to provide adequate illumination without the contrast and glare characteristics of visible bulbs.

The effect of making a space appear larger by brightening the peripheral enclosure may seem contradictory. Generally, a brightly lighted object against a more dimly lighted background will appear to advance or become closer than if the lighting were reversed. However, when the entire periphery is uniformly lighted to a bright level, this figure-ground contrast does not exist and the brightness draws attention to the periphery, making the overall enclosure seem larger (Tiedje 1987).

In addition to enhancing spaciousness and having a preferred quality of light, indirect wall and ceiling lighting appears to contribute positively to some more subjective design problems in underground space. For example, by simply raising the overall

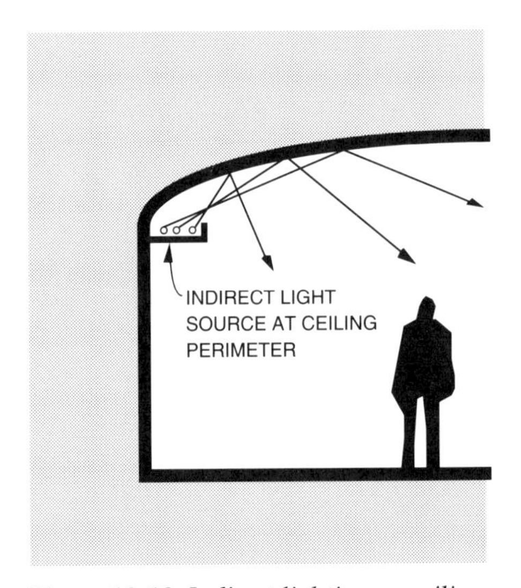

Figure 10-19: Indirect lighting on ceilings makes a space appear higher.

Figure 10-20: Indirect lighting on the ceiling of an underground shopping concourse in Montreal makes a relatively low space appear higher.

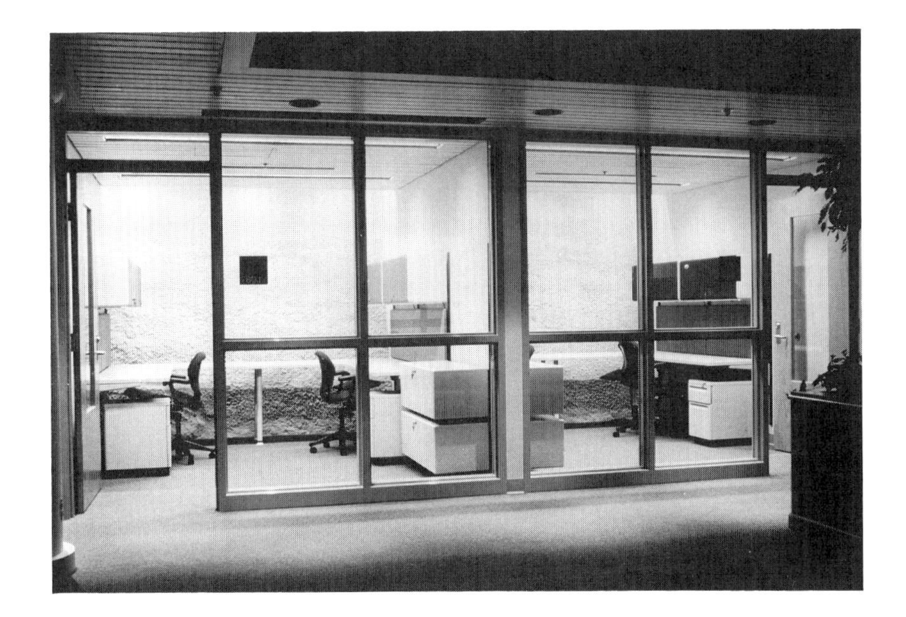

Figure 10-21: In this deep underground office area at the University of Minnesota, uniform indirect lighting is used on perimeter walls to make spaces appear larger and to highlight the texture of the exposed shotcrete finish. (Architects: John Carmody and Mike Melman)

level of illumination, associations with darkness are offset. In addition, by using full-spectrum light sources, indirectly lighted walls and ceilings can appear to be naturally lighted since the light source is not visible. In some cases, indirectly lighted ceilings create the feeling of being under the sky rather than a ceiling.

PATTERN 10-6: DARK, AMBIGUOUS BOUNDARIES

To enhance a feeling of spaciousness in underground settings, leave the peripheral surfaces in darkness to give the impression of infinite space.

In apparent contradiction to Pattern 10-5, which recommends high, uniform illumination on walls and ceilings to increase spaciousness, designers and some researchers have suggested that spaciousness can also be enhanced if the enclosure or periphery of a space is in darkness and thus its boundaries cannot be clearly perceived (Tiedje 1987; Ankerl 1981). In a museum or church setting, objects in the foreground are placed under bright light while the room periphery remains dark. This creates a feeling of awe and mystery as objects appear to float in a black void (Flynn et al. 1988). Brightly lighted objects in the foreground advance in relation to the dimly lighted background.

A notable set of examples of this design approach are the rock cavern subway stations in Stockholm, Sweden. Suspended light fixtures direct high levels of illumination downward to the floor, while the ceiling and walls of the caverns are dimly lighted. Attention is focused on the floor and furnishings which appear to some extent to float in an undefined dark cavern.

While this approach does seem to create an illusion of infinite space which is desirable in creating a spacious environment underground, it also creates a predominantly dark space. Darkness, particularly in a cave-like setting, is one of the characteristics often associated with negative imagery in underground facilities. Using this approach to create an unusual, mysterious environment may be quite stimulating and thus may be acceptable in a setting where people do not spend long periods of time (i.e., a subway or a museum), but relying on darkness to improve the habitability of windowless settings where people spend long periods of time seems to be a questionable strategy.

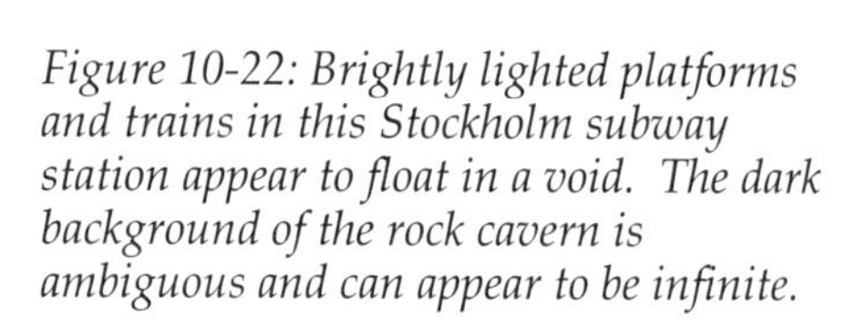

Figure 10-22: Brightly lighted platforms and trains in this Stockholm subway station appear to float in a void. The dark background of the rock cavern is ambiguous and can appear to be infinite.

PATTERN 10-7: PATTERNS OF LIGHT AND SHADOW

Figure 10-23: Patterns of light and shadow create variety in the interior environment, define spaces, and can be used to direct people along paths to important destinations. Lighting is effectively used in this underground museum to direct attention to the exhibits.

Create varied patterns of light and shadow in underground buildings to provide visual stimulation, to define social spaces, and to highlight pathways and landmarks that will aid in orientation.

Many of the patterns in this chapter have suggested techniques for creating a particular effect such as indirect lighting to achieve spaciousness or full-spectrum light to simulate the color of sunlight. It is important in lighting design, however, to recognize the multifaceted role lighting plays at various scales within a building. With respect to lighting, a building interior will be more stimulating, more legible, and ultimately emulate the desirable characteristics of the natural world if there are variations at many scales and in many ways in the lighting design. This does not imply variation simply for the sake of it, but variation to reinforce the definition of pathways and social spaces as well as to create special places and reflect different functions.

In *A Pattern Language*, Alexander et al. (1977) address this issue in a number of ways. "In a building with uniform light level, there are few 'places' which function as effective settings for human events. This happens because to a large extent, the places which make effective settings are defined by light." The authors suggest that people are naturally attracted to light, and thus it can be used to direct movement by increasing light levels at major destination points along a pathway. In effect, the system of paths, activity nodes, and landmarks described in Chapter 8 can be reinforced by light patterns of varying intensities. The key point is that the definition of space using light can only occur if there are corresponding areas of darkness.

Figure 10-24: Even in a simple corridor patterns of light and shadow create visual interest. The indirect light washing the walls creates a feeling of spaciousness as well, making the corridor appear intermittently wider.

Alexander et al. (1977) further emphasize the need for "pools of light." In their view, "Uniform illumination . . . serves no useful purpose whatsoever. In fact, it destroys the social nature of space and makes people feel disoriented and unbounded." They indicate that individuals concentrate better under a pool of brighter light with a less bright background than they do in uniform light. They further suggest that light must define boundaries not only for individual spaces but also to reinforce the common identity of groups functioning together in a space.

Finally, Alexander et al. state that humans did not evolve under a uniform sky but in places "with dappled light which varies continuously from minute to minute." This not only begins to suggest that nature may be a useful model for lighting design, but also that there are qualities of light in certain settings that should not be overlooked. They point out that the best-loved places in buildings are often defined by non-uniformities of light (window seats, verandas, and fireside corners), and that filtered light in particular has wonderful qualities: "Light filtered through a leafy tree is pleasant—it lends excitement, cheerfulness, gaiety, and we know uniform lighting creates dull, uninteresting spaces." Patterns of light and dark that correspond with the social function of spaces and achieve some of the special qualities of natural light will contribute to the creation of a rich, complex, and stimulating interior environment.

CHAPTER 11
by John Carmody

Life Safety

Design Issues and Problems

Life safety is frequently mentioned as an important design issue related to placing people in underground facilities. One reason is that most underground buildings present some physical constraints that require special design features to ensure basic safety in an emergency. A second reason is that fear of entrapment from fire, flood, or other disaster represents an underlying negative association with underground space. Thus, the perception of safety is important to ensure the occupants' sense of well-being and overall acceptance of an underground facility.

Figure 11-1: Fear of entrapment from fire, flood, or other disaster represents a basic negative association with underground space.

Generally, the natural and manmade disasters to be considered in design are fire, explosions, earthquakes, and floods, with fire being by far the danger of greatest concern in most underground buildings. All buildings must be designed so that unsafe conditions are avoided, emergencies are detected, the unsafe conditions (i.e., fire or flood) are alleviated as soon as possible, and people are evacuated to places of safety within a reasonable period of time. While the detection and nature of various types of emergencies differ, the fundamental design problem of efficiently evacuating people to places of safety is present in all types of disasters.

The purpose of this chapter is to present the life safety problems inherent in underground structures, to identify general design objectives, and then present possible design responses in the form of patterns. This chapter is not intended to cover all aspects of life safety in buildings nor is it intended to be a precise building code document. Individual underground facilities often present unique safety problems which must be analyzed by designers and local code officials. This chapter is instead intended to define key issues and suggest conceptual design solutions drawn from researchers attempting to develop standards in this evolving area (Degenkolb 1981; Wise and Wise 1984; Sterling et al. 1988; Tong 1990; Littlechild 1989). The focus is on fire safety and the evacuation of people. Fire is not only the most common emergency situation, it is also a major life-threatening result of explosions and earthquakes as well. Structural design for earthquakes as well as waterproofing and drainage design to prevent flooding are beyond the scope of this chapter. In Appendix D, the specific life safety features of three underground facilities are presented.

The key problems associated with emergencies, particularly fire, in underground facilities are:

1. The underground is generally associated with fear of entrapment in a fire, flood, or earthquake.
2. Underground facilities do not have windows and may have layout patterns and egress systems that are unfamiliar, which leads to longer evacuation times and may engender fear and anxiety about escape.
3. Without windows, there is no daylight to provide light in a power failure nor any view out to maintain orientation and guide an escape during an emergency.
4. People must travel up rather than down stairways to evacuate an underground facility. This requires considerably more exertion than downward travel, slowing exit speeds, and the direction of travel is into the rising smoke rather than away from it.
5. To offset a sense of confinement as well as provide orientation and stimulation in underground facilities, interconnected and open interior spaces with glass partitions are desirable. This openness tends to conflict with using major entrance and circulation areas as compartmentalized, fireproof corridors and egress routes.

Figure 11-2: Entrance and egress to this 70-meter-deep subway station in St. Petersburg, Russia, occurs through a single escalator shaft. This type of entrance to an underground space reinforces feelings of confinement and fear of entrapment. The greatest concerns over emergency egress arise for deep, isolated facilities with high occupancy levels.

6. Because underground buildings are largely not visible and have no windows, fire fighting is difficult. Fire fighters cannot see the fire, they cannot see people to rescue through windows, and windows and doors cannot be broken to ventilate the fire or enter the building.
7. Because of the enclosed, windowless nature of underground buildings, positive pressure builds during a fire which can reduce the fire-resistant capabilities of construction materials.
8. In a fire in an enclosed underground space, oxygen levels can be depleted in the vicinity of the fire. If air suddenly reaches the fire area, an explosive "blow-back" can occur as partially burned materials ignite. This problem may be exacerbated by an "exhaust only" smoke removal system.
9. Because underground spaces are below grade, flooding from natural causes or sprinklers activated in a fire cannot drain naturally out of the building.
10. In some site conditions, combustible gases can collect around underground structures, leading to the danger of explosion.

Emergency Evacuation

The efficient, safe evacuation of an underground facility has several components. When an emergency occurs, it is well established that people usually do not immediately respond by leaving the building (Nelson and MacLennan 1988). There is a reaction time that involves information seeking and decision making. To the degree that people cannot see the evidence of the emergency (i.e., smoke or fire) and may be unfamiliar with the building, they are more likely to continue to seek information and delay evacuation. People obtain information related to emergency

Figure 11-3: With limited exposure and points of entry, underground buildings present problems for fire fighters. This entrance pavilion is one of the few visible elements of a multistory museum and office complex.

evacuation in two ways: (1) direct alarm and/or voice communication, and (2) a set of visual cues about egress routes that includes signs, lighting, and the layout pattern of the facility.

Alarm and voice communication about the nature of the emergency and how to respond would seem to be a critical way of reducing the confusion and delays in evacuation that are likely to occur in an unfamiliar setting. Effective voice communication would require a detection and surveillance system run from a control center that is capable of coordinating evacuation and other emergency systems.

The visual cues required for effective egress raise a broad set of issues in underground design for people concerning the legibility of the environment and the ability of people to find their way. As discussed in Chapter 8 (Layout and Spatial Configuration), lack of spatial orientation is one of the basic problems in underground buildings. This is because the overall mass and configuration of the building is not visible and the lack of windows reduces reference points to the exterior. To overcome the physical constraints of being underground, the internal organizing principle of the facility must be understood. To the degree that a building is legible with a layout that is easy to visualize and understand, emergency evacuation will be enhanced.

Although a building with a clear organizing principle is important to emergency evacuation, there are still many related problems to be overcome in an underground facility. Various unfamiliar or unconventional safety concepts may be used that do not correspond to the normal way of exiting a building in an emergency. For example, in a deeper building it may be advisable to take refuge in another portion of the building and eventually await evacuation by using elevators since going up several flights of stairs is too strenuous or even impossible for some. In other cases, the main entrance and circulation through the building may occur in open spaces (i.e., glass-enclosed elevators in an atrium), while safe evacuation routes may involve corridors and stairwells completely unfamiliar to users entering in the normal way.

This potential for evacuation routes and procedures to be unfamiliar means that efficient, safe evacuation requires a number of mutually reinforcing strategies. In addition to an architecturally legible layout and emergency alarm and voice communication systems, signs and emergency lighting are important as well. Without windows admitting daylight, emergency lighting in an underground facility is even more critical along egress routes during a power failure.

Inaccessibility for Fire Fighting

By nature, underground buildings are less visible and less accessible from the exterior. Because the source of a fire cannot be seen, it is more difficult for fire fighters to attack it by conventional means. Doors and windows are not as available to be broken for entry or to ventilate the fire, nor can people be seen or rescued through windows. If fire fighters enter through the top of an underground facility they may face the rising heat and smoke, making the approach more dangerous and difficult. These physical constraints have several implications for life safety systems underground. Since the overall configuration of underground facilities is unlikely to be fundamentally changed to improve fire fighting, there must be overcompensation in other areas to ensure fire prevention and safe egress. Control centers with good surveillance, effective automatic fire suppression systems, and smoke ventilation are essential to provide fire fighters with information and to control the fire with minimal need for fire fighters to enter the spaces during dangerous phases of the emergency. The need for fire department access may require special tunnels or shafts to be built for this purpose.

Figure 11-4: Unlike conventional buildings where the egress movement is usually downward, people in underground spaces must walk upstairs. This requires more physical exertion and people are traveling in the same direction as rising heat and smoke. In very deep underground structures, egress by climbing many flights of stairs is unfeasible for many people.

Smoke and Fire Development

In underground buildings, fires may be confined to spaces with no connection to the outside, causing conditions different from and potentially more dangerous than those found in above-grade buildings. The confinement of a fire within a space interferes with the dissipation of heat, gases, and smoke, greatly enhancing the radiative feedback to the seat of the fire and increasing initial burning rates. Oxygen reduction causes inefficient combustion, resulting in fires that generate dense smoke and carbon monoxide. High temperatures often occur because of the heat buildup due to inadequate heat venting. Proper engineering design of ventilation systems to operate under typical underground fire conditions is essential for spaces such as these.

Another related concern is the potential creation of a high pressure atmosphere. During a fire in a confined space (such as a room of a building), the atmosphere is a mixture of smoke, fire gases, and air. A smoky atmosphere and a normal atmosphere usually behave essentially the same (except when the sprinkler system is engaged) with regard to movement. As the fire grows, both the pressure and the temperature increase. The volume of gases in a room could increase by a factor of three or more if unconfined. Every cubic foot of fresh air introduced into the burning space is expanded by this factor before it is displaced as a smoky mixture. As the hot gases move away from the fire, they cool rapidly, thus contracting to their original volume. But, even though the displaced gases eventually cool to the ambient temperature, the effect of the expansion during fire conditions is a net increase in volume of displaced smoke of approximately twice the volume of the spaces involved (Carmody and Sterling 1983).

A critical problem in this potentially high pressure environment is that fire-endurance ratings for construction materials are based on conditions of negative or neutral pressure. The endurance of these materials will be reduced in positive pressure conditions, raising questions concerning required endurance ratings in enclosed conditions (Degenkolb 1981).

An obvious solution to alleviating the buildup of smoke, heat, and pressure in enclosed spaces is to mechanically ventilate the fire area to remove smoke and pressure. If the smoke is exhausted in this manner and there is no air supply, a negative pressure will be created and oxygen will be depleted. This increases the possibility for a "blow-back" type of explosion if air is suddenly introduced into this oxygen-starved environment.

Innovation in Underground Life Safety

In relatively shallow below-grade buildings, life safety techniques are not remarkably different from those found in conventional buildings. Well-known techniques for fire suppression, smoke control, and evacuation using stairways appear sufficient for structures extending one to three levels into the ground. Once underground developments become deeper and more isolated from the surface, however, the problems are less analogous to conventional buildings. Access may be extremely limited — for example, a chamber 100 meters below grade may be

Design Objectives for Life Safety

1. Minimize hazardous, combustible materials or separate them from occupied areas.
2. Construct a fire-resistant building.
3. Construct an earthquake-resistant building where appropriate.
4. Provide systems for early detection of emergencies and alarm systems with directive information for occupants.
5. Remove smoke from the area of the fire and suppress or extinguish the fire as quickly as possible.
6. Provide for the efficient evacuation of people from areas of danger to places of safety (either within or outside the facility).

reached by a single shaft, or a network of tunnels or mined chambers may extend hundreds of meters into a hillside with no vertical shafts to the surface. In these cases, innovative approaches to life safety must be developed. Innovations are constantly evolving for buildings such as hospitals where patients cannot be evacuated, or high-rise structures that present physical constraints for escape and fire fighting. More unconventional analogous environments worth exploring include submarines, ships, airplanes, or spacecraft. To achieve safe conditions in isolated environments, providing refuge for people may be required rather than immediate evacuation, and extremely high standards for fire prevention, communication, and suppression systems may be necessary.

Design Patterns Related to Life Safety

This section presents several design approaches for ensuring life safety in underground facilities that meet the design objectives stated previously. The intention is to present the basic pattern or concept, discuss its characteristics, and illustrate it with a representative drawing and/or photograph. This does not imply that the pattern should be replicated in this exact manner. Many diverse design responses can be developed based on the objectives and approaches presented here. (See Chapter 6 for a discussion of putting these patterns into a larger context.)

In approaching life safety issues in underground facilities, it is important to recognize that strategies for prevention, detection, suppression, and evacuation must be conceived as an integrated package. The physical constraints may inhibit using ideal evacuation or fire fighting procedures, but these may be compensated for by excellent prevention, detection, and suppression systems. Although the patterns that follow are presented as isolated concepts, and not all are valid in all cases, they must be viewed as pieces of a well-coordinated overall approach.

The patterns discussed here are intended to complement those in other chapters, particularly those related to developing clear entrances and layouts (Chapters 7 and 8) and clear sign systems (Chapter 9).

Life Safety Patterns

11-1: Clear Internal Organization and Egress System

11-2: Safe Vertical Egress—Stairwells, Elevators, and Escalators

11-3: Compartmentalization and Places of Safe Refuge

11-4: Clear Signs and Emergency Lighting

11-5: Effective Detection, Alarm, and Communication Systems

11-6: Effective Smoke Removal and Air Handling

11-7: Effective Fire Suppression

11-8: Fire-Resistant Construction and Restriction of Hazardous Materials

PATTERN 11-1: CLEAR INTERNAL ORGANIZATION AND EGRESS SYSTEM

Provide a clear emergency egress system by using a simple, understandable layout. When possible, egress paths should correspond with familiar circulation patterns used to enter and leave the facility. When unconventional or unfamiliar egress routes are required, they should be clearly highlighted and explained.

Evacuation of a conventional building in an emergency, also known as emergency egress, is based on a few simple principles. Once an alarm is sounded or an emergency discovered, people proceed through a sequence of spaces to the exterior, which is considered a place of safety. In a typical excavation sequence, the spaces are increasingly fire resistant and safe (i.e., a room to a corridor to a smoke-proof stairwell to an exterior door). There is a given maximum distance from any point in the building to the exit, usually in the range of 75 to 400 feet. This distance varies depending on the type of occupancy and other factors such as the presence of hazardous materials, which reduces acceptable distances, and the presence of various life safety systems (i.e., automatic sprinklers, smoke venting, and fire-resistant construction), which makes increased distances permissible. The concept of setting a maximum distance to an exit is obviously related to a calculation of an acceptable amount of time required for evacuation.

An important aspect of designing buildings for safe egress is that reaching an exit door to a place of safety does not necessarily mean reaching a door to the outside. Usually exit distances are measured to places of relative safety in the sequence of spaces (i.e., a stairwell that eventually leads to an exterior door). Another basic principle in egress design is avoiding entrapment in spaces or

Figure 11-5: Lack of spatial orientation and unfamiliarity with underground buildings may cause delays in emergency evacuation. Wayfinding problems occur in complicated underground settings. Design patterns such as this central atrium space in an underground shopping center in Kyoto, Japan helps people maintain orientation and provides a visual connection to the surface.

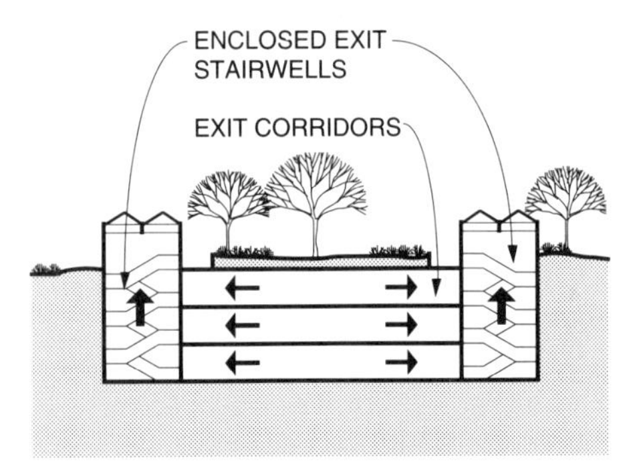

Figure 11-6: Shallow underground buildings utilize conventional egress techniques. People pass through corridors to stairwells that exit on the surface.

corridors that have only one way out. Thus, dead-end corridors are undesirable and limited in length. Likewise, in most spaces over a certain size there must be at least two paths of escape.

In general, underground facilities can be designed to provide safe egress and meet conventional building codes. However, there are two major distinctions between conventional and below-grade spaces that have an important impact on egress design: (1) underground spaces may present physical constraints that require unconventional egress techniques, and (2) unfamiliarity with these techniques and lack of spatial orientation in general introduce potential wayfinding problems underground.

Shallow underground buildings extending three stories or less into the ground usually present no highly unusual physical constraints. Most likely the egress system can be designed similar to an enclosed conventional building with corridors leading to enclosed stairwells that exit directly to the surface (see Figure 11-6). Unless penetration of the surface is severely restricted, stairwells can occur frequently enough to meet conventional exit distances.

In deeper underground facilities, however, these familiar conventional egress techniques may not be feasible. For example, networks of mined caverns such as those proposed for development in Minneapolis, Minnesota, cannot provide frequent, closely spaced stairwells to the surface. The proposed egress system relies on the use of a system of long, smoke-proof corridors (pressurized in case of fire) referred to as exit passageways that lead to stairwells or exterior portal entrances. This permits great flexibility in shaft location since the required distance to a door entering the exit passageway can be met and the length of the passageway itself is unlimited (Figures 11-7 and 11-8). Similar passageway systems have been utilized in industrial facilities with large floor areas — in some cases, enclosed passageways are suspended overhead while in others they are located beneath the floor. The egress system for deep mined facilities can take many forms depending on factors such as where shafts must occur and whether there is access through tunnels as well as shafts. Figures 11-9 through 11-11 illustrate three egress schemes for a proposed archives facility in deep mined space.

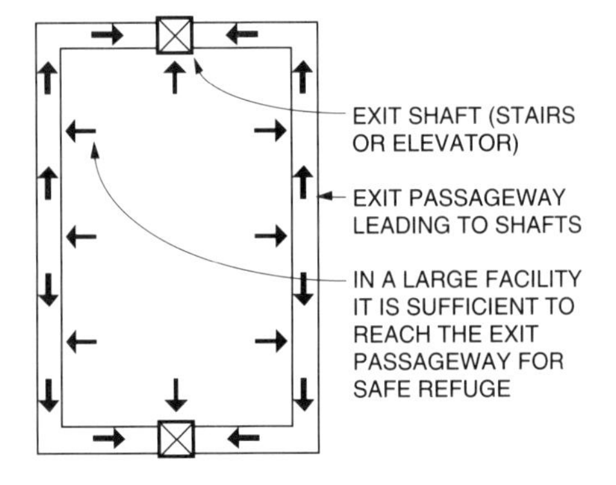

Figure 11-7: This plan illustrates the use of long exit passageways around the perimeter of an underground facility to provide egress. When shafts are far apart, exit passageways can be used to meet exit distance requirements.

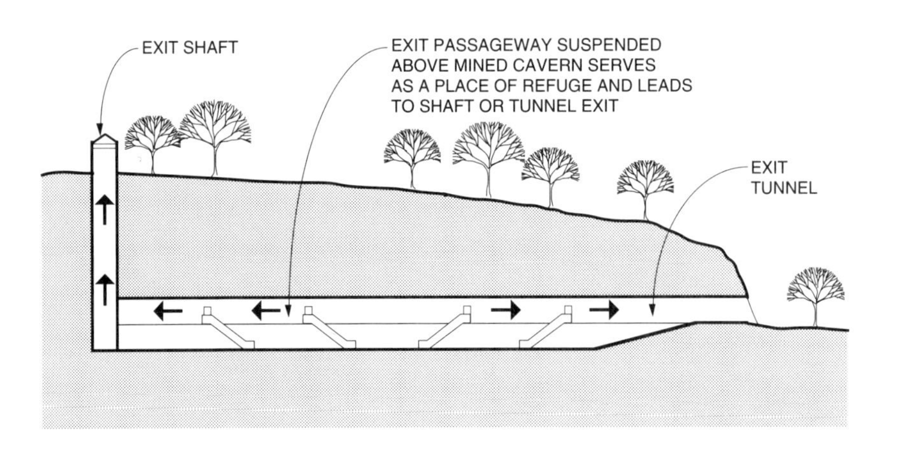

Figure 11-8: In deep mined space, the distance to shaft and tunnel exits may be considerable. In this illustration, long exit passageways that lead to stairwells and enclosed elevator lobbies are suspended above the cavern floor to provide egress.

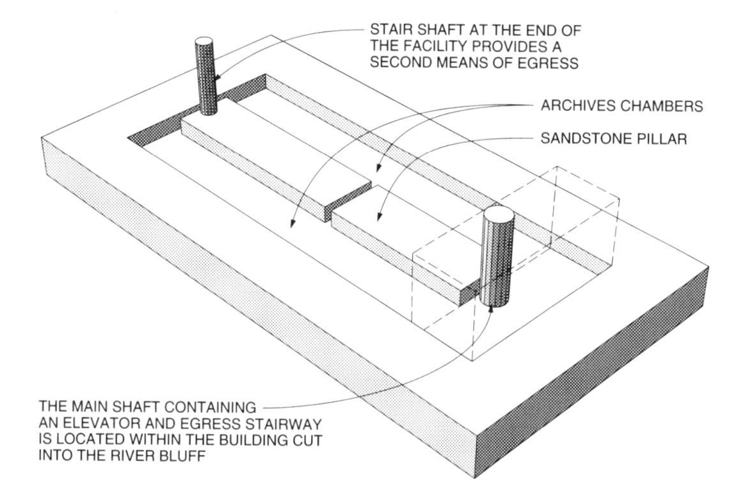

Figure 11-9: This cutaway view shows one egress design for a proposed archives facility in deep mined space at the University of Minnesota. This approach places shafts at both ends of the 100-foot-deep chambers. At one end the main access shaft is within a deep cut building that extends down to the mined space level, while a smaller shaft containing a stairway is located at the other end. This layout is simple to understand and provides egress in two directions from any point.

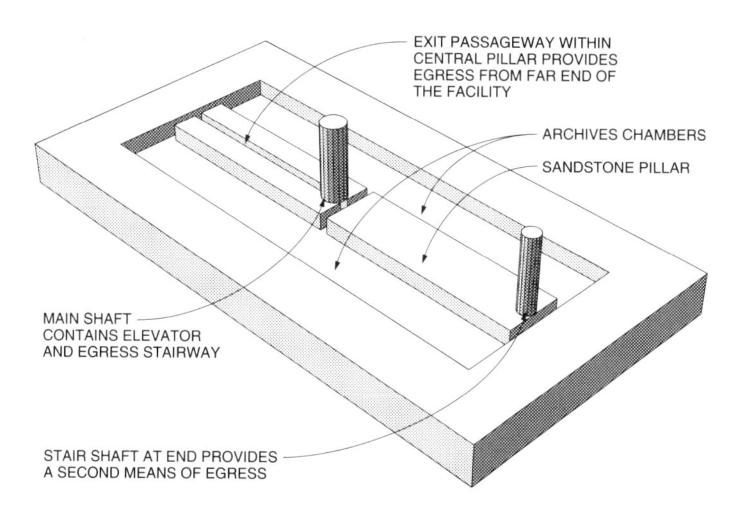

Figure 11-10: This egress design for the proposed archives facility in deep mined space is for a condition where the main access shaft must be located in the center of the plan. A smaller shaft containing a stairway is located at one end, providing a second means of egress. This layout results in a "dead end" condition at the other end, however, since the main shaft is in the middle. This is resolved by placing an exit passageway within the pillar leading from the far end to the central egress shaft. With the passageway, egress is provided in two directions from any point.

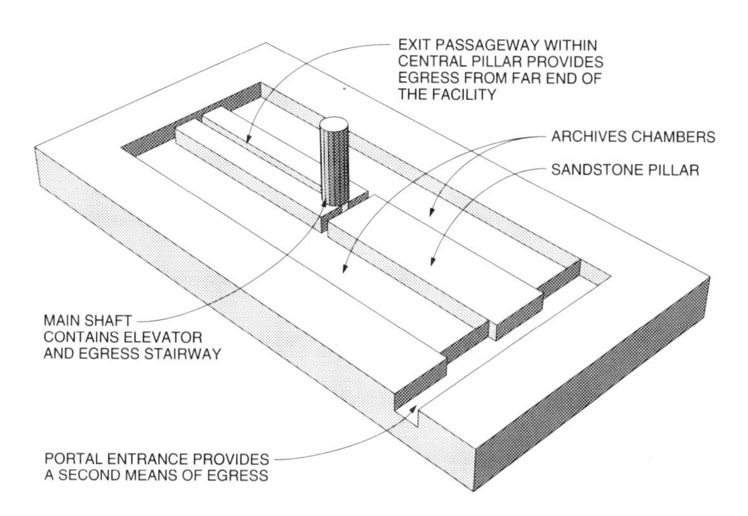

Figure 11-11: This cutaway view shows another egress design for the proposed archives facility in deep mined space at the University of Minnesota. This approach is for a condition where there is horizontal access to the facility through a tunnel from the river bluff that provides a second means of egress. Similar to Figure 11-10, this layout results in a "dead end" condition at the other end since the main shaft is in the middle. This is resolved by placing an exit passageway within the pillar leading from the far end to the central egress shaft. With the passageway, egress is provided in two directions from any point.

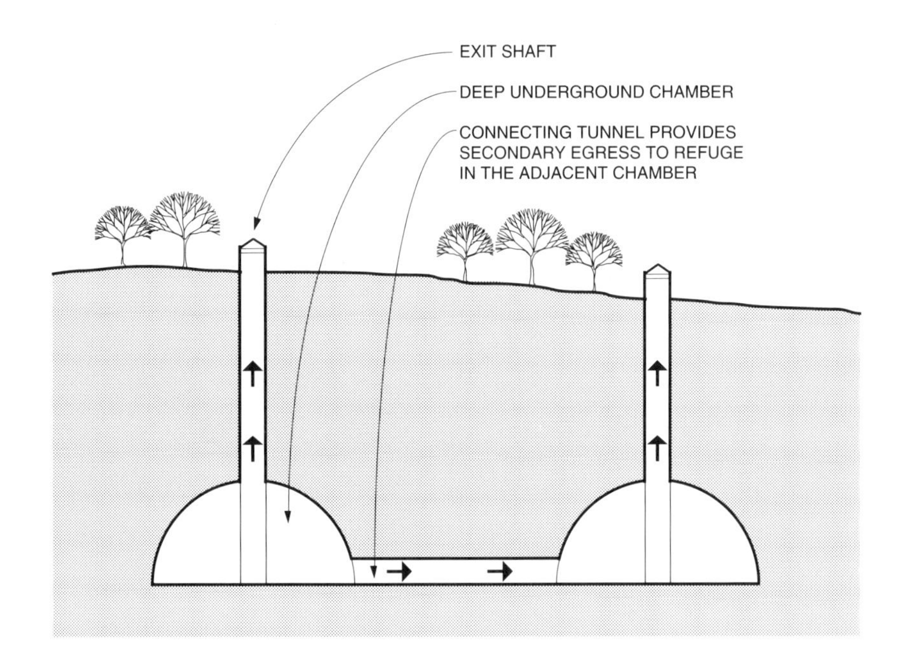

Figure 11-12: Deep isolated underground chambers may only have a single elevator for access and egress. This illustrates the use of an exit passageway through a tunnel to an adjacent facility which provides a place of refuge.

Another unconventional egress situation arises for extremely deep facilities reached only through a long elevator shaft (see Figure 11-12). Not only are stairwells inappropriate beyond a certain depth, multiple points of egress may also be impossible to provide. In such a case, safe egress may mean leaving one portion (or compartment) of the facility to find refuge in another until the emergency is over and people can be rescued. Another possibility is egress through a tunnel to another space or point of egress some distance away.

While these unconventional egress systems may be necessary to provide safe evacuation of deep underground facilities, they raise some questions about providing a clear, unambiguous system that people will understand and follow in an emergency. In general, underground buildings are unfamiliar and spatial orientation is a problem in everyday wayfinding. In his book *Wayfinding in Architecture*, Romedi Passini (1984) suggests that there are three important characteristics to enhance legibility of a building (that is, for orientation to be maintained). First, the internal organizing principle of the building must be understood. Orientation will also be enhanced by understanding the external organizing principle — that is, the overall form and volume of the building. Finally, orientation within the building is improved by spatial correspondence. This refers to making relationships between spaces, particularly indoors/outdoors and aboveground/underground, more visually accessible and articulate. Many of the patterns in Chapter 8 suggest techniques that contribute to creating an underground building with clear organizing principles. Examples of these patterns are a major building thoroughfare, a sunken courtyard, and an interior atrium.

Fire safety researchers reinforce these principles of creating simple, unambiguous building layouts to ensure efficient evacuation (Pauls 1988; Nelson and MacLennan 1988). Exit routes should be simple and there should be assurance that they lead to safety. Problems will be more likely to arise with unusual arrangements of corridors including curving or angular shapes and exit enclosures and doors that cannot be differentiated. The uncertainty introduced by complex and unclear layouts and egress paths will lengthen the decision-making and investigation time during an emergency, thus delaying evacuation.

The problem of using exit passageways and other unconventional egress techniques is that they are not familiar and not the way people entered the space. In studying behavior in fire situations, Jonathan Sime (1985) has noted that "the pattern of movement both toward and away from the threat is mediated by the degree of familiarity of the individual with accessible persons or places ... in an emergency people are even more likely to be drawn toward the familiar than under normal circumstances." Sime and others have noted that most people seek to leave a building by the same path through which they entered it.

Figure 11-13: The major exit stairwell in the CME Building in Minneapolis, Minnesota, is a bright red cylindrical form that is clearly visible on each floor of the seven-story-deep facility.

The extent to which wayfinding during emergencies is a problem depends on the number of people in a facility and their experience with it. Wayfinding is of greatest importance in facilities open to the public (i.e., stores, subways, museums) rather than those limited to occupants familiar with egress systems and procedures. When there are fewer people in a facility, a legible egress system is likely to be more important since there may be no one to follow or provide information.

To the degree that it is possible, the layout of underground buildings should be simple and clear. Egress paths should correspond with familiar circulation patterns used to enter and leave the facility. When secondary routes of escape are necessary, they should be highlighted and explained as much as possible. For example, it may be desirable for stair shafts or exit passageways in a complex underground environment to be brightly colored, unmistakable architectural forms (see Figure 11-13). This must be accompanied by extensive signs and possibly maps of the facility.

The goals in designing an effective egress system are to evacuate all occupants within a given time in a way that minimizes confusion, panic, and exertion. The physical layout of the egress system, which is addressed in this pattern in a general way, is made up of several possible components discussed in more detail in the patterns that follow (11-2: Safe Vertical Egress and 11-3: Compartmentalization and Places of Safe Refuge). Emergency egress is also enhanced by other systems and techniques described in Pattern 11-4: Clear Signs and Emergency Lighting, and Pattern 11-5: Effective Detection, Alarm, and Communication Systems.

PATTERN 11-2: SAFE VERTICAL EGRESS – STAIRWELLS, ELEVATORS, AND ESCALATORS

Design stairwells, elevators, and escalators to maximize safe vertical egress. Make egress stairwells enclosed, smoke-proof, ventilated, and open in the center to provide visual access. Elevators used for egress in deeper facilities require enclosed, smoke-proof, ventilated lobbies with voice communication to the surface.

Vertical egress is usually the final component of the overall evacuation sequence in a building. In most cases, vertical egress is an enclosed, smoke-proof, positively pressurized, ventilated stairwell which leads to an outside door. In an underground facility, people must ascend rather than descend the stairs, which has some important implications. The speed of exiting upward is slightly slower; more importantly, however, it is assumed that people are fatigued after only one minute of ascending stairs compared with five minutes when descending. Based on this assumption, most people will be fatigued after ascending four to six stories of stairs. Resizing stairs to have wider treads and shorter

Figure 11-14: A stairwell with an open central space enhances orientation and provides visual access between the surface and people below who may need assistance.

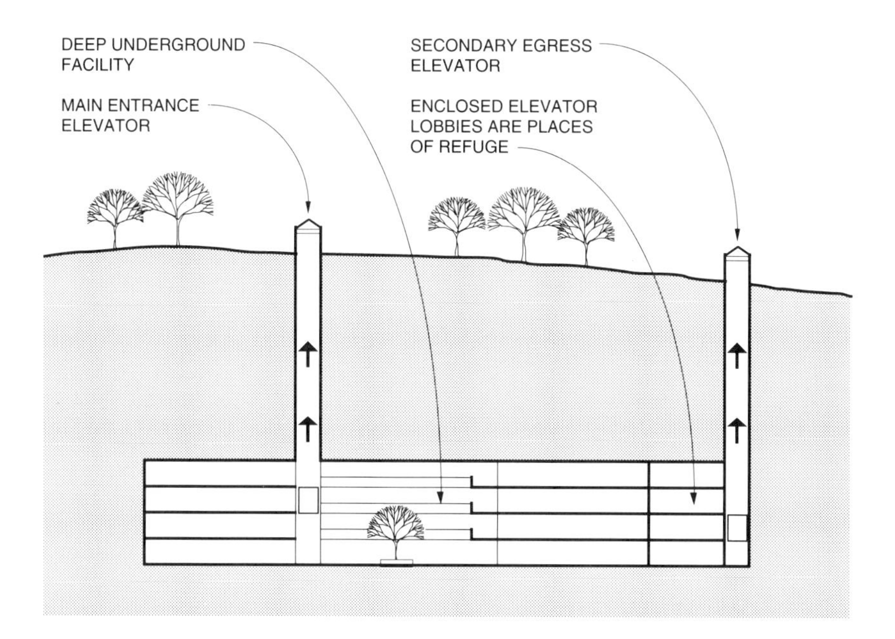

Figure 11-15: In deep isolated underground space, elevators may be the only feasible means of egress. In this illustration, one elevator serves as the major means of entrance while a second elevator is primarily to facilitate emergency egress. Enclosed elevator lobbies provide places of refuge for people awaiting elevators.

risers will reduce fatigue somewhat, and increasing stairwell capacity to hold the entire building occupancy removes the time pressure for evacuation. Nevertheless, there appears to be a limit to vertical egress on stairs in an upward direction.

The stairwell may also be a point of entry for fire fighters, a place of refuge for people unable to ascend to the top, and in some cases an important circulation space within the building. One design concept for an enclosed stairwell is to create an open space in the center which enhances spatial orientation and provides visual access between the surface and people below who may require assistance. If a stairwell is a place of refuge and a major point of egress as well as fire department entry, it should be designed to accommodate these functions. For example, it could contain standpipes and hoses as well as two-way voice communication on several levels.

In many public underground facilities, escalators are used to provide an efficient and somewhat effortless means of vertical circulation. Circulating through an underground building using escalators is particularly desirable since orientation is maintained by descending in relatively open, central areas and there is greater visible activity and interaction with other people. As a means of emergency egress, however, escalators are generally not completely enclosed like an emergency stairwell with fire-resistant doors and positively pressurized, separate air supply. Nevertheless, they will be used by people because they are the familiar way of entering and leaving the building. This is not a problem if the fire is not in the vicinity of the escalators; however, when the fire is nearby it is important to stop the escalators and redirect people to other places of egress. In a recent fire at a London subway station, people attempted to escape on escalators only to be brought up into the fire zone in the mezzanine at the top (Fennell 1988).

Another aspect of escalator design that will enhance emergency egress is the control of smoke to prevent it from rising through the open spaces around the escalators. Permanent edges hanging down from the ceilings on each floor can serve to trap smoke in a "smoke reservoir" and prevent it from spreading immediately into the escalator shafts (see Figure 11-16). This concept can also utilize smoke curtains that drop down mechanically in case of an emergency. This approach depends on smoke alarms and the capability for exhausting the smoke from each reservoir (see Pattern 11-6).

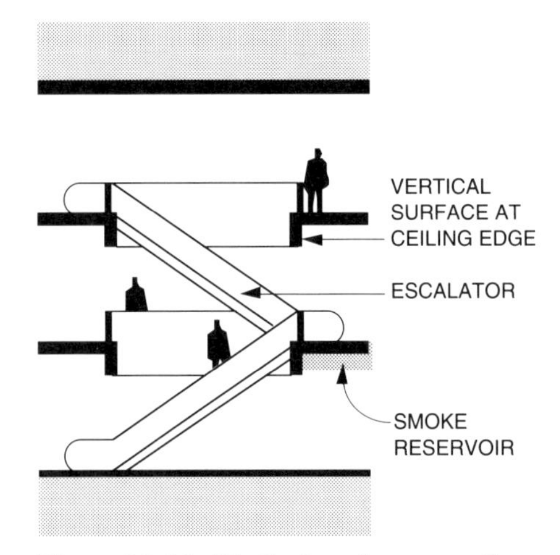

Figure 11-16: Vertical surfaces near the ceiling around escalator shaft enclosures contain smoke within a reservoir and prevent its spread to other floors.

A final means of vertical egress is to utilize elevators. In conventional buildings, elevators are usually not available for egress – people are directed to stairwells and the fire fighters control the elevators and may utilize them for entry or rescue. Unlike stairs or escalators, an elevator provides no continuous path to the surface. People must wait and depend on the actions of others in order to escape by elevator. Also, the speed and capacity of elevators for total evacuation are likely to be inadequate unless there is safe refuge near the elevators of sufficient size to hold all those waiting to exit. Elevators also have the disadvantage of providing an open vertical shaft vulnerable to smoke, since it is difficult to seal and pressurize elevator shafts. In addition, people in the elevator cannot see the existence of smoke or fire on a particular floor until the doors open, exposing them to possible harm.

In spite of the traditional avoidance of elevators for egress, they may be the only reasonable alternative in deeper underground facilities. Clearly they must be used for mobility-impaired people as well as for those unable to ascend numerous flights of stairs. In order to maximize safety in elevator egress, there should be enclosed, smoke-proof elevator lobbies on each floor. These can be designed as places of refuge with separate air handling, positive pressurization during a fire emergency, and two-way communication.

Unfortunately, enclosed elevator lobbies may conflict with the desire for openness in underground space, particularly if the elevator is a major means of entrance to the facility. One design approach is to form a safe lobby by utilizing roll-down steel doors or horizontally sliding wall barriers that only are activated in emergencies. In very deep isolated spaces where stairways clearly do not provide reasonable egress, it may be advisable to provide two sets of elevators: (1) those used for normal circulation which can be architecturally open (i.e., glass-enclosed elevators in an atrium), and (2) those designated for emergency use only with enclosed lobbies serving as refuge areas on each floor.

PATTERN 11-3: COMPARTMENTALIZATION AND PLACES OF SAFE REFUGE

Create compartments within underground facilities that serve as places of safe refuge during emergencies. Separate compartments with fire-resistant walls and ventilate each compartment as a separate zone.

Figure 11-17: Automatic roll-down steel shutters cover glass partition walls to create a place of refuge in the elevator lobbies that overlook this large central space. Under normal circumstances, the glass walls provide an open feeling and help people maintain orientation within the building.

Compartmentalization is a basic concept of fire safety in many if not most conventional buildings. It is an important aspect of egress design as discussed in Patterns 11-1 and 11-2. Generally, compartmentalization refers to creating separate zones or spaces within a building so that if a fire or other emergency occurs in one zone, people can escape to another zone that is a place of relative safety. This implies fire-resistant walls and automatically closing doors between zones. It also implies separate air handling in the compartments and the ability to pressurize certain zones while exhausting others in order to prevent smoke from crossing the barriers between compartments (see Pattern 11-6: Smoke Removal).

In conventional buildings, compartmentalization is commonly implemented by creating enclosed, smoke-proof stairwells which, in effect, are separate zones and serve as places of refuge. Likewise, different floors of buildings often function as separate compartments with no openings permitting air or smoke to penetrate from floor to floor. In high-rise buildings it is sometimes considered sufficient to evacuate the floor where a fire occurs as well as the floors immediately above and below the emergency, but not the entire building. Where people are simply unable to evacuate a building such as in a hospital, floors are divided into compartments so that patients can be moved from zones of danger into adjacent compartments that serve as places of refuge.

In underground settings, compartmentalization and providing places of safe refuge act as a useful and often necessary strategy to

Figure 11-18: In this 2000-foot-deep test laboratory, people must go to a refuge area in case of an emergency and await rescue. Conventional stairwells and multiple egress paths are not feasible.

provide adequate safety. At a minimum, different floors of underground facilities as well as stairwell enclosures and elevator lobbies should be designed as separate compartments. Possibly a space opening directly into the stairwell on each floor could serve a dual purpose as a meeting room or lounge, for example, and also as a place of refuge. Large and complex facilities should be divided into separate zones or compartments, and vestibules between compartments can further ensure smoke separation. Deeper, more isolated underground structures may rely on providing places of safe refuge where people may wait for rescue instead of using multiple escape routes.

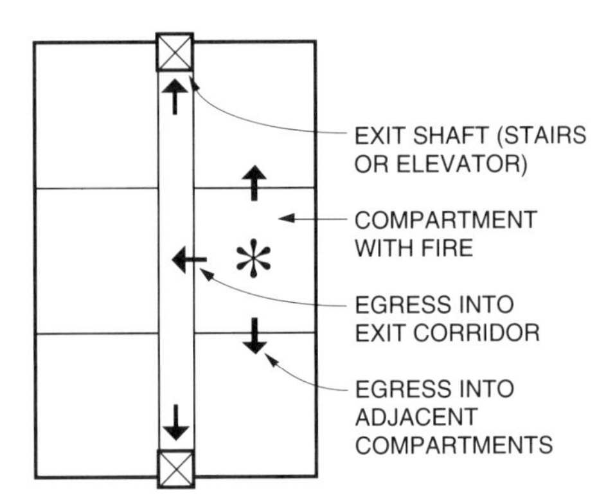

Figure 11-19: In this schematic plan of an underground development with limited points of exit, compartmentalization is used. In addition to conventional egress through corridors during emergencies, people can be evacuated to other adjacent compartments in the complex.

The use of compartmentalization and places of refuge is not as familiar to the public as simply evacuating a building. In particular, waiting in a safe haven for rescue may be unacceptable to people unless the procedure is well understood and there is reassurance that rescue is coming. This approach requires two-way voice communication in each refuge area with a control center that is able to see and coordinate the emergency (see Pattern 11-5).

A potential problem associated with using compartmentalization for safety purposes is that it may conflict with architectural goals such as creating a feeling of openness in windowless underground spaces. A multistory atrium is one desirable strategy, and the use of interconnected spaces divided at most by a glass partition wall is another. If compartments are sufficiently large and barriers occur at natural divisions within the facility plan, this may not be a great problem.

In conventional buildings, atriums are treated as a special type of compartment with certain additional fire safety requirements. Moreover, within a compartment there can be complete openness. Glass partition walls are not sufficiently fire resistant to serve as barriers between compartments but can be used extensively within them. This problem was addressed in the life safety code developed for deep mined space in Minneapolis where, within a compartment, glass walls of unlimited area were considered acceptable along corridors if they met certain requirements—i.e., wired, tempered, or laminated glass and protected by 135°F (37°C) sprinkler heads 6 feet (1.8 m) on center directed at both sides. For walls that do not form corridors (within a suite of offices, for example), plain glass partitions can be used with no limitations (Sterling et al. 1988).

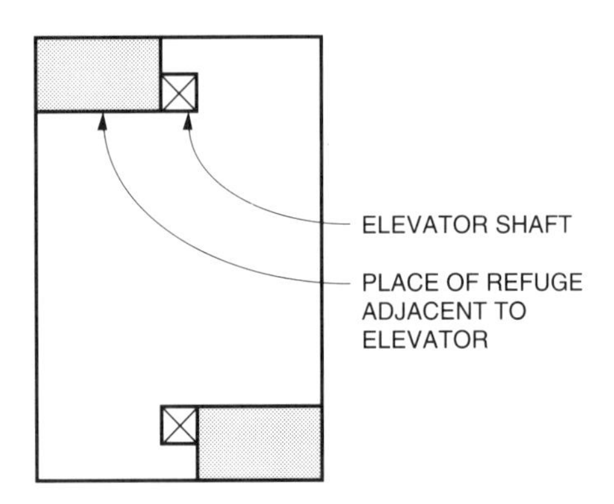

Figure 11-20: This schematic plan of an underground development illustrates the use of places of refuge adjacent to exit shafts. These compartments are smoke-proof, separately ventilated, and have two-way voice communication with the control center.

Doors between compartments can be left open as long as they close automatically in emergencies. To create a greater sense of openness, however, roll-down barriers or large horizontally sliding partitions may be used. Another similar approach that does not result in full compartmentalization is the use of smoke curtains that drop down in emergencies only to a level above head height. This contains smoke within a certain zone while permitting people to pass below (see Pattern 11-6).

Where complete separation of compartments is desired, barrier walls must have a substantial fire-resistance rating and pipes and ducts penetrating the walls must be sealed. If possible, duct penetration between compartments should be eliminated completely, but if it is unavoidable, these ducts should have automatically closing dampers to prevent smoke from crossing from one zone to the next.

PATTERN 11-4: CLEAR SIGNS AND EMERGENCY LIGHTING

Provide clear signs and emergency lighting along paths of egress.

While designing a clear layout and egress system is a major goal in underground facilities, people still must rely on signs in emergencies to direct and reinforce them toward exits or places of safety. This is particularly true in large, complicated buildings or where evacuation routes and procedures are unfamiliar.

Because of the potential problems in underground facilities, designing a clear, effective system of emergency signs is essential. In addition to typical exit signs near doorways, arrows or other directional signs are useful along corridors to provide further direction and reinforce people along the path. Since smoke collects near the ceiling, signs on the lower walls and floor are recommended in addition to traditional overhead exit door signs.

Graphical symbols are desirable, especially where visitors speaking various languages are anticipated. Also, in complex environments with many people such as a subway station, visual displays of emergency messages can help inform and direct people.

Another important aspect of enhancing safe egress in underground facilities is the provision of emergency lighting. Without windows to provide daylight in a power failure, emergency lighting becomes even more essential. Because of smoke gathering at the ceiling, some lighting on lower walls of corridors is desirable. In addition to general lighting, emergency power for illuminated exit signs is essential as well. Emergency lighting should be available within 10 seconds of a power failure.

Figure 11-21: Emergency exit and directional signs and emergency lighting are essential in underground spaces.

One innovative approach to emergency signage and illumination is the use of photoluminescent systems. Luminous materials consist of crystals, mainly zinc sulfide, that absorb and store light energy from artificial lighting. When the light source is interrupted, as in a power failure, they emit the light energy and appear to glow brightly in total darkness. The glow diminishes over time but is quite strong for up to an hour and is visible to dark-adapted eyes up to eight hours. These luminous materials are manufactured in the form of paints, sheets, and tapes (Krokeide 1988).

In a full installation, luminous materials are installed on lower walls and floors in the form of directional arrows; continuous bands define walls of passageways. Other important safety elements can be highlighted such as exit doors and door handles, exit route maps, fire extinguishers, phones, and alarms. Luminous materials can also be used to highlight important architectural forms and details. For example, the form of a major cylindrical stair shaft could be outlined and the stair nosings and rails within could be highlighted as well. Luminous systems are relatively low cost with high reliability and could contribute to a sense of security since no power is required and a complete installation can be extensive and reassuring. In recent tests, luminous systems performed as well as conventional emergency lighting and were preferred by some subjects (Webber and Hallman 1988).

PATTERN 11-5: EFFECTIVE DETECTION, ALARM, AND COMMUNICATION SYSTEMS

In underground facilities, provide effective detection, alarm, and two-way voice communication systems.

Because underground buildings are less visible and accessible, it is difficult for fire fighters to see and attack the fire as well as rescue people inside. This handicap can be offset to some extent if the facility has very effective systems for early detection of emergencies, and a two-way voice communication system between a control center and various points of refuge and other key spaces throughout the building. The *Life Safety Code* (NFPA 1991) requires that high-rise structures include a fire alarm system utilizing voice communication and two-way telephone communication for fire department use. This system must operate between the central control station and every elevator car, every elevator lobby, and each floor level of exit stairs. This type of system seems appropriate for deep and complex underground facilities, particularly since wireless communication devices may not always work underground. The ability to see the fire and supervise evacuation may be enhanced by a closed-circuit television system as well.

A critical problem in evacuating any facility is the delay caused by investigation and decision making. In an underground facility this delay can be increased due to the unfamiliar setting and possibly unconventional means of providing egress or refuge. Techniques for reducing delays include effective detection and alarm systems, as well as directive announcements over a public address system with accurate information about the emergency and evacuation procedures. Effective early detection requires smoke detectors and, where appropriate, devices for the detection of combustible gases that may originate either inside or outside the structure. Smoke detectors are particularly important because they will trigger an alarm at a much earlier stage than an automatic sprinkler system, which does not operate until an area is beyond human tolerance.

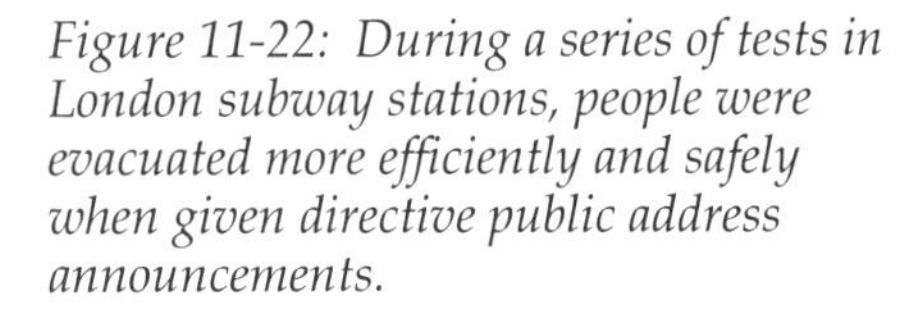

Figure 11-22: During a series of tests in London subway stations, people were evacuated more efficiently and safely when given directive public address announcements.

Effective communication during an emergency evacuation has become a critical issue in underground life safety due to the deaths caused by confusion and misdirection in the November 1987 fire in a London subway station (Fennell 1988). Subsequently, researchers have tested the effectiveness of several approaches to communication in a subway emergency (Sime et al. 1990; Proulx and Sime 1991). These include: (1) alarm only, (2) two officers directing people out plus a non-directive public address announcement, (3) a non-directive public address announcement from the control center, (4) a directive public address announcement from the control center, and (5) a directive public address announcement from the control center plus two officers directing people out.

The final two approaches, which utilized directive public address, were the most effective and resulted in the shortest evacuation times. Directive announcements (such as instructing people which exit to use or even that they should remain in a certain part of the station and escape by train) are particularly important in a complex setting where even officers directing people may not have an overview of the emergency.

In order for detection, alarm, communication, fire fighting, and evacuation to work effectively, a control center is needed with emergency or standby power for critical functions. According to the *Life Safety Code* (NFPA 1991), a central control station for high-rise structures should contain the systems listed below. These also are appropriate for complex or deep underground facilities:

- Voice fire alarm system panels and controls
- Fire department two-way telephone communication service panels and controls
- Fire detection and fire alarm system annunciation panels
- Elevator floor location and operation annunciators
- Sprinkler valve and water flow annunciators
- Emergency generator status indicators
- Controls for any automatic stairway door unlocking system
- Fire pump status indicators
- A telephone for fire department use with controlled access to the public telephone system

According to the *Life Safety Code* (NFPA 1991), high-rise structures must provide standby power for the following functions: (1) emergency lighting system, (2) fire alarm system, (3) electric fire pump, (4) central control station equipment and lighting, (5) at least one elevator serving all floors, transferable to any elevator, and (6) mechanical equipment for smoke-proof enclosures.

Other researchers have proposed that large underground facilities should have the capability to monitor fires with closed-circuit television and thermal cameras (Li 1989). Any unconventional egress techniques such as directing people to a place of refuge to await rescue will require specially designated two-way communication to these locations. Critical systems like these must also be monitored and operated from the control station and be supplied with standby power.

PATTERN 11-6: EFFECTIVE SMOKE REMOVAL AND AIR HANDLING

Provide an effective smoke removal system so that smoke is mechanically exhausted from the zone where the fire occurs, and outside air is supplied to adjacent zones.

Removing smoke effectively in a fire is one of the most critical components of an overall life safety system for underground facilities. In an enclosed, windowless environment smoke, heat, and pressure build up quickly. Smoke accumulation inhibits evacuation and ultimately smoke is responsible for 80 percent of all fire-related deaths.

The design of a mechanical smoke removal system is based on the following principles: (1) the normal air handling system must be shut down to avoid recirculating smoke, (2) in the zone in which the fire occurs smoke should be exhausted directly to the outside, and (3) in the zones adjacent to the fire, 100 percent outside air should be supplied with no exhaust to create a positive pressure. The positive pressure is intended to keep smoke from moving into these adjacent zones. Other critical components of the egress system (i.e., stairwells and exit passageways) as well as refuge areas must also be positively pressurized. Corridors should not be used in place of ducts for air handling.

This smoke venting approach results in negative pressure in the zone where the fire occurs. In a relatively small space air will be drawn from adjacent spaces by infiltration. If the compartments are well sealed, however, this negative pressure could hinder the operation of exhaust fans. If negative pressure is built up and then fresh air suddenly enters the space, a "blow-back" explosion can occur as oxygen enters the oxygen-depleted environment. A related type of problem occurs in multistory atriums where exhaust fans placed high in the space do not always effectively remove smoke that has cooled and settled near the floor. The conventional solution is to provide supply air from the floor of the atrium to facilitate smoke removal through the roof. Using a similar

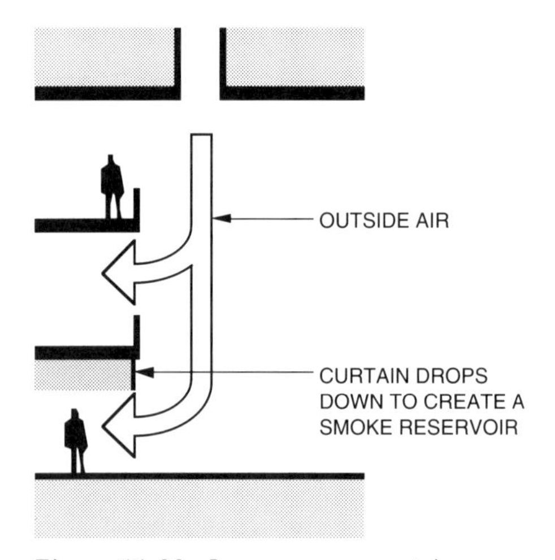

Figure 11-23: In open areas curtains can drop down to create smoke reservoirs. Each reservoir has a separate exhaust system.

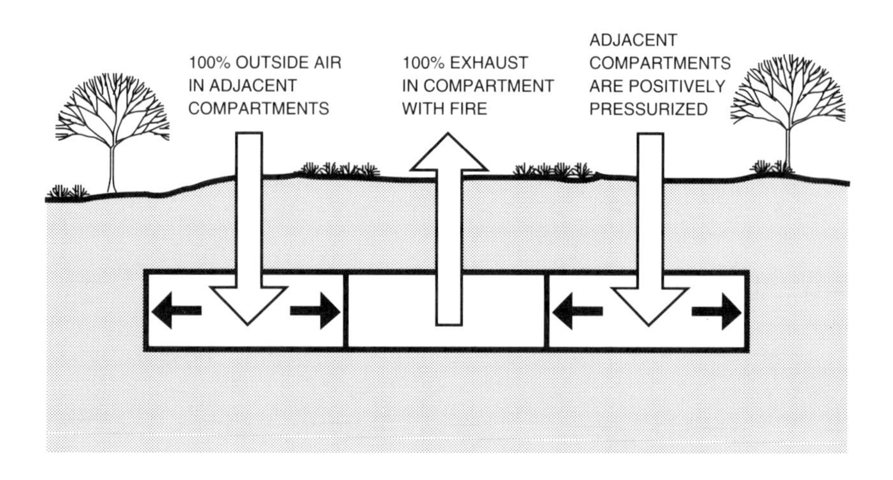

Figure 11-24: Smoke is exhausted from the fire zone and adjacent compartments are positively pressurized.

approach, supplying air from a low position in a compartment of an underground facility may be desirable to enhance smoke removal through exhaust ducts placed near the ceiling.

A final aspect of smoke removal involves the definition of a fire zone or compartment. Clearly, if an underground building is separated into a series of distinct, smoke-proof compartments, the emergency air handling system should be designed to exhaust or supply each compartment separately. In some cases, however, compartments may be quite large or the building function may require large open areas. In these cases, the use of smoke curtains that drop from the ceiling to a level just above head height can subdivide a space into a number of "smoke reservoirs." This approach is intended to trap the smoke in a certain area but permit people to cross beneath the curtains at any point for evacuation. For this method to work effectively, smoke detectors must activate the curtains and then exhaust fans and ducts must remove the smoke from the reservoir (Littlechild 1989).

PATTERN 11-7: EFFECTIVE FIRE SUPPRESSION

Use automatic sprinklers or other fire suppression systems in all underground facilities.

In underground facilities that present potential constraints for fire fighting and evacuation, effective automatic fire suppression systems are another key component of an overall life safety system. In various code documents, automatic sprinkler systems are required for underground spaces over a certain size or minimal number of occupants (NFPA 1988; Sterling et al. 1988). Automatic sprinkler systems are considered very effective at detecting and extinguishing fires. Ninety-eight percent of all fires in a sprinklered area are extinguished within an 11-square-foot area. The major drawback to these systems is that they are not activated until considerable smoke and heat are generated. Thus, it is strongly recommended that activation of alarms, smoke venting, and other emergency systems be triggered by smoke detectors, not by the detection devices inherent in an automatic sprinkler system.

Extinguishing fires with water is not always an acceptable solution. For example, the water may cause more damage than the fire in a computer room or a library of valuable manuscripts. One alternative fire suppression system uses halons (halogenated hydrocarbons). These chemicals can be tolerated by humans and can be implemented as soon as a fire is detected. Another suppression system utilizes carbon dioxide; however, people must be evacuated before the system can be engaged. It extinguishes fires by diluting the oxygen content of the air and preventing combustion. Carbon dioxide systems are considered effective against chemical and electrical fires with high temperatures. In deep isolated spaces the development of even more sophisticated automatic fire fighting/suppression systems may be required. For example, it has been suggested that fire-fighting robots may be an effective approach in these enclosed environments (Ogata et al. 1990).

PATTERN 11-8: FIRE-RESISTANT CONSTRUCTION AND RESTRICTION OF HAZARDOUS MATERIALS

Figure 11-25: Fire-resistant construction materials such as masonry walls and steel doors are recommended in underground facilities. However, techniques must also be developed to provide safety without creating a claustrophobic, undesirable interior design. The entrance to these underground offices is designed to preserve a sense of openness by using wire-glass with automatic sprinkler heads in order to meet fire separation requirements.

Construct underground buildings with fire-resistant materials and methods. As much as possible, avoid the placement of hazardous or flammable materials in habitable underground facilities.

Perhaps the most obvious and basic component of an overall life safety system for underground space is not allowing hazardous and combustible materials to be present. When these materials are required for certain manufacturing processes, for example, they must be stored in completely separate areas that have significant restrictions concerning occupancy.

In a similar sense, fire occurrence and damage will be minimized by the use of fire-resistant materials and construction methods. Generally, Type I or II construction is required for underground spaces in U.S. building codes (NFPA 1991). However, some use of wood and other combustible materials for finishes and furnishings is highly desirable to humanize underground environments and must be permitted to some extent.

The fire-endurance ratings for various walls, floors, and ceilings have been established by fire testing in furnaces that are operated at a negative pressure or, at best, a neutral pressure. These tests measure the fire endurance of a particular type of construction under similar conditions. According to the National Bureau of Standards and the Canadian Research Council, however, the typical pressure buildup in a fire may be in the range of 0.10 to 0.12 inches of water column. When the building is sprinklered, the pressure buildup will be in the range of 0.05 to 0.06 column inches of water.

Degenkolb points out that the Los Angeles Fire Department panel furnace is conventionally run with a positive pressure of

0.045 near the top of the panel, a neutral pressure about one-third up from the bottom, and a slight negative pressure at the bottom of the panel opening. Wall assemblies that have received a one-hour rating in other furnaces have failed after about 45 to 50 minutes in the Los Angeles furnace. Doors that have received a 30-minute rating in negative-pressure furnaces and have also survived a hose stream test have difficulty passing a 20-minute test in a positive-pressure furnace, and that is without adding the hose stream at the end of the fire test (Degenkolb 1981).

These fire tests evaluate an assembly under specific fire conditions that do not necessarily resemble real fire conditions in an underground building. It is possible that where one-hour fire resistance has been acceptable in aboveground buildings, underground structures with potentially higher positive pressures may require a greater level of fire resistance.

APPENDIX D

Life Safety Features of Three Underground Facilities

This appendix is in three parts. The first two sections on the Civil and Mineral Engineering Building and the Moscone Center were written by Raymond Sterling. The third section on the Les Halles complex in Paris, France, was written by Olivier Huet, an architect in Paris.

The general principles of life safety in complex underground facilities were presented in Chapter 11. In this appendix three examples of projects, representative of large or complex occupied underground facilities, are described in terms of their special life safety features.

Civil and Mineral Engineering Building—University of Minnesota

The Civil and Mineral Engineering Building is located on the Minneapolis campus of the University of Minnesota. The 50,000-square-meter structure includes classrooms and laboratories as well as office space. The building was planned as a demonstration of an energy-conserving, underground building. Completed early in 1983, the building takes advantage of geological conditions in the Minneapolis-St. Paul area to create inexpensive mined underground space.

As illustrated in the accompanying figures, the building is approximately 95 percent below grade and includes two distinct types of underground space—the more conventional cut-and-cover space near the surface and deep mined space in the bedrock. An approximate 15-meter-thickness of soil lies above the bedrock, in which up to three floor levels of cut-and-cover space occur. The soil is underlain by a 9-meter-thick layer of limestone that acts as a natural roof over the space mined out of the softer sandstone below. The mined space is connected to the building above by two shafts through the limestone. The resulting mined space, used mainly for laboratories with some offices, is on two levels, with the lowest floor level 35 meters beneath the surface.

The spaces in the building fall into four distinct areas:

- A student/classroom area contains the department office, classrooms, student lounge and study area, and computer facilities. These spaces extend up to two levels below ground and have considerable access to windows and natural light through a sunken courtyard entrance and a skylighted circulation space.
- A faculty office area extends two stories below ground around a separate sunken courtyard.
- Part of the research laboratories and graduate student work spaces is located in a three-story-deep cut-and-cover area of the building. The dominant space in this area is the main structures laboratory. The laboratory's floor is approximately 10 meters below grade and its roof is approximately 10 meters above grade to allow overhead crane access to the loading dock area. Many of the other research, work area, corridor, and elevator spaces were designed to open onto the structures laboratory area for access and view.
- The remainder of the laboratory space and the offices of the Underground Space Center are located in the mined space portion of the building. This two-story space is approximately 5000 square meters in area and is distributed around a central rock pillar which supports the

limestone above. Initially, a portion of the lower level of the space was left unfinished. This will be converted to additional office and storage space during 1992.

Special Life Safety Considerations for Fire Emergencies

The life safety provisions for this novel building design were worked out between the architect and University building code officials in consultation with other building code officials and the local fire department.

The life safety aspects of the cut-and-cover spaces in the building are not unusual. The occupant loads are not particularly high and exits not difficult to provide. The upper portion of the building is divided into compartments separated by fire-resistant construction, and exiting is possible through some individual windows plus three exit stairways and an exit passage into an adjacent building. The building is fully sprinklered and has a fire safety monitoring system connected to two annunciator panels near the loading dock and in the department main office.

The main design aspect requiring adjustment during the design process was the protection of spaces opening onto the main structures laboratory. The atrium provisions of the State Building Code (which follows the U.S. model Uniform Building Code) were applied and restricted the spaces that could open directly onto the structures laboratory. Windows from interior faculty offices that had been planned to overlook the laboratory were deleted from the design, and a second level corridor overlooking the laboratory had to be enclosed. All interior window areas opening onto the laboratory were protected by fire shutters which would be closed in case of fire.

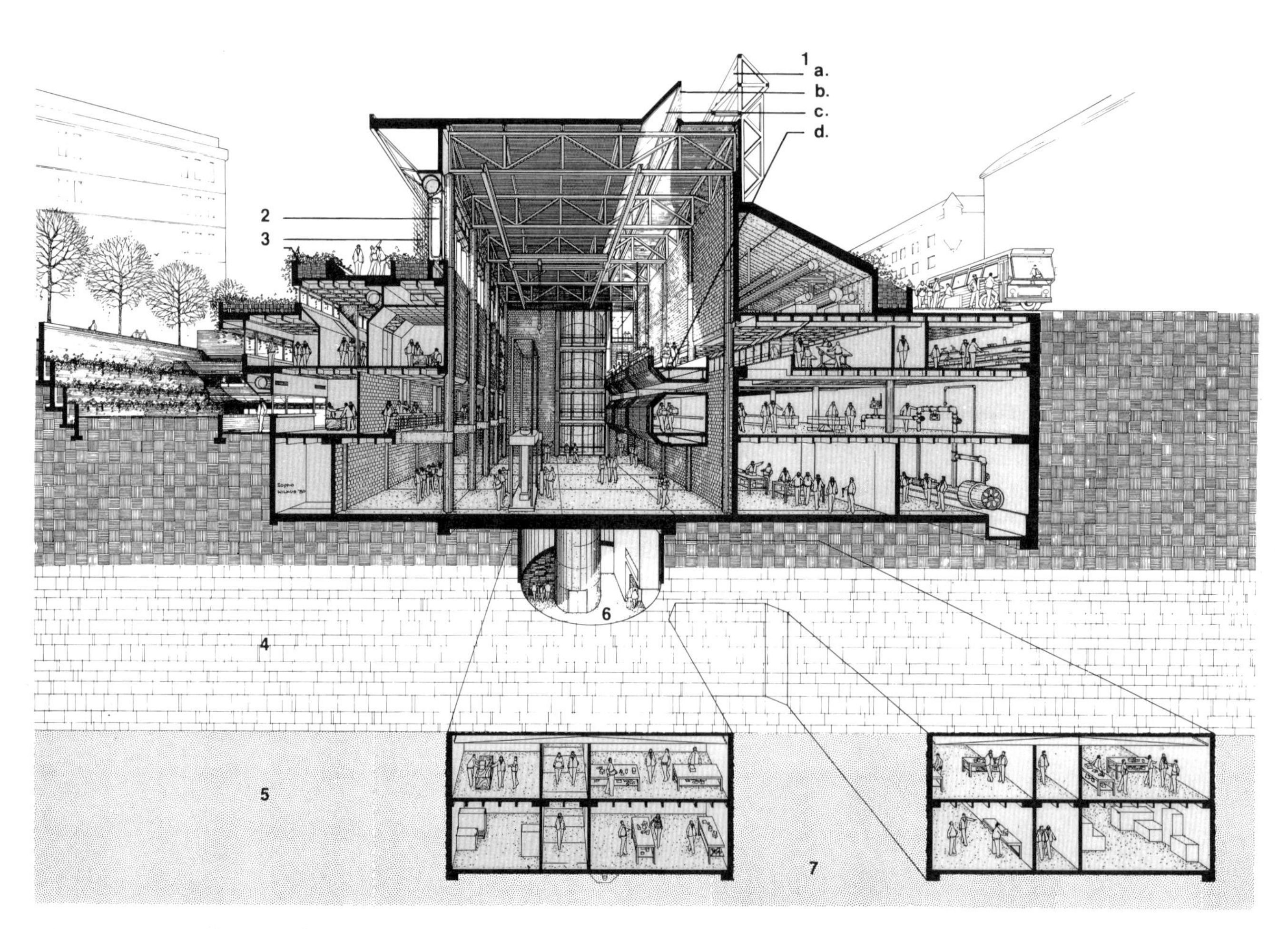

Figure D-1: Section – Civil and Mineral Engineering Building at the University of Minnesota. (Source: BRW Architects)

The design of the safety aspects for the mined space was based on the availability of two separate fire- and smoke-protected exit stairways from the mined space and the dividing of the space itself into two compartments each served by one of the exit stairways. Separate ventilation systems are used for each compartment and are controlled to exhaust air and smoke from the fire zone and to supply air to the other zone in case of a fire. Each exit stairway is contained in one of the two shafts that serve the mined space. The large shaft also contains the building's two passenger elevators, the vertical chases to bring sunlight and view to the lowest level of the building, and mechanical/electrical equipment space. The small shaft contains (beside the stairway) the freight elevator and mechanical/electrical equipment space. Open chases in the shafts (such as for light and view systems) are protected from occupied spaces by automatically operated fire shutters.

Because of the depth of the building and the fact that elevators are programmed to return directly to the surface in case of a fire alarm, all occupants of the lower levels are faced with a stair climb of 30 to 35 meters to reach the surface. The stairwells would be enclosed and pressurized during a fire to keep smoke out of the stairwell. The stairwells serve as exits for higher levels of the building and discharge directly to the building exterior. For occupants who are unable to make this climb, a refuge area is provided within the limestone rock in each shaft. This is supplied separately with pressurized fresh air and is equipped with communication systems.

Experience

The building has not experienced any serious fires or life safety emergencies. The building did suffer from a significant number of false alarms in the first two years of operation. These were traced mostly to the accumulation of dust on the smoke detectors from operations in the structures laboratory and on concealed detectors in the false floor of the computer room. The false alarms had a very negative effect on the willingness of the mined space occupants to respond to alarms because of the 35-meter stair climb involved.

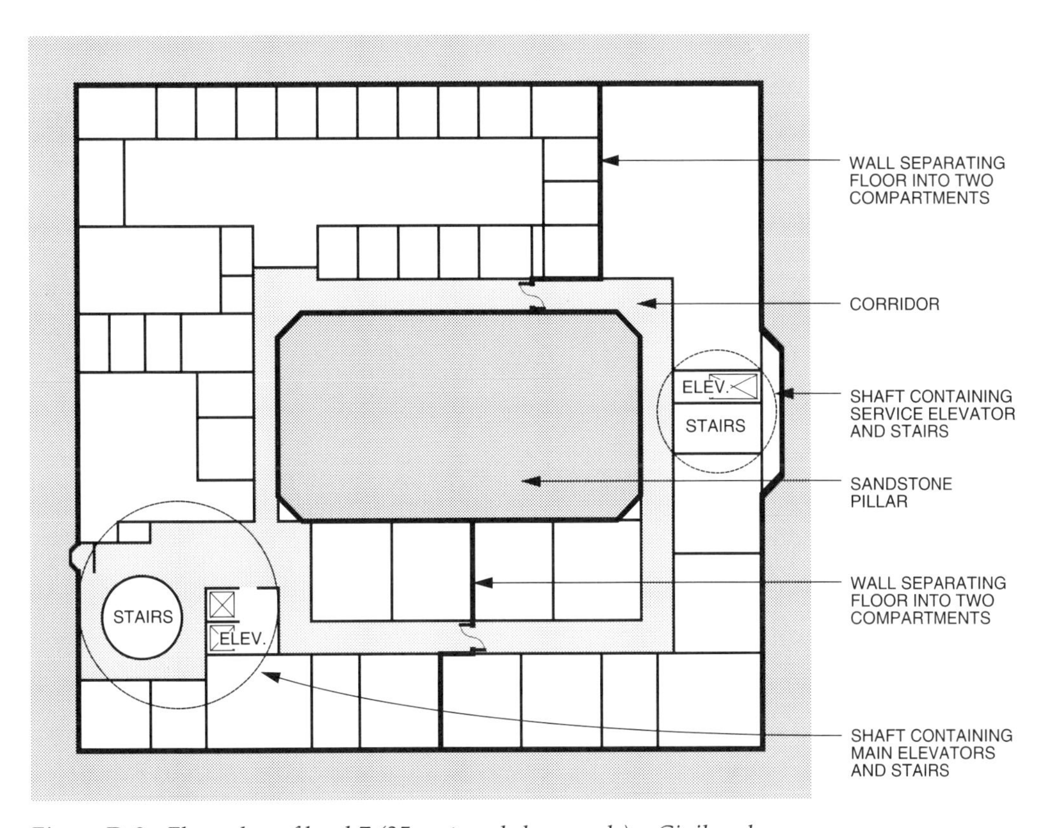

Figure D-2: Floor plan of level 7 (35 meters below grade) – Civil and Mineral Engineering Building at the University of Minnesota.

Moscone Convention Center

Located near downtown San Francisco, the 60,400-square-meter convention center is almost entirely below grade except for a relatively small entrance pavilion on the surface. The convention center was opposed by groups resisting the new development and the massive scale of the convention center in particular. The referendum that authorized the convention center provided that the facility be built underground if financially feasible (Kornsand 1980). Construction was started in 1978 and completed in 1981.

The center occupies an oversized city block, 256 meters by 160 meters, and serves as the focal point of the Yerba Buena Redevelopment area. The center has a 25,500-square-meter column-free main exhibit hall. Concrete arches spanning 84 meters across the exhibition space are also designed to support future development and/or landscaping on the roof of the exhibition area. The main exhibition floor is located from 4.9 to 9.1 meters below grade. Surrounded by earth berms, the rooftop is actually above existing grade and provides a clear height of 11.3 meters over the exhibit area.

The convention center is entered through a 2,800-square-meter, glass-enclosed pavilion on the surface. The two lower levels are reached by escalators, elevators, and stairs from the entrance lobby. As many as 31 individual meeting rooms with capacities from 50 to 600 people can be created with partitions on the mezzanine level. On the lowest level is the main exhibit hall (which can be subdivided into three separate areas), a 2,800-square-meter main ballroom, a kitchen that can serve 6,000 people, and 12 loading docks reached by ramps on the building perimeter. The main exhibit hall can hold 20,000 people with an additional 4,000 in other spaces. Administrative offices and a security/fire control office are located on the mezzanine. A first aid station is located on the exhibit hall level.

Fire/Life Safety Features

The following description of the fire/life safety features is based on a paper by Norman Kornsand, Rolf Jensen & Associates, San Francisco, the fire safety consultants for the project (Kornsand 1980).

The applicable building code and fire marshal regulations did not allow the construction of an assembly room with an occupant load of 1,000 or more in a basement unless safety features were as effective as those in similar use buildings at or above ground level. The provisions incorporated into the design and operating procedures for the building were sufficient to satisfy this requirement.

The key elements of the fire safety features of the convention center are:

- Means of egress.
- Fire suppression.
- Smoke removal.
- Early fire warning.
- Voice communication and public emergency reporting system.
- Annunciation of signals and fire emergency response.
- Emergency power.
- Fire management program.

The particular difficulties posed by the underground convention center are:

- Large occupancy: Occupant loads may reach 20,000 in the exhibit hall and 4,000 in other spaces.
- Mobility-impaired access: Handicapped persons or infirm occupants are unable to use stairs or escalators.
- Unfamiliar surroundings: The occupants are infrequent visitors and are unfamiliar with the building.
- Visual noise: Banners, signs, lights, etc., that are part of the exhibits interfere with the recognition of exits.

The main exhibit hall has 22 exits with a total width of 143 meters. Eighteen of these exits are 6.1-meter-wide straight stairs leading from the exhibit floor directly to

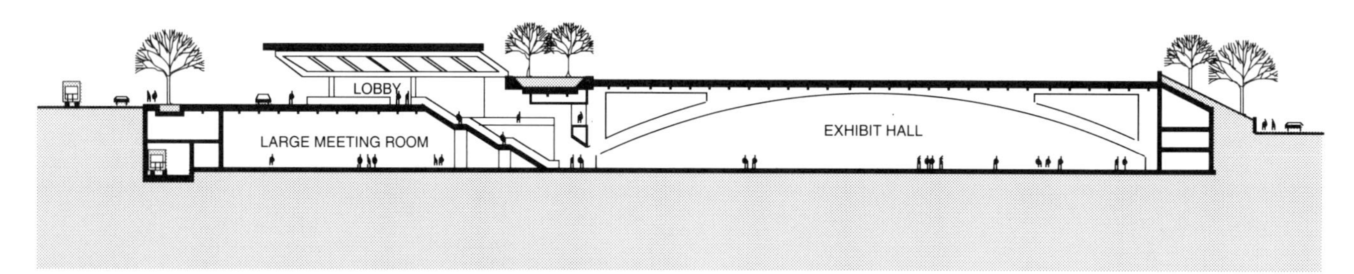

Figure D-3: Section – Moscone Convention Center, San Francisco, California, USA.

the outside. The stairs are for the most part placed at 27.5-meter intervals along the north and south sides of the exhibit hall and positioned between the paired concrete arches that support the roof. Four 8.4-meter-wide ramps provide other emergency-only exit routes not requiring the use of stairs. These ramps also function as truck ramps, but double Class A-3 hour closures separate these exit ramps from the truck dock areas in an emergency. In addition, the main entrance lobby, escalators, elevators, and stairs are separated from the exhibit hall by two-hour fire-resistant construction. The exit signage was specially designed to stand out visually within the exhibit hall.

An exit analysis carried out as part of the design indicated that if the exhibit hall were fully occupied (20,000 people), it could be evacuated in slightly over nine minutes. Of this time, people would not be within a protected enclosure for only 2.5 minutes.

The fire suppression systems were designed to use wet sprinkler systems with ordinary temperature-rated fusible link closed sprinklers. All fixed protection was at the ceiling level to accommodate the changing exhibits. The sprinklers were designed to allow for the high combustible load of typical exhibits (up to 100 kilograms of combustible material per square meter of arena) and the high ceiling height of the exhibit hall. The design criteria were established as 8.15 liters per minute per square meter over the hydraulically most remote 372 square meters. In addition, fire department hose connections with 61 meters of 25-millimeter diameter hard rubber hose were provided at special fire command modules located at each end of each double arch roof support. This layout allows the flexible hose to reach anywhere within the main hall. Two electrically driven 95-liter-per-second fire pumps are provided. These can be operated from the emergency generation system and can be supplied from either two remote connections to the San Francisco water supply or from two 117-cubic meter on-site reservoirs.

Although the roof of the convention hall is above ground it is constructed of reinforced concrete to permit future construction above the exhibit hall. This arrangement precludes penetrations in the roof assembly and the use of gravity heat and smoke venting. Mechanical smoke removal is used and 11 smoke removal zones are designated in the building. Eight smoke exhaust fans with a capacity of 18.9 cubic meters per second are activated to remove smoke from the exhibit hall, and fan discharge is regulated to limit negative pressures on the exit doors.

Ionization smoke detectors are used as early warning detectors in the main exhibit hall. The hall is divided into

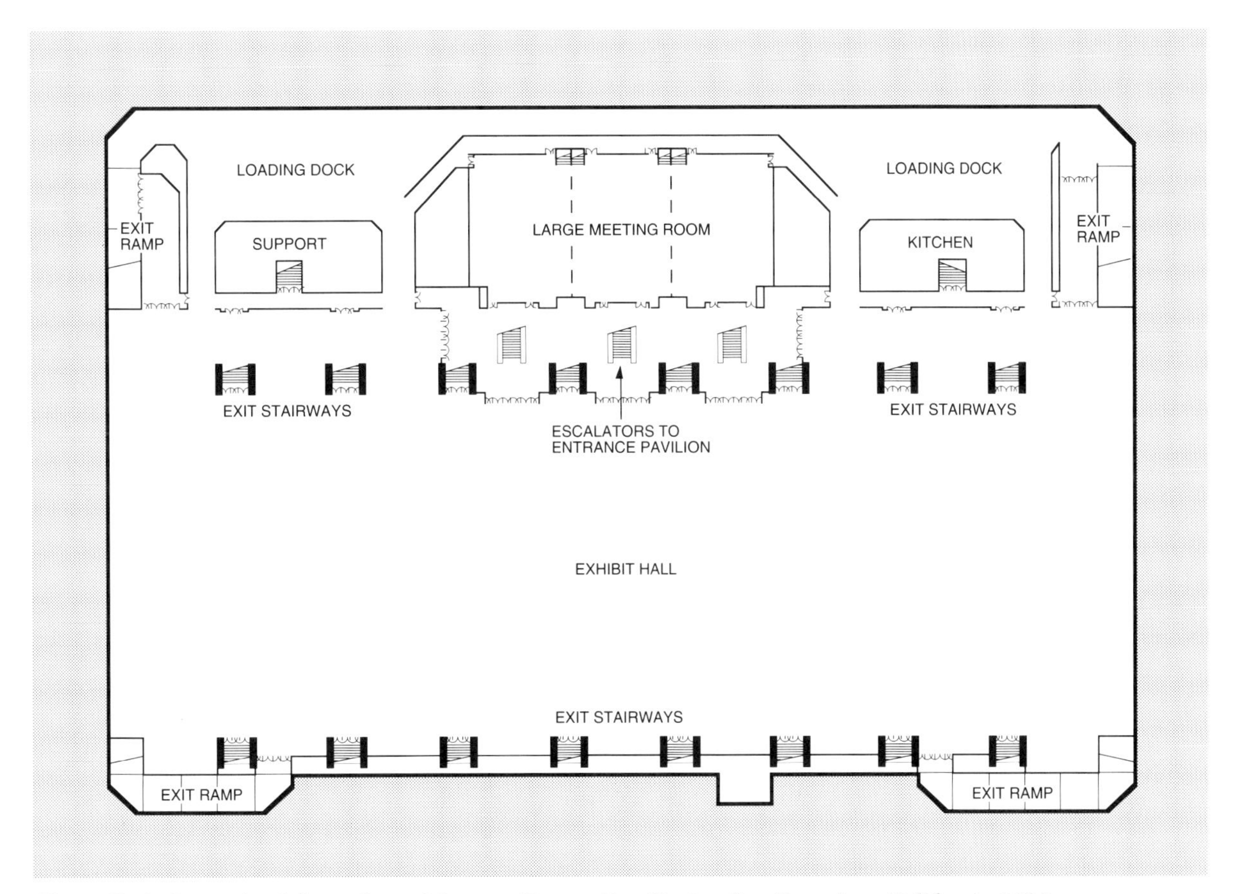

Figure D-4: Lower level floor plan – Moscone Convention Center, San Francisco, California, USA.

three detection zones representing the possible subdivision of the hall. Unlike sprinkler activation, the activation of a smoke detector does not automatically initiate a public warning and building egress but alerts the control center and the fire department to the condition. The smoke detection system is deactivated during the set-up and dismantling of exhibits when trucks are operating in the hall.

All sensors and emergency systems are linked to the control center, and the location and status of emergency conditions or systems are displayed. A separate emergency communication system is provided using glass-covered phone jacks. When the glass is broken the annunciator panel automatically indicates the position of the jack being used.

Three on-site diesel engine generator sets provide emergency power to the following systems:

- Exit lighting.
- Emergency lighting.
- Fire alerting and supervisory systems.
- Emergency communication systems.
- Fire pumps.
- Passenger elevators.
- Smoke removal and emergency ventilation fans.

An active fire management program was developed for the operation of the center. It includes:

- Controls on the storage and use of dangerous substances and appliances.
- Specific guidelines for the construction of exhibition booths.
- A regular maintenance and testing program for the emergency system.
- An on-site trained fire brigade for emergency verification and quick response.

Experience

The Moscone Convention Center has been in operation about 10 years and has had no incidents requiring outside intervention. A small boiler fire was automatically controlled by the sprinkler system. The presence of a manned control center and the delay in notifying external agencies for certain types of alarms (e.g., smoke detectors) have been valuable in controlling the disruption caused by false alarms. The fire marshal responsible for the project also noted that automatic door closing devices, which allow fire doors to be open during normal conditions, are very important to reduce the danger of door wedges being used (Carlson 1991).

LIFE SAFETY IN LES HALLES UNDERGROUND COMPLEX

The final phase of redevelopment of Les Halles, formerly the central wholesale market of Paris, has recently been completed. A sizable portion of this huge complex is underground (more than 300,000 square meters) including a network of roads, subway stations, parking lots, cultural and sports facilities, commercial areas, and space required for technical infrastructure (Figure D-8). At the bottom of the construction, 30 meters below street level, are the stations serving the subway and "regional express network" (RER).

In France, the public building code forbids access to any structure at the second underground level or any level six meters or more below the surface. But in a case of large underground developments such as Les Halles (or "le Grand Louvre"), studies are made at the early stages of the project and special dispositions may be adopted.

Life safety of the visitors in Les Halles concerns principally:

- Elimination of water infiltration.
- Maintenance of adequate ventilation and air conditioning.
- Detection and control of disasters (especially fire).

Water Infiltration

The water table is 30 meters below ground level, and had to be taken into consideration both during the construction of the building and also in its maintenance. To avoid the decompression of soil around the huge excavations, it was necessary to create a waterproof wall to limit water infiltration. The operation was performed under protection of numerous water pumping stations. At the end of the work, it was decided to maintain the water table below its natural level: 20 pumping stations work permanently to accomplish this task.

Ventilation and Air-conditioning

Air is renewed at the rate of 5 to 8 cubic meters per hour and per visitor. Given the large number of visitors, this requires considerable ventilation rates. Four HVAC plants assure building ventilation and are used as smoke exhausting systems in case of fire (Figures D-9 and D-10). Thousands of square meters of pipes are necessary.

Air-conditioning was indispensable, given the heat generated by the large number of visitors and the low amount of heat loss occurring from the underground building.

The placement of exhaust chimneys was not easy due to the density of the surrounding buildings. In some cases it was necessary to buy existing buildings and empty the interior, thus transforming them into exhaust chimneys.

Detection and Control of Disasters

The arrangements for public life safety are based on the following principles:

- The underground roadway network forms an "intervention access" for fire fighters and other individuals involved in safety operations. Security telephones and fire control equipment are available at regular intervals, and the entire network is surveyed from an underground headquarters using video cameras and remote control sensors. Emergency electrical generators are available to assure the function of the lighting system and ventilation (seven generators are needed for the Les Halles complex: two for the roadway network, five for the parking and commercial area). Controlled roads leading from the roadways to underground pedestrian pathways facilitate access to the complex.
- Evacuation of visitors from commercial areas through the roadway network is not possible. The public areas are compartmentalized in 3000- to 6000-square-meter areas, over one or at most two levels, and are separated by fireproof walls and doors. In the case of fire or accident in one compartment, the smoke is extracted through the exhaust air ducts which are operated at above normal speed (Figure D-10). The occupants are conducted to the outside through the emergency stairs. Ordinary stairs are closed by metallic curtains to avoid smoke propagation.
- The north and south parking lots constitute two different security areas separated from roadway network and pedestrian pathways by fireproof walls and doors. They have their own emergency stairs to the outside.
- Each emergency staircase serves several compartments and, in some cases, the RER transit

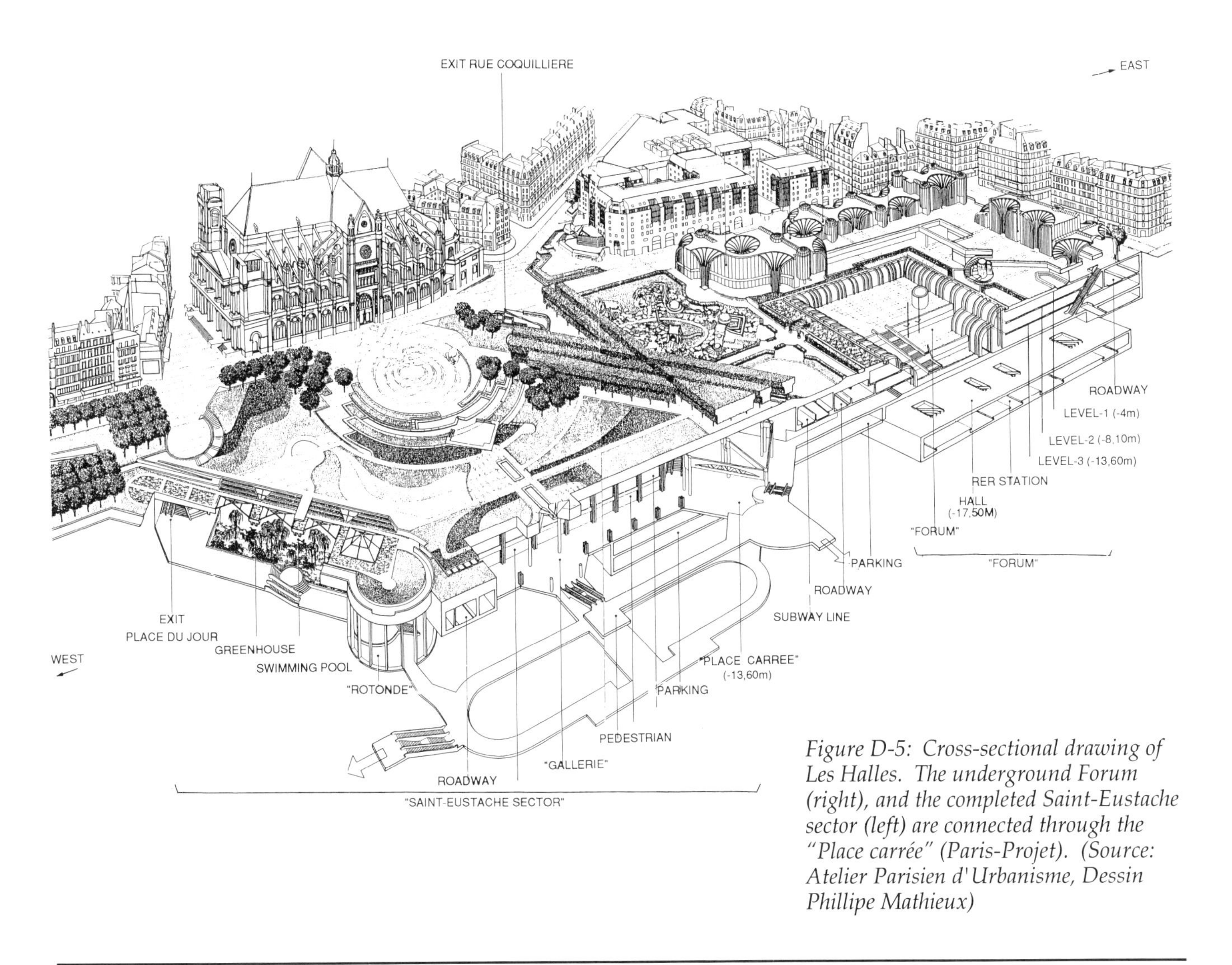

Figure D-5: Cross-sectional drawing of Les Halles. The underground Forum (right), and the completed Saint-Eustache sector (left) are connected through the "Place carrée" (Paris-Projet). (Source: Atelier Parisien d'Urbanisme, Dessin Phillipe Mathieux)

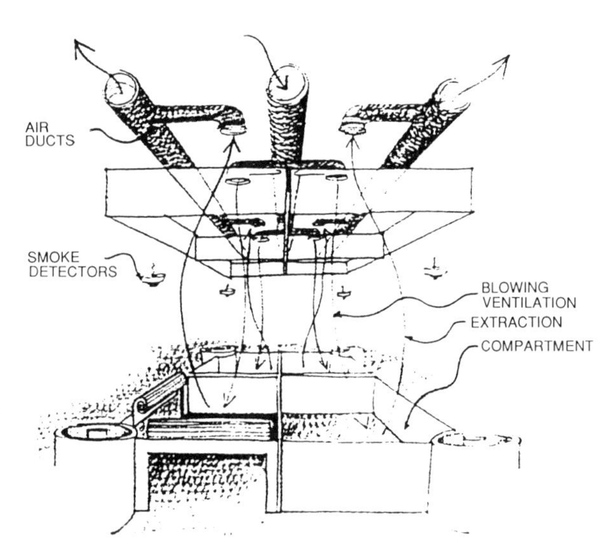

Figure D-6: The operation of the ventilation system under normal conditions at the Les Halles complex.

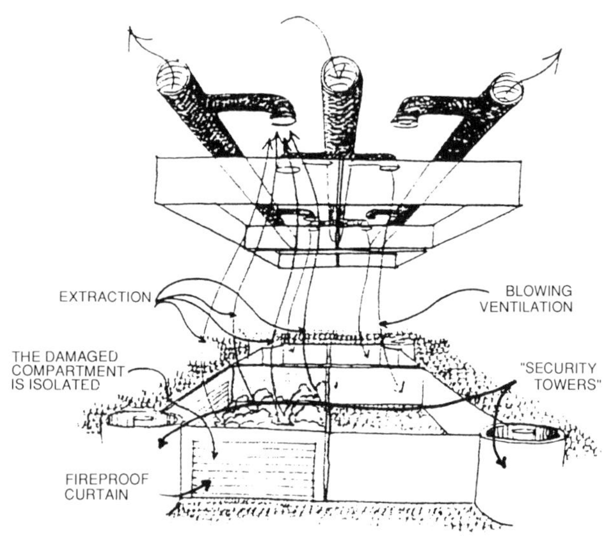

Figure D-7: In case of fire, smoke is removed through the air extraction duct, operating at above normal speed. The isolation of the compartment is assured by lowering a fireproof curtain (10 ans d'activités aux Halles).

station. The maximum distance between two emergency exits is 50 meters. The stairs are usually grouped in "security towers" which contain three spiral staircases intertwined but completely independent, which communicate to three different levels. The center of the tower is dedicated to the air-conditioning system.

- The underground areas are equipped with standard fire detection equipment, sprinklers, and pressurized fire hydrants.
- In addition to the control center monitoring and controlling the roadway network mentioned above, independent control centers exist for the commercial areas/walkways and for the parking areas. These three control centers are connected through direct telephone lines and are equipped with computers. Each control center is permanently occupied by a security staff which receives all information on public utilization and operation of the installations in the space under its control, and has the power to initiate maintenance operations or emergency procedures, if necessary. Computers store and analyze the received information and can help in the formulation of decisions. Each post can independently control much of the equipment under its jurisdiction. Certain functions, however, such as the closing of fireproof doors, the operating of ventilation systems, and suppression of the "security towers" are operated automatically through remote sensors present in each compartment.
- The staff required to assure security and life safety is quite significant—50 security agents, specially trained in fire fighting and life safety. Some technicians have also been trained to assist fire fighters in case of disaster. All together, 70 people assure life safety in Les Halles.

Experience

Accidents have been low in number and modest in importance. At least in part, this reflects the careful attention given to disaster planning during the conception of the project. During the initial stages of planning in 1972, members of the design team visited underground complexes all over the world. The lessons learned at these other sites were incorporated into the design and have helped make Les Halles a reference building in the matter of underground city planning.

References: Part 2

Chapters 5-11 and Appendix D

Aksugür, E. 1979. The effect of hues of walls on the perceived magnitude of space in a room under two different light sources having different spectral distributions. *Architectural Bulletin* 4:22-47 (as cited in Kuller 1981).

Alexander, C., S. Ishikawa, and M. Silverstein, with M. Jacobson, I. Fiskdahl-King, and S. Angel. 1977. *A Pattern Language*. New York: Oxford University Press.

Ankerl, G. 1981. *Experimental Sociology of Architecture*. New York: Mouton (as cited in Tiedje 1987).

Aubree, A. 1978. Artificial lighting during the day of a deep room. Illuminating Engineering Society Conf. (as cited in Wise and Wise 1984).

Bain, B.A.

—1989. The entry experience: Preferences of the mobility-impaired. *Changing Paradigms*. Proc., Environmental Design Research Association Annual Conf., EDRA 20, North Carolina State Univ.

—1990. Approaching buildings: A conceptual model of the entry sequence. *Coming of Age*. Proc., Environmental Design Research Association Annual Conf., EDRA 21, Univ. of Illinois at Urbana-Champaign.

Barton, M., M. Spivack, and P. Powell. 1972. The effects of angle of light on the recognition and evaluation of faces. *Journal of the Illuminating Engineering Society*, April: 231-34 (as cited in Wise and Wise 1984).

Bennett, D.J. 1978. Notes on the underground. *Earth Covered Buildings and Settlements*. Conf. Proc., Ft. Worth, Tex., ed. F. Moreland. Government Printing Office, Conf-7805138-P2.

Birkerts, G. 1974. *Subterranean Urban Systems*. Industrial Development Division, Inst. of Science and Technology, Univ. of Michigan.

Birren, F. 1983. Color and psychotherapy. *Interior Design*, Dec. (as cited in Mahnke 1987).

Bitter, C., and J.F. van Ierland. 1967. Appreciation of sunlight in the home. *Proceedings of the Conference on Sunlight in Buildings*: 27-37. Rotterdam: Bouwcentrum International.

Bobrick, B. 1981. *Labyrinths of Iron*. New York: William Morrow and Company, Inc.

Boyce, P.R. 1980. *Human Factors in Lighting*. London: Applied Science Publishers.

Brill, M., S. Margulis, and E. Konar. 1983. *Using Office Design to Increase Productivity*. Buffalo Organization for Social and Technological Innovation, in association with Westinghouse Furniture Systems.

Canter, D. 1976. *Environmental Interaction*. New York: International University Press (as cited in Wise and Wise 1984).

Carlson, L. 1991. Personal communication, Aug. 14.

Carmody, J., and R. Sterling.

—1983. *Underground Building Design: Commercial and Institutional Structures*. New York: Van Nostrand Reinhold. ISBN 0-442-28746-1.

—1987. Design strategies to alleviate negative psychological and physiological effects in underground space. *Tunnelling and Underground Space Technology* 2 (1): 59-67. Pergamon Press.

—1990. Underground space on earth: Analog for a lunar base. *Proc.,Space 90, Engineering, Construction, and Operations in Space*, Albuquerque, N. Mex.

Clearwater, Y.A., and R.G. Coss. 1991. Functional aesthetics to enhance well-being in isolated and confined settings. *From Antarctica to Outer Space: Life in Isolation and Confinement.* New York: Springer-Verlag.

Cochran, C.D., and S. Urbanczyk. 1982. The effect of availability of vertical space on personal space. *Journal of Psychology* 3:137-40 (as cited in Tiedje 1987).

Collins, B. 1975. *Windows and People: A Literature Survey.* Washington, D.C.: NBS Building Science Series.

Cooper-Marcus, C. 1985. *Design Guidelines: A Bridge Between Research and Decision-Making.* Center for Environmental Design Research, Univ. of Calif., Berkeley. Report CEDR-WP08-85.

Coss, R.G., Y.A. Clearwater, C.G. Barbour, and S.R. Towers. 1989. *Functional Decor in the International Space Station: Body Orientation Cues and Picture Perception.* NASA Technical Memorandum 102242.

Cuttle, K. 1983. People and windows in work places. *Proc. Conf., People and the Physical Environment Research.* New Zealand: Ministry of Works and Development.

Dantsig, N.M., P.N. Lazareo, and M.V. Sokolov. 1967. *Ultraviolet Installations of Beneficial Action.* CIE (Commission Internationale de l'Eclairage) Publication 20: 67.

Deasy, C.M. 1985. *Designing Places for People: A Handbook on Human Behavior for Architects, Designers, and Facility Managers.* New York: Whitney Library of Design.

Degenkolb, J.G. 1981. Fire protection for underground buildings. *Underground Space* 6 (2): 93-95. Pergamon Press.

Demos, G.D., S. Davis, and F.F. Zuwaylif. 1967. Controlled physical environments. *Building Research* 4:60-62 (as cited in Collins 1975).

Doubilet, S., and T. Fisher. 1986. Hong Kong Bank. *Progressive Architecture* 3:86.

Feller, R.P., et al. 1974. Significant effect of environmental lighting on caries incidence in the cottom rat. *Proc. Society for Experimental Biology and Medicine,* 1065-68.

Fennell, D. 1988. *Investigation into the King's Cross Underground Fire.* London: The Department of Transport.

Flynn, J.E., A.W. Segil, and G.R. Steffy. 1988. *Architectural Interior Systems.* Second Edition. New York: Van Nostrand Reinhold.

Flynn, J.E., and T.J. Spencer. 1971. The effects of light source color on user impression and satisfaction. *Journal of the Illuminating Engineering Society,* April:167-79.

Fritzell, C., and U. Ranhagen. 1980. Human beings underground. *Subsurface Space,* Vol. I. Proc., Rockstore 80, Stockholm.

Gerlach, K.A. 1974. Environmental design to counter occupational boredom. *Journal of Architectural Research,* Sept. 15-19 (as cited in Wise and Wise 1984).

Gilmer, R. 1966. *Industrial Psychology.* New York: McGraw-Hill.

Gurovskiy, N.N., F.P. Kosmolinskiy, and L.N. Mel'nikov. 1986. Proyektirovaniye usloviy zhizni i raboty kosmonavtov. (Designing the Living and Working Conditions of Cosmonauts.) NASA Technical Memorandum 76497 (as cited in Wise and Rosenberg 1988).

Hane, T. 1989. Application of solar daylighting systems to underground space. *Tunnelling and Underground Space Techology* 4 (4): 465-70. Pergamon Press.

Hane, T., K. Muro, and H. Sawada. 1991. Psychological factors involved in establishing comfortable underground environments. *Urban Underground Utilization '91,* Proc. 4th Int. Conf. on Underground Space and Earth Sheltered Buildings, Tokyo, Japan.

Hashimoto, S., N. Yamaguchi, and M. Kawasaki. 1989. *Experimental Research on the Aromatheraputic Effect of Fragrances in Living Environments.* Tokyo: Institute of Technology, Shimizu Corporation.

Heerwagon, J. 1990. Windows, windowlessness and simulated view. *Coming of Age.* Proc., Environmental Design Research Association Annual Conf., EDRA 21, Univ. of Illinois of Urbana-Champaign.

Heerwagon, J., and G. Orians. 1986. Adaptations to windowlessness: A study of the use of visual decor in windowed and windowless offices. *Environment and Behavior* 8 (5): 623-39.

Holister, F.D. 1968. *A Report on the Problems of Windowless Environments.* A report to the Greater London Council. London: Hobbs the Printers, Ltd.

Hollon, S.D., P.C. Kendall, S. Norsted, and D. Watson. 1980. Psychological responses to earth sheltered, multilevel and aboveground structures with and without windows. *Underground Space* 5 (3): 171-78. Pergamon Press.

Hollwich, F. 1980. *The Influence of Ocular Light Perception on Metabolism in Man and in Animals.* New York: Springer Verlag.

Holm, W., and G. Roessler. 1972. Sunlight in dwellings. *Proc. CIE Study Group Symposium,* Varna, Bulgaria, Oct. (as cited in Collins 1975).

Hopkinson, R.G. 1967. The psychophysics of sunlighting. *Proceedings of the Conference on Sunlight in Buildings,* 13-17. Rotterdam: Bouwcentrum International.

Hopkinson, R.G., and J.B. Collins. 1970. *The Ergonomics of Lighting.* London: MacDonald Technical and Scientific.

Hou, X., and Y. Su. 1988. The urban underground space environment and human performance. *Tunnelling and Underground Space Technology* 3 (2): 193-200. Pergamon Press.

Hughey, J.B., and R.L. Tye. 1983. Psychological reactions to working underground: A study of attitudes, beliefs and valuations. *Underground Space* 8 (5-6): 381-91. Pergamon Press.

Imamoglu, V. 1986. Assessing the spaciousness of interiors. *O.D.T.U. Mimarlik Fakultesi Dergisi* 7 (2): 127-37. Bahar (as cited in Tiedje 1987).

Imamoglu, V., and T.A. Markus. 1973. The effect of window size, room proportion and window position on spaciousness evaluation of rooms. *Windows and Their Function in Architectural Design.* Proc., CIE Conference, Istanbul, Turkey.

Inui, M. 1980. Views through a window. *Daylight*: Proc., CIE Symposium, Berlin, Germany, 323-32 (as cited in Wotton 1981).

Inui, M., and Miyata. 1973. Spaciousness in interiors. *Lighting Research and Technology* 5 (2): 103-11.

Itten, J. 1970. *The Elements of Color.* New York: Van Nostrand Reinhold.

Jackson, G.J., and J.G. Holmes. 1973. Let's keep it simple - daylight design. *Light and Lighting,* Feb.: 59-60, and March: 80-82 (as cited in Collins 1975).

Kaye, S.M., and M.A. Murray. 1982. Evaluations of an architectural space as a function of variations in furniture arrangement, furniture density, and windows. *Human Factors* 24 (5): 609-18 (as cited in Wise 1985).

Keighley, E.C. 1973. Visual requirements and reduced frustration in offices - A study of multiple apertures and window area. *Journal of Building Science* 8:311-20 (as cited in Collins 1975).

Kornsand, N.J. 1980. Convention center offers fire protection design challenge. *Specifying Engineer* 43 (5): 75-80.

Krokeide, G. 1988. An introduction to luminous escape systems. *Safety in the Built Environment,* ed. J.D. Sime. London: E. and F.N. Spon.

Kuller, R.
–1980. Non-visual effects of daylight. *Proc. Symp. on Daylight: Physical, Psychological and Architectural Aspects*: 172-81. Commission International De l'Eclairage.
–1981. *Non-Visual Effects of Light and Color: Annotated Bibliography.* Stockholm: Swedish Council for Building Research.

Larson, C.T. (ed.). 1967. *The Effect of Windowless Classrooms on Elementary School Children.* Architectural Research Laboratory, Dept. of Architecture, Univ. of Michigan (as cited in Collins 1975).

Lavianna, J.E., R.H. Mattson, and F.H. Rohles. 1983. Plants as enhancers of the indoor environment. *Proc. Human Factors Society, Vol. II,* Norfolk, Va.

Les Halles: achèvement d'un projet, *Paris-Projet* n°25-26, 1985.

Lesser, W. 1987. *The Life Below the Ground: A Study of the Subterranean in Literature and History.* Boston: Faber and Faber.

Levin, H., and L. Duhl. 1984. Indoor pollution: Lighting, energy, and health. *Architectural Research.* New York: Van Nostrand Reinhold.

Lewy, A.J., et al. 1982. Bright artificial light treatment of a manic-depressive patient with a seasonal mood cycle. *American Journal of Psychiatry* 139:1496-98 (as cited in Mahnke and Mahnke 1987).

Li, K.C. 1989. Fire protection in caverns. *Rock Cavern - Hong Kong.* Proc. Seminar, Hong Kong, Dec. 8-9, 1989, eds. W.A. Malone and P.G.D. Whiteside. Institute of Mining and Metallurgy. ISBN 1 870706 14 5.

Linn, C. 1988. Lighting makes airport club, business center relaxing, inviting. *Architectural Lighting* 2 (8): 34-37.

Littlechild, B.D. 1989. Fire engineering design proposal for a large commercial complex in a cavern in Hong Kong. *Rock Cavern - Hong Kong.* Proc. Seminar, Hong Kong, Dec. 8-9, 1989, eds. W.A. Malone and P.G.D. Whiteside. Inst. of Mining and Metallurgy. ISBN 1 870706 14 5.

Longmore, J., and E. Ne'eman. 1974. The availability of sunshine and human requirements for sunlight in buildings. *Journal of Architecture Research* 3 (2).

Lynch, K. 1960. *Image of the City.* Cambridge, Mass.: MIT Press.

Maas, J.B., J.K. Jayson, and D.A. Kleiber. 1974. Effects of spectral differences in illumination on fatigue. *Journal of Applied Psychology* 59 (4): 524-26.

Mahnke, F., and R. Mahnke. 1987. *Color and Light in Manmade Environments.* New York: Van Nostrand Reinhold.

Manning, P. (ed.). 1965. *Office Design: A Study of Environment.* Liverpool, Pilkington Research Unit, Liverpool Univ. Dept. of Building Science (as cited in Collins 1975).

Markus, T.A. 1967. The significance of sunshine and view for office workers. *Proc. Conf. on Sunlight in Buildings,* 59-93. Rotterdam: Bouwcentrum International.

Mayron, L.W., J. Ott, J. Amontree, and R. Nations. 1975. Light, radiation, and dental caries. *Academic Therapy* 10 (4): 441-48.

Mayeron, L.W., J. Ott, R. Nations, and E.L. Mayron. Light, radiation, and academic behavior. *Academic Therapy* 10 (1): 33-47.

Mel'nikov, L.N. 1978. Komnaty psikhologicheskoy razgruzki (Psychological relief rooms). *Mashino stroitel* 1:33-34 (as cited in Clearwater and Coss 1989).

Menchikoff, A. 1975. La Perception des Volumes. *Psychologie,* July: 48-51 (as cited in Wise 1985).

Mori, K. 1988. Solar energy technology for use in future cities. *A New Frontier: Environments for Innovation.* Proc. Int. Symp. on Advanced Comfort Systems for the Work Environment.

Muro, K., H. Sawada, and T. Hane. 1990. Psychological issues on utilization of underground spaces. Tokyo: Institute of Technology, Shimizu Corporation.

National Fire Protection Association (NFPA). 1991. *NFPA 101 Life Safety Code.* Quincy, Mass.: National Fire Protection Association.

Ne'eman, and Hopkinson. 1970. Critical minimum acceptable window size: A study of window size and provision of a view. *Lighting Research and Technology* 2:17-27.

Neer, R.M., T. Davis, A. Walcott, S. Koski, P. Schepis, I. Taylor, L. Thorington, and R.J. Wurtman. 1971. *Nature* 229 (5282): 255-57.

Nelson, H., and H. MacLennan. 1988. *Fire Protection Engineering.* Quincy, Mass.: National Fire Protection Association.

NFPA. See National Fire Protection Association.

Nishi, J., F. Kamo, and K. Ozawa. 1990. Rational use of urban underground space for surface and subsurface activities in Japan. *Tunnelling and Underground Space Technology* 5 (1-2): 23-31. Pergamon Press.

Nuttall, N. 1988. Science. *New Scientist* 28 (April): 39.

Ogata, Y., T. Isei, and M. Kuriyagawa. 1990. Safety measures for underground space utilization. *Tunnelling and Underground Space Technology* 5 (3): 245-56. Pergamon Press.

Olds, A.R. 1985. *Nature as healer. Readings in Psychosynthesis: Theory, Process, and Practice*, 97-110. Toronto: Ontario Institute for Studies in Education.

Olds, A.R., and P.A. Daniel. 1987. *Child Health Care Facilities.* Washington, D.C.: Association for the Care of Children's Health.

Orians, G. 1980. Habitat selection: general theory and applications to human behavior. *The Evolution of Human Social Behavior* 49-66. Chicago: Elsevier (as cited in Heerwagon 1990).

Passini, R.

—1984. *Wayfinding in Architecture.* New York: Van Nostrand Reinhold.

—1985. Sign systems, maps, and wayfinding. *Proc.Int. Conference on Building Use and Safety Technology.*

Pauls, J. 1988. Movement of people. *Fire Protection Engineering.* Quincy, Mass.: National Fire Protection Association.

Paulus, P.B. 1976. On the psychology of earth covered buildings. *Underground Space* 1 (2) : 127-30. Pergamon Press.

Pilon, P. 1980. In Paris, a "city center" goes underground. *Underground Space* 5 (2): 102-20. Pergamon Press.

Porter, T., and B. Mikellides. 1976. *Color for Architecture.* New York: Van Nostrand Reinhold.

Proulx, G., and J. Sime. 1991. To prevent panic in an underground emergency: Why not tell people the truth? *Fire Safety Science.* Proc. 3rd Int. Symp. on Fire Safety Science. London: Hemisphere Publishing Corporation.

Rappoport, A., and R.E. Kantor. 1967. Complexity and ambiguity in environmental design. *APA Journal* 33 (4): 210-21, American Inst. of Planners.

Rohles, F.H., and W. Wells. 1977. The role of environmental antecedents on subsequent thermal comfort. *ASHRAE Transactions* 83:21-29 (as cited in Wise and Wise 1984).

Rosenthal, N.E., et al.
—1984. Seasonal affective disorder: A description of the syndrome and preliminary findings with light therapy. *Archives of General Psychiatry* 41 (Jan.): 72-80.
—1985. Antidepressant effects of light in seasonal affective disorder. *American Journal of Psychiatry* 142 (2): 163-70.

Ruys, T. 1970. *Windowless Offices.* M.A. Thesis, Univ. of Washington (as cited in Collins 1975).

Savinar, J. 1975. The effect of ceiling height on personal space. *Man-Environment Systems* 5:321-24 (as cited in Wise 1985).

Sawada, H., and T. Hane. 1991. Comparison between Japanese and American word imagery used to describe underground space. A paper presented at the Symp. for Utilization of Underground Spaces.

Scuri, P., and D. Skene. 1990. Spaces without windows. *Coming of Age.* Proc., Environmental Design Research Association Annual Conf., EDRA 21, Univ. of Illinois at Urbana-Champaign.

SEMAH. 1979. *10 ans d'activités aux Halles*, (Société anonyme d'économie mixte d'aménagement, de rénovation et de restauration du secteur des Halles).

Sharon, I.M., R.P. Feller, and S.W. Burney. 1971. The effects of lights of different spectra on caries incidence in the golden hamster. *Archives of Oral Biology* 16 (2): 1427-31.

Sillam, M. 1989. "L'aménagement des Halles," *Hygiène et prévention dans les ouvrages en sous-sol*, CEGIBAT.

Sime, J. 1985. Movement toward the familiar. Person and place affiliation in a fire entrapment setting. *Environment and Behavior* 17 (6): 697-724. Sage Publications.

Sime, J., G. Proulx, and M. Kimura. 1990. *Evacuation Safety in the Sub-surface Stations of Tyne and Wear Metro: Case Study of Monument Station.* Stage 2 of a use safety evaluation on behalf of Tyne and Wear Passenger Transport Executive, Newcastle upon Tyne, U.K.

Smith, R.D. 1986. Light and health - A broad overview. *Lighting Design and Application*, Feb.

Smith, R., and R. Holden. 1980-91. Personal communications with Univ. of Minnesota building officials.

Sommer, R. 1974. *Tight Spaces: Hard Architecture and How to Humanize It.* Englewood Cliffs, N.J.: Prentice Hall.

Spivack, M., and J. Tamer. 1981. *Light and Color: A Designer's Guide*. Washington, D.C.: American Institute of Architects Service Corporation.

Sterling, R.L., and J. Carmody. 1990. The experience with innovative underground structures at the University of Minnesota. *Proc. Int. Symp. on Unique Underground Structures*, Denver, Colo., June 12-15, 1990, 1(77):1-19, ed. R.S. Sinha. Golden, Colo.: CSM Press, Colorado School of Mines.

Sterling, R., J. Carmody, and W. Rockenstein. 1988. Development of life safety standards for large mined underground space facilities in Minneapolis, Minnesota, USA. *Proc. Third Int. Conf. on Underground Space and Earth Sheltered Buildings*, Shanghai, PRC.

Su, Y., and F. Peng. 1990. Psychological effect of underground space environment to human beings and the design countermeasures. *Tunnel and Underground Works Today and Future*. Proc. Int. Congress, International Tunnelling Association Annual Meeting, Cheng Du, PRC.

Tiedje, B. 1987. *Spaciousness - The Illusion and the Reality*. M.A. Thesis, Univ. of Washington.

Tilley, R.D. 1990. 3M Austin Center. *Architecture*, Aug.: 90-91.

Titus, W.C., M. Dainoff, M. Hill, R. Oskamp, B. McClelland, and R. Riley. 1977. The psychophysics of mass-space. *Man-Environment Systems* 6:370-71 (as cited in Wise and Wise 1984).

Tong, L. 1990. Fire - the harmful disaster for underground space use. *Tunnel and Underground Works Today and Future*. Proc. Int. Congress, International Tunnelling Association Annual Meeting, Cheng Du, PRC.

Ulrich, R.
—1979. Visual landscapes and psychological well-being. *Landscape Research* 4 (1): 17-23.
—1981. Natural versus urban scenes: Some psychophysiological effects. *Environment and Behavior* 13:523-56.
—1983. Aesthetic and affective response to natural environment. *Behavior and the Natural Environment*, eds. I. Altman and J.F. Wohlwill. New York: Plenum Press.
—1984. View from the window may influence recovery from surgery. *Science* 224:420-21.
—1986. Human responses to vegetation and landscapes. *Landscape and Urban Planning* 13:29-44.

Wada, Y., and H. Sakugawa. 1990. Psychological effects of working underground. *Tunnelling and Underground Space Technology* 5 (1-2): 33-37. Pergamon Press.

Watson, N., and I. Payne. 1968. The influence of fluorescent lamps of different color on the perception of interior volume. Environmental Research Group, Univ. of London (as cited in Kuller 1981).

Webber, G., and P. Hallman. 1988. Movement under various escape route lighting conditions. *Safety in the Built Environment*, ed. J.D. Sime. London: E. and F.N. Spon.

Wells, B. 1965. Subjective responses to the lighting installation in a modern office building and their design implications. *Building Science* 1:57-68 (as cited in Collins 1975).

West, M.J. 1986. *Landscape Views and Stress Response in the Prison Environment*. M.A. Thesis, Univ. of Washington.

Whitehead, L.A., B. Lee, J. Scott, and B. York. 1986. A demonstration of large scale core daylighting by means of a light pipe. *1986 International Daylighting Conference II*. Long Beach, Calif.

Williams, R. 1990. *Notes on the Underground*. Cambridge, Mass.: MIT Press.

Wilson, L.M. 1972. The effects of outside deprivation on a windowless intensive care unit. *Archives of Internal Medicine* 130:225-26.

Wise, B.K., and J.A. Wise. 1987. *The Human Factors of Color in Environmental Design: A Critical Review*. Dept. of Psychology, Univ. of Washington. A report to NASA.

Wise, J.A.
—1985. *The Qualitative Modelling of Human Spatial Habitability*. College of Architecture and Urban Planning, Univ. of Washington. A report to NASA.
—1986. A qualitative model of human spatial habitability. *30th Annual Meetings of the Human Factors Society*. Dayton, Ohio.

Wise, J.A., and E. Rosenberg. 1988. The effects of interior treatments on performance stress in three types of mental tasks. Grand Valley State Univ., Mich. CIFR Technical Report No.: 002-02-1988.

Wise, J.A., and B.K. Wise.
—1984. Humanizing the underground workplace: Environmental problems and design solutions. *First International Symposium on Human Factors in Organizational Design and Management*, eds. O. Brown and H.O. Hendricks. North-Holland: Elsevier Science Publishers BV.
—1988. (eds.) *The Human Factors of Underground Work Environments*. Center for Integrated Facilities Research, Grand Valley State Univ., Mich.

Wohlwill, J.F. 1983. The concept of nature: A psychologist's view. *Behavior and the Natural Environment*, eds. I. Altman and J.F. Wohlwill. New York: Plenum Press.

Wools, R., and D. Canter. 1970. The effect of the meaning of buildings on behavior. *Applied Ergonomics* 1 (3): 144-50 (as cited in Wise 1985).

Wotton, E. 1981. *Windows and Well-being in the Workplace*. Prepared for Health and Welfare Canada, Health Facilities Design, Ottawa, Ontario.

Wurtman, R.
—1968. Biological implications of artificial illumination. *Illuminating Engineer*, Oct.: 523-29.
—1969. The pineal and endocrine function. *Hospital Practice* 4 (Jan.): 32-37.

—1973. Biological considerations in the lighting environment. *Progressive Architecture* 9:79-81 (as cited in Levin and Duhl 1984).

Wurtman, R., M. Baum, and J. Potts (eds.). 1985. *The Medical and Biological Effects of Light.* Annals of the New York Academy of Sciences, 453.

Wyon, D.P., and I. Nilsson. 1980. Human experience of windowless environments in factories, offices, shops, and colleges in Sweden. *Proceedings of the Eighth CIB Triennial Congress*, Oslo, Norway.

Ylinen, J. 1989. Architectural design, spatial planning. *The Rock Engineering Alternative*, ed. K. Saari. Helsinki: Finnish Tunnelling Association.

Zamkova, M.A., and E.I. Krivitskaya. 1966. Effect of irradiation by ultraviolet erythema lamps on the working ability of school children. *Gig. i Sanit.* 3:41-44.

Index

A

B

C

D

E

F

G

H

I

J

K

L

M

N

O

P

Q

R

S

T

U

V

W

Z